# Recovering Autistic Children

## Second Edition

Edited by
Stephen M. Edelson, Ph.D.
Bernard Rimland, Ph.D.

Autism Research Institute, San Diego

RECOVERING AUTISTIC CHILDREN



The views and opinions expressed by the contributors to this book are not necessarily the views and opinions of the Autism Research Institute.

This book is not intended as medical advice. Its intention is solely informational and educational. Please consult a qualified medical or health professional if you wish to pursue the ideas presented.

Neither the editors, contributors, nor the sponsoring organization, the Autism Research Institute, is engaged in rendering professional advice or services to the individual reader. The ideas, procedures, and suggestions contained in this book are not intended as a substitute for consulting with a qualified physician and obtaining medical supervision regarding any activity, procedure, or suggestion that might affect your health. Neither the editors, nor contributors, nor the sponsoring organization, shall be liable or responsible for any loss, injury, or damage allegedly arising from any information or suggestion in this book.

Published by the Autism Research Institute
4182 Adams Avenue
San Diego, CA 92116, U.S.A.
www.AutismResearchInstitute.com

ISBN 0-9740360-1-3 (formerly ISBN 0-9740360-0-5)

PRINTED IN THE UNITED STATES OF AMERICA

# Contents


Acknowledgments ..... 5
Introduction to the Second Edition ..... 6
Introduction to the First Edition ..... 7
Part I Professional Perspectives ..... 13
*Chapter 1* The History of the Autism Research Institute and the Defeat Autism Now! (DAN!) Project (Rimland) ..... 15
*Chapter 2* Joining Hands to Overcome Autism (Green) ..... 26
*Chapter 3* What I Would Do If I Were a Parent of an Autistic Child: Recommendations Based on 25 Years of Research Experience (Edelson) ..... 38
Part II Parents Report Their Experiences ..... 45
Autism Symptom Profile: Matching Symptoms to Treatments ..... 46
*Chapter 4* Jackson's Story (Barnhart) ..... 49
*Chapter 5* Dillon's Story (Bayliss) ..... 54
*Chapter 6* I Am Sam (Bezalel) ..... 60
*Chapter 7* Story of Ryan and Stacy Blanco (Blanco) ..... 67
*Chapter 8* James (Burrell-Stella) ..... 77
*Chapter 9* My Son (Campbell-McBride) ..... 89
*Chapter 10* For the Love of Jake (Corcoran) ..... 94
*Chapter 11* A Very Tough Kid (Doggett) ..... 105
*Chapter 12* But What's Medically Wrong with My Children? (Duffield) ..... 123
*Chapter 13* There Is Hope (Hamilton) ..... 134
*Chapter 14* Becoming Aware of Our Son's Autism and Finding Hope for His Future (Helmick) ..... 142
*Chapter 15* Steven: Hopes, Prayers, and Progress (Hoffiz) ..... 154
*Chapter 16* My Son, the King of Metals (Holmes) ..... 160
*Chapter 17* When Lightning Strikes Twice (Jelen) ..... 165
*Chapter 18* Coming to Terms with Autism (Jepson) ..... 172
*Chapter 19* Michael… "That's Mike, Ed" (Kitt) ..... 177
*Chapter 20* Max's Story: A Homeopathic Cure of Autism (Lansky) ..... 185
*Chapter 21* Entering the World of Autism: A Mother's Story (Lewis) ..... 209
*Chapter 22* How Chelsey Changed Our Lives (McCandless) ..... 219
*Chapter 23* Through a Glass Darkly (Mead) ..... 232
*Chapter 24* Improving Every Day (Mendenhall) ..... 240
*Chapter 25* Hope Renewed (Miller) ..... 245
*Chapter 26* Austin's Journey (Parrott) ..... 251
*Chapter 27* Inspiration, Hope, Perseverance, and Success (Petrie) ..... 257
*Chapter 28* Love Never Fails (Rowe) ..... 263
*Chapter 29* Matthew's Story (Savage) ..... 273
*Chapter 30* Predetermined (Schlapfer) ..... 279
*Chapter 31* We Rescued Our Child from Autism (Seroussi) ..... 285
*Chapter 32* The Twinkle in His Eye (Sytsema) ..... 292
*Chapter 33* Doctor, Can You Tell Me What's Wrong with My Baby? (Vest) ..... 299
*Chapter 34* Against the Odds: A Story about Nikolai Young (Young) ..... 313

Part III How to Help Your Child: A Quick Start with Vitamin B6/ Magnesium and DMG ........ 323
*Chapter 35* Vitamin B6 (and Magnesium) in the Treatment of Autism ........ 325
*Chapter 36* The Most Air-Tight Study in Psychiatry? Vitamin B6 in Autism ........ 329
*Chapter 37* Vitamin B6 in Autism: The Safety Issue ........ 333
*Chapter 38* Dimethylglycine (DMG), a Nontoxic Metabolite, and Autism ........ 337
*Chapter 39* What Is the Right 'Dosage' of Vitamin B6, DMG, and Other Nutrients Useful in Autism? ........ 341
*Chapter 40* B6 and DMG Letters to the Editor, *ARRI* Newsletter ........ 344
*A.* Young Children ........ 345
*B.* School-Age Children ........ 355
*C.* Teenagers and Adults ........ 364
*Chapter 41* Abstracts of Studies of High-Dosage B6 (and often with Magnesium) in Autistic Children and Adults (1965-2005) ........ 372
Part IV How to Help Your Child: Other Treatment Modalities ........ 379
Parent Ratings of Behavioral Effects of Biomedical Interventions ........ 381
*A.* Autism ........ 382
*B.* Asperger Syndrome ........ 384
*Chapter 42* Vitamin C in the Prevention and Treatment of Autism ........ 386
*Chapter 43* Controlling Self-Injurious and Assaultive Behavior in Autism ........ 390
*Chapter 44* Puberty, Aggression, and Seizures ........ 394
*Chapter 45* *Candida*-Caused Autism? ........ 397
*Chapter 46* Our Children: Victims of Both Autism and Dogma ........ 400
*Chapter 47* Specific Carbohydrate Diet Reduces Autistic Symptoms ........ 404
*Chapter 48* Methylation: The Link Between Thimerosal and Autism? ........ 406
*Chapter 49* The 14th DAN! Conference: An Historical Event ........ 408
*Chapter 50* Two Letters to the Editor: Physician, Mom, Offer Success Stories ........ 411
*Chapter 51* Hyperbaric Oxygen Therapy: Dramatic Results Reported in Treating "Untreatable" Long-Term Neurological Damage ........ 413
*Chapter 52* Medical Marijuana: A Valuable Treatment for Autism? ........ 416
*Chapter 53* Clinical Use of Methyl-B12 in Autism ........ 423
*Chapter 54* New Therapy: Low-Dose Naltrexone for Immunomodulation ........ 427
*Chapter 55* Chelation: The Story Behind the Headlines ........ 430
*Chapter 56* Overview: Detoxification through Chelation Therapy ........ 433
Part V Appendices ........ 439
*Appendix A* Resources ........ 440
*Appendix B* ARI Internet Sites ........ 442
*Appendix C* Autism Treatment Evaluation Checklist (ATEC) ........ 444
*Appendix D* Abbreviations and Acronyms ........ 448
Index ........ 450

# Acknowledgments

We would like to express our gratitude to:

- The parents who share in this book the stories of their personal struggles with autism, and their successes. Their dedication and perseverance will provide valuable information and encouragement to countless families and professionals;

- Katharine Lawrence for her highly competent contributions to all phases of this book. We applaud the dedication, enthusiasm, and energy she devotes to her efforts to help families and their children;

- Tory Mead for her work on the initial phase of this project and for inviting many of the parents who contributed these wonderful stories about their children;

- Anna Mae Gushue for her help with preparing the book. Thanks also to Tom Bennett for help with the photos, and to the McCullough family. Several people proofread the book and provided us with constructive feedback: Dianne Doggett, Ray Hausler, Mary Lawrence, Dorothy Long, Arkady Mak, M.D., Ph.D., and Cindy Terry; and

- The many thousands of families and professionals worldwide who have supported the efforts of the Autism Research Institute over the past three-and-a-half decades.

# INTRODUCTION TO THE SECOND EDITION

It is unusual to change the title of a book between the first and second editions, but we have done so. Why? The original title, *Treating Autism,* was, in 2003, intended to be a bit provocative, since conventional thought held that autism was an untreatable lifelong disability. Drugs provided partial, symptomatic relief, in some cases, but with significant risk of serious side effects. However, such enormous progress has been made in developing effective treatments between 2003 and now, 2006, that we have changed the title to *Recovering Autistic Children.* It is fair to say that more progress has been made—and more autistic children have recovered—in these three years than in the prior three decades.

For the first time in history, in October 2004, at the Autism Research Institute-sponsored Defeat Autism Now! (DAN!) conference in Los Angeles, a group of recovered autistic children was introduced to, and interviewed before, a cheering crowd of 1,200 parents and professionals. One year later, a second group of recovered, formerly autistic children appeared onstage at our DAN! conference in Long Beach, California. Recovery, which was once thought to be an impossibility, then to be a rarity, is becoming commonplace. Visit www.Autism-RecoveredChildren.com to see videos of these historic events.

The Autism Research Institute has a list of approximately 1,000 recovered, or nearly recovered, autistic children whose parents have volunteered to discuss their children's recovery with the media. The message that Autism is Treatable; Recovery is Possible must reach a wider audience.

Please see pages 8-10 for a brief description of the updated and expanded sections of this new edition.

# Introduction to the First Edition



The Autism Research Institute (ARI), which was founded in 1967, has since then advocated a parent-driven revolution in the treatment of autism. ARI's basic premise is that parents are the best source of information on what helps—and what doesn't help—autistic children. Thanks to the information provided by parents, ARI's efforts have been remarkably successful.

It began with a few reports—"I removed milk from my child's diet, and he's a new person." "I started my daughter on the megadose nutrients, and she's talking now." "We eliminated yeast, and the tantrums stopped." The few reports snowballed into hundreds, then thousands. Every day parents contact ARI, describing incredible improvements in their autistic children as a direct result of a wide range of biomedical treatments. Growing numbers of physicians, many of whom are themselves parents of autistic children, are reporting that these interventions are changing the lives of their own children, and the lives of their patients.

The effective treatment methods that have evolved, as the result of the combined efforts of parents and professionals, are referred to collectively as the Defeat Autism Now! (DAN!) program.

The majority of these successful biomedical interventions involve nutritional and dietary approaches. Very few involve drugs, which are still the only treatment modality employed by the mainstream medical community. ARI's quarterly newsletter, the *Autism Research Review International (ARRI)*, often publishes readers' letters about these successful new treatments, but there is not enough space in the *ARRI* to accurately depict the dramatic ways in which they can benefit children with autism spectrum disorders.

The aim of this book is to provide in-depth stories written by parents and doctors who have used the rational, non-drug biomedical treatments recommended by ARI to improve the lives of autistic children. We hope these stories will give parents hope and direction, and provide physicians and other healthcare practitioners with real-life evidence that the era of simply drugging and institutionalizing autistic children has given way to an era of effectively treating them, frequently bringing about major improvement, and often recovery.

This book may be approached in several ways:

1. You can read the entire book from cover to cover to develop a broader and better understanding of how different parents, coming from different perspectives and caring for a very diverse group of children, have successfully used a variety of biomedical treatments.



2. You can use the Autism Symptom Profile on pages 46 and 47 to compare your child's symptoms with those of the children who are described in the book. In this way, you can focus on the successful treatment of children who are most similar to your own child.

3. You can use the Index to look up specific topics that are of special concern, such as failure to speak, aggression, or tantrums, or to learn what interventions have been helpful.

This book is divided into five parts:

- **Part I** contains chapters written by Drs. Bernard Rimland, John Green, and Stephen M. Edelson. Dr. Rimland describes his introduction to autism when he and his wife discovered that their two-year-old son, Mark, was autistic. Dr. Rimland then shares with the reader valuable insights based on his 50 years of experience with autism. Dr. Green describes his perspective as a physician who has successfully treated many autistic individuals and provides the reader with an excellent introduction to the DAN! approach. Dr. Edelson discusses what he would do if he were a parent and suggests ways in which parents may determine if a treatment truly helped their child.

- **Part II** consists of 31 parent-written accounts of how autistic individuals have benefited from the DAN! approach. These are only a small sampling of those who have improved, and even recovered, as a result of effective biomedical approaches to autism. We hope that as you read the true stories in this book, you will gain both inspiration and practical guidance from the parents and professionals who are revolutionizing the treatment of autistic children. The word "hopeless" is being eliminated from the vocabulary of autism. Part II also includes chapter updates completed in late 2005 for this Second Edition.

- **Part III**, "How to Help Your Child: A Quick Start with Vitamin B6/Magnesium and DMG," provides a great deal of information from various sources on the use of vitamin B6 with magnesium and dimethylglycine (DMG) in treating autism. Included are 58 "Letters to the Editor" from the *ARRI* that were written by parents and some professionals to report their experience with vitamin B6 with magnesium and DMG. ARI has received many hundreds of such letters from parents describing remarkable improvement in their children as a result of using these supplements. Of all the biomedical treatments for autistic individuals, including drugs, the use of vitamin B6 with magnesium has received the most scientific support (22 positive research studies to date, including 13 double-blind controlled experiments; information about these studies is included in Chapter 41). Although research on the use of DMG to treat autism has been sparse, there is much evidence showing that it is a very safe and often highly effective nutritional supplement.



- **Part IV**, "How to Help Your Child: Other Treatment Modalities," consists of research findings from ARI's parent surveys and recent articles from the *ARRI* on a large variety of useful interventions. Two tables include the most recent analysis of the Treatment Effectiveness Survey. The first table, based on the responses of over 24,500 parents, permits you to compare the safety and efficacy of virtually all the drugs used in treating autism with a great many nutritional supplements and diets. Inspection of this table will demonstrate why the DAN! approach, which emphasizes special diets and supplements, is so much safer and more effective than the drugs prescribed by conventional doctors. A second table presents treatment rating results for those with Asperger syndrome. The *ARRI* articles provide important information to help understand and treat autistic individuals as well as information on promising and emerging treatments.

- **Part V** consists of several Appendices:

- **Appendices A** and **B** provide a list of resources and ARI's websites that provide information to parents and professionals. Almost all of the information sources list websites. For those who do not own a computer, most public libraries offer free access to the Internet. Additionally, the *ARRI* provides up-to-date news on biomedical and educational research. Past issues of the *ARRI* and an index are available at www.AutismNewsletter.com. The publication list of the Autism Research Institute is available both on its website and in printed form from ARI (4182 Adams Avenue, San Diego, CA 92116, U.S.A., fax: 619-563-6840). The ARI publication list provides access to many books, videos, audiotapes, specialized information packages, and other items.



- **Appendix C** presents the Autism Treatment Effectiveness Checklist (ATEC). The ATEC allows parents to evaluate the effectiveness of a treatment and/or measure the progress of their child. Professionals and researchers also use the ATEC to evaluate the efficacy of various treatments. (This form may also be printed from ARI's website, which provides an immediate no-cost scoring service.)

- **Appendix D** provides a list of Abbreviations and Acronyms.

We wish to emphasize that the biomedical approaches described in this book are most effective when combined with intensive educational approaches. One of the most important benefits of biomedical treatments, as many parents tell us in their chapters, is that they "open the children up" to the experience of learning. We strongly encourage parents to pursue educational and biomedical treatments concurrently to maximize their children's progress.

ARI advises parents who are initiating biomedical treatments to refrain from mentioning these treatments to the child's teachers, therapists, grandparents, neighbors, etc., to see if improvement is spontaneously noticed by these observers. We have heard from hundreds of parents that teachers have asked them, "What is going on? Billy has learned more in the past week than in the past two months!" What a joy it is to hear such remarks!

## Part I

# Professional Perspectives



Part I provides the historical background and discusses many of the concepts and treatments involved in the biomedical approach to autism. The authors are Bernard Rimland, Ph.D., director of the Autism Research Institute in San Diego; John Green, M.D., medical director of The Ever-Green Center in Oregon City, Oregon; and Stephen M. Edelson, Ph.D., assistant director of the Autism Research Institute in San Diego.

# — Chapter 1 —
# The History of the Autism Research Institute and the Defeat Autism Now! (DAN!) Project

By Bernard Rimland, Ph.D.
Autism Research Institute, San Diego, California



It all started with the birth of my own autistic son, in 1956. Mark was a screaming, implacable infant who resisted being cuddled and struggled against being picked up. He also struggled against being put down. Our pediatrician, Dr. Black, who had been in practice for 35 years, had never seen or heard of a child like Mark. Neither Dr. Black nor I, who at that time was three years beyond my Ph.D. in psychology, had ever seen or heard the word "autism." It was not until Mark was two years old that my wife, Gloria, remembered reading, in one of her old college textbooks, about children like Mark, who looked through people rather than at them, and who accurately repeated radio commercials and nursery rhymes, but did not engage in communicative speech. I went out to the garage, found the dusty box of old college texts, and there, five years after I had earned a Ph.D. as a research psychologist, I saw the word "autism" for the first time. Today autism is an all-too-familiar word—even to high-school students.

Autism was *extremely* rare in those days, occurring perhaps once or twice in every 10,000 live births. Slowly but surely, the prevalence was rising. In my summary of research on the prevalence of autism, published in an article I wrote for the *Autism Research Review International (ARRI)* in 1989, I reported that a number of studies showed autism to occur on average in 4.5 children per 10,000 live births. In 1995, I published an editorial in the *ARRI* announcing that an epidemic of autism appeared to have started. The medical authorities jeered. "Impossible!" they said, "It is not a real increase—it is just an increase in awareness." They were wrong—the increase is very real.

More recently, in 2002, I reported that studies conducted in both the U.S. and the U.K. showed that autism now occurs in 45 to 68 children out of 10,000 live births—an increase of 1000 to 1500% in a decade! And studies show that the increase cannot be attributed to changes in diagnostic criteria or greater awareness. Later chapters in this book will help explain the causes of the epidemic, and suggest approaches to deal with it.

Starting with the several references cited in my wife's old text, I began to read everything I could find on the subject of autism. I was appalled to find that it was uniformly believed, and presented as an established fact in every textbook, that autism was an emotional (psychological) disorder. The only treatment recommendations were psychoanalysis or other forms of psychotherapy for both the mother and the child. The mother was required to acknowledge her guilt, and confess that she hated the child and wished it had never been born. The child, in so-called "play therapy," was provided with a paper or clay image of a woman (his mother) and was encouraged to tear it to bits, thus expressing his hostility toward his mother, whom the psychotherapists were positive had caused his autism. There were a few drugs that were also used with autistic children, but then, as now, the idea was not to treat the autism but to slow the children down enough to make life tolerable for those who must deal with them.



I decided to read everything I could possibly find on the subject of autism, not only to learn what might be done to help Mark, but also to try to understand on what basis the psychiatrists had decided that mothers were to blame for their children's autism. After four years I had read everything I could find on the subject of autism, including translations of the foreign language articles I could not read myself. I learned that, despite the supreme confidence (arrogance) with which the authorities proclaimed the mothers were to blame, I could find no shred of scientific evidence for such a belief. The book I wrote, *Infantile Autism: The Syndrome and Its Implications for a Neural Theory of Behavior*, won the Century Award in 1964, and resulted, as I had intended, in destroying the belief in the "psychogenic hypothesis" that autism was an emotional disorder caused by bad mothering. Instead, I successfully argued, the biological causes of autism must be sought.

The resulting publicity—I had overnight become *the* world authority on autism—resulted in many invitations to speak at universities and medical schools, and in my receiving many letters and phone calls from other parents, as well as from a number of research scientists interested in exploring the ideas presented in *Infantile Autism*.

In 1965, having been favorably impressed by the excellent results achieved by Ivar Lovaas at UCLA in teaching autistic children with the behavior modification techniques now called applied behavior analysis, or ABA (professionals at the time, of course, overwhelmingly derided Lovaas' work), I founded the Autism Society of America (ASA) to provide a nationwide forum for informing parents about such new and important developments. Two years later, in 1967, I founded the Autism Research Institute

(ARI) as a center for collecting, analyzing, and disseminating research on the cause and treatment of autism. Founding the ASA, as well as the ARI, were expressions then, as now, of a lack of confidence in the community of professionals who dealt with autism.

One of the first letters I received was from a mother in Canada who was experimenting with high doses of certain vitamins in the treatment of her autistic child. It seemed to me to be a rather crazy idea, but she was reporting good results. The Canadian mother sent me a letter that she had received from her own mother, the child's grandmother, who was a nurse in a psychiatric hospital in Saskatoon. The grandmother's letter observed that two sophisticated young psychiatrists, Drs. Abram Hoffer and Humphry Osmond (who later became my friends and colleagues), were experimenting with large doses of vitamin B3 on their adult schizophrenic patients. The grandmother wrote that she and the other psychiatric nurses and staff members could see quite remarkable improvement in the patients that Hoffer and Osmond were treating with "megavitamin" B3. The improvement was clearly better than that seen in the patients being treated by the other psychiatrists, who used only drugs. Nevertheless, to the surprise and disappointment of the nursing staff, the traditional psychiatrists refused to see what was so clearly evident to everyone else, that Hoffer's and Osmond's megavitamin treatments were in fact effective. Since I was so keenly aware that the psychiatric establishment had shown a total lack of intellectual integrity by falsely blaming the mothers for causing autism, on the basis of no data, it did not surprise me that the psychiatric establishment could also be deluding itself with regard to the efficacy of treatments. Hoffer and Osmond had published a number of scientific controlled double- and triple-blind studies supporting their initial findings. It made no difference to the great majority in the psychiatric establishment who were—and still are—hooked on drug treatments.

Over a period of several years I began to hear from other mothers, in California, New York, Georgia, and elsewhere, that they were, on their own, trying high doses of vitamins on their autistic children, and that certain vitamins, especially vitamin B6, seemed to be helping. There was so much consistency in these reports that I decided to conduct a large-scale study of several of the most promising vitamins, and in the late 1960s I undertook such a study, based on several hundred autistic children whose parents had contacted me seeking help and advice.

The first problem was to find flavored vitamins, since some of the vitamins of interest, especially B6 and B3, are very bitter. I wrote to all 26 vitamin manufacturers in the *Thomas Register* to ask if they would be willing to make flavored vitamins for a study we were planning on autistic children. Twenty-four of the 26 companies did not reply. One of the two who replied simply said, "Not interested." The other company, Kirkman Labs of Portland, Oregon, said, "Certainly, we'll be glad to help. Just tell us what you need." A very welcome, and very important, letter! Remember, in those days, the late '60s, autism was extremely rare—probably only one or two children per 10,000, and almost no one had even heard the term "autism."

Kirkman Labs worked diligently with us for many months, sending us sample after sample of tablets flavored to mask the taste of B3 and B6, so they would be palatable to autistic children. Kirkman did this at their own expense, which must have been considerable. Without them we would have failed. As a parent and as a researcher, I will forever be grateful to Kirkman Labs, which continues to manufacture vitamins and other products tailored to the needs of autistic children.



The results of my first study were quite positive, especially for vitamin B6. At the time of this writing I am aware of 22 studies of vitamin B6 as used in autistic children, conducted by researchers in seven countries, and all studies but one have provided positive results (see Chapter 41 for information about these studies). (The only study not reporting benefits involved only nine children.) Adding magnesium to the B6 has repeatedly been found to be essential for best results. Eleven of the studies have been double-blind, placebo-controlled studies. Nevertheless, a great many articles and textbooks representing the views of the medical establishment still continue to say that vitamin therapy for autism has not been proven, or that it is unsafe. Both contentions are false—just as their view was false that autism was caused by bad mothering.

As the years went on, I continued to find, repeatedly, that the parents, especially the mothers, were remarkably effective at identifying treatments that were helpful to their autistic children. They were also very observant in detecting factors that caused their children to become worse. In 1967 we began to systematically collect such data from parents of autistic children and to include on our questionnaires items about the effects of vaccines on the children. Many parents had reported their children to get markedly worse after the DPT (diphtheria/pertussis/tetanus) shot. In recent years, as the number of vaccines given infants increased from three to 22, the number of parents reporting vaccine-related deterioration of their children has skyrocketed.

We also began collecting information about the effects of milk and wheat on children's behavior, since many parents were telling us that their children did much better on a casein-free and/or gluten-free diet.

For too many years, autism research had largely been confined to descriptive efforts (What are the symptoms? What brain areas and functions are affected?) or to trying various psychiatric drugs, developed for other purposes, which might bring about reduction of symptoms. Even with such limited goals, progress was far from encouraging.

Drugs, in particular, quite apart from their harmful side effects, have absorbed far too much research funds, time, and attention. Autism has never been caused by a deficiency of Ritalin or Risperdal. I recently heard the same interesting comment from two psychiatrists, both mothers of autistic sons. One physician mother was from Maryland, the other from California: "It is one thing to be looking in the *Physicians Desk Reference* for a drug for another mother's child. When it is your own child, you see the same words with very different eyes."



Since its establishment in 1967, the Autism Research Institute has had, as a major priority, the tracking of promising treatments for autism. Intensive study of the scientific literature, and analysis of case reports from literally thousands of parents of autistic children, convinced us that there is much that can be done *now* to help the children. Progress in the acceptance of useful medical interventions is painfully slow—it is not uncommon for a safe and effective treatment to be available for decades before it is widely implemented. Hoffer's and Osmond's discovery in the early 1950s that vitamin B3 confers major benefits to adults with acute-onset schizophrenia is still largely ignored by the psychiatric establishment. Another more recent example is the use of small amounts of folic acid, a very safe B vitamin, as a means of preventing severe birth defects. It is estimated that over 25,000 cases of mental retardation could have been prevented in the U.S. if widespread use of folic acid supplements had been recommended when the discovery was first announced in the 1960s, rather than 30 years later, in the 1990s. There are a multitude of similar examples.

It was very evident that there were a number of treatments, largely discovered by the mothers of autistic children, that were much more effective than the drugs being used by the psychiatric establishment, and certainly much safer.

In 1994, after a series of discussions with my esteemed colleagues Sidney Baker, M.D., and Jon Pangborn, Ph.D., we decided to call together a think-tank of exceptionally competent and open-minded physicians and scientists who were interested in the ideas that we shared, and could help us make sense of them. The purpose would be to identify treatments—safe treatments—for which there is credible evidence of efficacy. Once these efficacious treatments were identified, an attempt would be made to find why they work, so their efficacy could be improved.

The Autism Research Institute convened the first Defeat Autism Now! (DAN!) conference in Dallas in January, 1995. The attendees were approximately 30 physicians and scientists, from the U.S. and Europe, with special expertise in autism research and treatment. Psychiatry, neurology, immunology, allergy, biochemistry, genetics, and gastroenterology were among the fields represented. A number of attendees were, like Jon Pangborn and me, parents of autistic children.



The conference was a great success: there was a cordial meeting of the minds and a very rapid consensus among the participants, most of whom had never met each other before, as to the most useful approaches to treatment.

The participants agreed that one of the major priorities of the DAN! Project should be the publication of a document representing the best ideas and practices of those in attendance, so that they could share their expertise with physicians everywhere who were interested in bringing about real improvement in the diagnosis and treatment of autism, as quickly as possible. The document, *Autism: Effective Biomedical Treatments* (often referred to as the DAN! Clinical Manual or the DAN! Protocol), was first published in February 1996. It was updated in January 1997, April 1999, September 2001, October 2002, and September 2005. It represents a consensus statement of the state-of-the-art alternative medical approach to the treatment of autism. (The 1996 version covered 41 pages; the 2005 version, 328 pages!)

Follow up DAN! conferences were held annually for five years, going to twice a year in 2001, to further advance the treatment of autism. The conferences have produced a base of physicians who wish to employ rational, scientifically sound approaches to the diagnosis and treatment of autism, and who regard psychoactive drugs as their last choice, not their first.

The *Effective Biomedical Treatments Manual* represents the best thinking of some of the very best minds in the field of autism. The planning of the DAN! conferences and think tanks and the arduous work of putting together the ideas expressed at the DAN! conference were undertaken by my two exceptionally talented colleagues:

- Sidney M. Baker, M.D., a graduate of and former faculty member of the Yale Medical School and former director of the Gesell Institute of Human Development, who has extensive training and experience in pediatrics, allergy, immunology, neurology, biochemistry, and computer science.

- Jon Pangborn, Ph.D., a fellow of the American Institute of Chemists and Certified Clinical Nutritionist, who is also the father of an autistic son. Now a private consultant, Dr. Pangborn was formerly president of Doctor's Data, a major medical laboratory, and very probably has studied more biochemical workups of autistic patients than anyone else on Earth.

Drs. Baker and Pangborn have worked together on the biochemistry of autism since the early 1980s. Although the writing of the Manual is done by the Baker and Pangborn team, new ideas and careful refinement of concepts already in the Manual take place at DAN! "think-tank" conferences of leading physicians and researchers, which range in duration from a day to a weekend. Eighteen DAN! think-tanks have been convened by the Autism Research Institute thus far.



*Autism: Effective Biomedical Treatments* was written for:

- Physicians who wish to apply state-of-the-art medical knowledge and technology to the process of diagnosing and treating their autistic patients. (Visit www.AutismResearchInstitute.com, or write ARI: 4182 Adams Avenue, San Diego, CA 92116, U.S.A., or fax 619-563-6840, for referrals near you.)

- Parents of autistic children who, having received a copy of the DAN! Manual, will take it to the child's physician to see if the physician may be willing to undertake the intensive workup suggested. If that physician is not interested, the parents may wish to seek another physician.

One of the consequences of the huge upsurge in autism during the past decade has been a great number of autistic children born into families in which one or both parents are physicians. A good many of these physician-parents, after having explored conventional medicine's approaches toward dealing with autistic children, and finding them ineffective, have joined the ranks of DAN! doctors. At the Autism Society of America's annual conference in San Diego in July, 2001, and again at ASA's conference in Indianapolis in July, 2002, the Autism Research Institute has sponsored panel presentations titled "Physicians who have successfully treated their own autistic children." These videos can be viewed on ARI's website: www.AutismResearchInstitute.com.

Jaquelyn McCandless, M.D., a board certified psychiatrist and neurologist, was about to retire when her 14th grandchild, Chelsey, was diagnosed autistic. Dr. McCandless accepted the challenge. After diligent research, she adopted the DAN! approach. Her story is told in her excellent, very helpful book, *Children With Starving Brains*, also available from ARI. You will also find a chapter and two articles by her in this book.

Afterword: Oh yes! You are wondering about my son Mark, whom we were told to institutionalize and forget at age five, who was still in diapers at seven and did not ask or answer a question until age eight. Mark began to improve dramatically when we started behavior modification and vitamin B6 with magnesium. Later, dimethylglycine (DMG) also helped greatly. Mark, now 50, is still on megadose B6 and magnesium, lives at home with his parents, attends a day program for mentally disabled adults, takes the city bus to the day program, makes daily visits to the art galleries and coffee shops in the neighborhood, and has turned out to be a remarkably talented artist, discovered at age 22. Mark has been interviewed about his art on NBC, CBS, CNN, and PBS. (He confided to the CBS interviewer, "I *like* being famous.") He did the illustrations for his sister Helen Landalf's book for children, *The Secret Night World of Cats*, and had the pleasure of meeting with Dustin Hoffman, as Hoffman prepared for his role in *Rain Man*. We are proud of Mark. Not such a bad outcome, after all!

Now, with all that said:



**What is a parent to do?**

The first choice for parents is obviously to find a well qualified DAN! doctor nearby and get the lab tests done to identify what is needed to correct whatever metabolic problems the lab tests reveal. That is much easier said than done. There are too few DAN! doctors, and often their first available appointment is many months in the future. Some are so busy they will not enroll any new patients.

If you are one of the many parents whose child's autism started during the second year, and you believe (correctly, I think, in most cases) that vaccines played a causal role, you will need the help of a competent physician to help with the mercury (and other heavy metals) detoxification process.

Several of the parent-authored chapters that follow will be helpful to you in understanding and implementing the detoxification process. Our ARI *Mercury Detoxification Consensus Report*, the product of our mercury detoxification think-tank, is available free on www.AutismMercuryDetox.com or by mail for $5.00 (ARI, 4182 Adams Ave., San Diego, CA 92116).

What would I do if I could not get a timely doctor's appointment? I would do exactly what I have been suggesting to parents for over three decades: Place the child on high-dose vitamin B6 and magnesium, and on dimethylglycine (DMG), for a trial period of at least six weeks, to see if these very safe non-prescription nutritional supplements will help. Also, as I have been suggesting for over three decades, the child should be placed on the gluten-free, casein-free (GFCF) diet for at least several months, again on a trial basis.



Should you start all of these treatment approaches at once? That is debatable. If you were doing a scientific research study, you would try only one approach at a time, so as not to confuse the effect of treatment X with treatment Y. Many parents do choose to try one treatment at a time, so they can better understand the effects on the child.

On the other hand, you are not undertaking a scientific experiment in order to publish an article in a professional journal but rather are trying to help your child, and you know time should not be wasted. Most parents feel that their primary job is to help the child as much as possible and as quickly as possible, so they will put off teasing out the differential effects of the various treatments until later on. These parents often will try several interventions at once, such as the B6/magnesium, the DMG, and the GFCF diet. I am somewhat more disposed toward the latter approach: "Help the child first, worry later about exactly what it is that's helping the child."

You may be wondering how you can be sure that the interventions I suggest will really help your child. There's no way to be sure without trying them—every child is very different from every other child—but I am very confident that these interventions will help a large percentage of the children on whom they are tried and will harm none of them. Here is why I believe these interventions are very worth trying:

1. There are many excellent scientific studies showing that B6/magnesium as well as the GFCF diet are effective. Less scientific evidence is available on the efficacy of DMG, but like B6/magnesium and the GFCF diet, it is very safe. (Chapter 41 summarizes the studies showing B6/magnesium to be effective.)

2. I have been getting informal feedback from many thousands of parents in letters, phone calls and personal conversations since the late 1960s. The following parent stories in this book, and the "Letters to the Editor" in Chapter 40, are a small sample of the very encouraging input that I have received concerning vitamin B6/magnesium and DMG.

3. The Autism Research Institute has been collecting formal parent surveys on the effects of various drugs, diets, supplements, and other interventions since 1967. The tables on pages 381-385 present the statistics ARI has compiled over the past 36 years showing how parents (over 24,500 of them!) have rated the various interventions. Our conclusions are solid: B6 and magnesium, DMG, and the GFCF diet are very worth trying. So are a number of other non-drug treatments, but I'd start with these recommended interventions, to be augmented later, after some more trial and error, with some of the other safe nutritional supplements that are listed at the bottom half of the tables. As the tables show very clearly, the nutritional supplement and special diet approaches are far safer and far more likely to be helpful than any drug.



Before undertaking the above mentioned treatments, or *any* treatments for that matter, there are two things I would do:

1. I would complete an Autism Treatment Evaluation Checklist (ATEC) about the child, before any treatment is started (i.e., do a baseline ATEC), and periodically, say every two weeks, or every month, complete an additional ATEC form for the child. That will permit you to keep track of any changes as a result of the interventions, over time. The ATEC is a simple, one-page means of evaluating the effect of various interventions on your child. Appendix C includes a copy of the ATEC and information about its use. Your ATEC responses may be entered also at www.ARI-ATEC.com, and the total scores and subscores will be immediately provided. There is no cost for this service.

2. I would refrain from mentioning that I was trying these interventions to others in the child's environment, such as teachers, babysitters, relatives, and neighbors—especially teachers and ABA therapists,

who are likely to keep accurate written records of the child's progress. We have heard from hundreds of parents over the years that they have, on our advice, refrained from mentioning to the teachers the use of the GFCF diet, or the use of B6 and magnesium and/or DMG, and in many cases, within a few days, the teacher has come to the parent asking: "What is going on? Johnny has made more progress in the past week than he has in the past two months." By keeping your trials of new interventions a secret from teachers and others in the child's environment, you provide yourself with an invaluable opportunity to benefit from such unbiased observations. Each child thus becomes, in effect, a subject in a double-blind "mini-study."



**The gluten-/casein-free diet** is explained in many excellent books authored by mothers (usually) of autistic children. These books contain a wealth of how-to information, sources and resources, and kitchen-tested recipes. Since my culinary skills are limited to making toast and boiling eggs, I can do no better than heartily recommend some of these books, which are available from ARI (see also www.AutismNDI.com):

1. Lisa Lewis, Ph.D., *Special Diets for Special Kids* I and II.

2. Karyn Seroussi, *Unraveling the Mystery of Autism and Pervasive Developmental Disorder: A Mother's Story of Research and Recovery.*

3. Sally Ramsey, *The Cheerful Chemist's No Casein, No Gluten, Sugar Optional Cookbook.*

4. Bruce Semon, M.D., Ph.D. and Lori Kornblum, *Feast Without Yeast; 4 Stages to Better Health.*

## — Chapter 2 —

# Joining Hands to Overcome Autism

By John Green, M.D.
The EverGreen Center, Oregon City, Oregon

*Dr. Green, a specialist in clinical ecology and nutritional medicine and a DAN! practitioner, works in Oregon City, Oregon. You'll notice that his name appears in several of the other stories in this book.*



I have been practicing medicine for 27 years. My first five years in practice were spent discovering that much of what I was taught in medical school proved ineffective at resolving chronic health problems. Subsequently, over the past 22 years, my focus has been on learning how to treat patients with chronic "mystery" illnesses, which are generally poorly responsive to conventional therapies.

The first teachers in this new medicine I have been learning were patients. They asked penetrating questions; they tried new interventions—diets, vitamins, herbs, detoxification, colonics, breathing exercises, visualizations, energetic therapies, etc.; and they brought me books, tapes, and phone numbers of healers who had helped them. In some cases my skepticism was too strong, but in many cases the changes I saw in my patients helped me to listen and learn from their experiences. This helped me find other doctors with minds and hearts open to learning and teaching better ways to care for our patients. The most important groups of like-minded physicians in my "upbringing" in medicine are the American Holistic Medical Association, the American Academy of Environmental Medicine, the American Enzyme Potentiated Desensitization (EPD) Society, and the Defeat Autism Now! (DAN!) group.

Over the years I have encountered four main challenges in this work. The first arises from medical training, which teaches us to group patients by diseases, in order to study the disease, and treat the disease rather than the patient. This stereotypic process fails to adequately address such important variables as biochemical individuality, belief systems, individual susceptibility and vitality. Also, by reducing patient problems to specialty areas, such as gastroenterology, neurology, psychiatry, and immunology, we in effect separate our patients into parts. Who is to reconnect the whole and unify the patient? Autism, as discussed below, is a multifactorial illness, with tissue injury occurring through a variety of self-reinforcing mechanisms. Autistic patients require an integrative approach to treatment, rather than a reductionistic approach. So M.D.-type doctors need to learn to think holistically in order to best help autism spectrum disorder (ASD) kids.

The second challenge relates to time and money. There is so much to explore related to a person's illness—the patient's story, the family dynamic, laboratory tests, response to past treatments, which treatments are appropriate, priority and sequencing for specific interventions, and evaluation of response to treatment. With every patient, a doctor faces constraints on time and money, which influence the therapeutic milieu. In each case it is necessary to develop a way of working within these constraints in order to optimize the resources of the patient and the family. In some cases this requires approaching treatment in an empirical and often intuitive fashion. In other cases where resources are relatively unrestricted, there is an opportunity to do more testing and develop treatments based on the results. These patients who receive more in-depth investigation have provided help in understanding how to treat some of the aspects of autism in other children.



In working with ASD patients from all walks of life, it has proven extremely helpful to use phone, fax, and both types of mail. I encourage families to report in monthly with progress updates and any questions, and this helps us to reduce office visits to about half the frequency we would otherwise need. This decreases demands on the family in many ways, including missed work time and school or therapy time. Many families have learned to be very succinct about encapsulating for me a summary of the past month, including response to interventions, assessment of current status (I use a symptom checklist and score sheet to help with this), and update on diet and exactly which supplements and medications are being given (including dosage). Some parents even send videos of their children to vividly show how they're doing.

The third challenge relates to risk and uncertainty. If we choose to provide no medical treatment to an autistic child, we risk losing the opportunity of bringing about major change in the "golden" first five years, and this is one of the saddest losses. If we choose, as have the DAN! doctors, to offer the treatments that have been shown to be effective in many children, even if lacking the endorsement of the medical establishment, we face other risks:

- One risk is lack of insurance coverage, which is common and desperately needs to be changed.

- Another risk is adverse action by authorities, including regulatory institutions. In extreme cases, child abuse allegations have been made against parents by child protective services because children were receiving treatments not approved by the medical establishment. Innovation is risky. There is the risk of uncertain outcome with new therapies, and the sometimes greater risk of ostracism or attack by defenders of the status quo. Several DAN! doctors, including myself, have been subjected to investigation by the state medical licensing board related to treatments that have helped many autistic children. The experience of undergoing investigation by an intrinsically antagonistic medical board is harrowing, expensive, and degrading, even when the doctor is cleared of any "wrongdoing." I personally know several doctors who have lost their licenses for stepping out of the box in order to offer innovative and effective treatments. Dr. Andy Wakefield's experience as a whistleblower epitomizes the injustice inherent in a medical system that can be so self-serving as to shoot the messenger.

- An additional risk is that a child might be harmed by a treatment. In fact, to date the therapies derived from the DAN! Protocol are remarkably safe, with no reports of serious injury or irreversible harm to my knowledge—the one exception being a case stemming from a drug error caused by two similar-sounding medications. *[Editors' note: please see page 430.]* Nevertheless, prudence is essential; and we continue to investigate gentler, less expensive, and easier ways of treating such problems as toxic metals, yeast and bacterial overgrowth, allergies and autoimmunity, inflamed bowels, and circulatory and metabolic problems.

- Still another risk for professionals is psychological. Autism is a very complex disease, and committing to treat affected children calls upon all of our emotional resources. Children are unpredictable in their responses to interventions as simple as eliminating one food from their diet, or giving a probiotic or a B vitamin. It is both inspiring and humbling to travel along with families in their journey through autism and its vagaries. It is common to find that children who have similar lab findings and symptom profiles may respond quite differently to the same treatment. This requires the doctor to work hard at dropping personal demands that we must get it

> right the first time. It may be as valuable to learn what does not help a child as what does help, if we can stay tuned in and use this information to better shape our approach to treatment. But if the doctor is heavily invested in a particular treatment that has failed, the disappointment or frustration may occlude the doctor's view of what comes next. So we doctors and parents need to be almost as resilient as the children.

The fourth of the challenges I have encountered derives from our Western materialistic (Newtonian) view of reality and illness. Whereas an illness is actually an expression of a body that is out of balance struggling to restore balance, we tend to think of illnesses as "entities," ascribing to them an almost physical existence. We doctors also seek to objectify and quantify people's experience of illness, i.e., "Rate your pain on a 10-point scale," "How many stools per day?" "Her mercury level is only 4 ppm." We do need data to assess and prioritize approaches to treatment. But we can be led astray by invalid data. For example, one autistic child I am treating has had three IQ tests over three years. The first time, at age four, she scored 68, or significantly retarded. The second time, at age 5½, she scored 89, or mildly subnormal. The third time, at age seven, she scored 100 or "average." Is her intelligence increasing with treatment, or are the numbers invalid, changing because of her improving ability to relate to the testing process? In her case, the latter seems to be true. But if her parents had accepted the first test score, expectations for this child would have been very low, focusing mainly on training her to get along in life. Now expectations focus on educating her to help her thrive and contribute in life.



In many cases, the parent knows best. This was illustrated by one secretin study in which psychologists evaluating ASD kids treated with either placebo or active secretin were unable to distinguish treatment with placebo from treatment with active hormone. Parents, on the other hand, were able to identify the active therapy with a high degree of confidence.

We must strike a balance between knowing the data about the illness and knowing the patient's experience. Quantifying symptoms and measuring lab results can help us to better monitor progress and change therapy, but if we rely too heavily on data, our work can become sterile and devoid of love. Autistic children are confronted with pain, frustration, fear, and confusion in their lives. These are issues each of us must face at times in our own lives. Children are wonderful models and teachers for us if we can share our humanness with them and allow our own deeper issues to be touched by their suffering and their buoyancy. My office walls are papered with delightful drawings produced by artistic autistic children who convey their love, their hope, or simply an overflowing of their perceptions to be shared with anyone.

Eight years ago a mom brought her four-year-old autistic son, Jordan, to me for evaluation. He was only the third autistic person I had treated, and at that time mom knew more about the disease and its treatment than I did. We approached his treatment together, with mom helping me to let go of stereotypes I had acquired about autism as an untreatable illness. She also gently helped me to access tools that I'd used in investigating many other types of chronic illness, i.e., looking at his biochemistry, allergies, gut flora, toxins, and general nutritional adequacy, and supporting the strengths of the family. Jordan has made great progress over these years, doing well academically, becoming involved in religious training, and demonstrating real talent as a musical performer. His main residual difficulties are a mild speech impediment, mild respiratory allergies, somewhat concrete thinking, and a tendency to obsess about certain subjects. Last week we had a detailed conversation about what it means to be autistic and what it is to obsess. He described being autistic as a different way of thinking. He said he knows he is obsessing when mom says, "Couldn't we talk about something else now?" Jordan has a delightful sense of humor, a very affectionate nature, and a striking concern about justice. Jordan and his mother really opened for me the world of treating autistic children.



I began to see a few other affected kids, and then in 1999 another mom brought a deluge of ASD kids after I began treating her daughter. She had been to a meeting I was attending in another state on autism treatments. When I introduced myself and my practice location in a question-and-answer period, she searched me out after returning home. After her daughter began to improve under my care, she referred others in her network to me. I became acquainted with more parents of ASD children and was amazed at the devotion, intelligence, and commitment that are common to these people. The severity of the autism epidemic became palpable to me, and a growing sense of urgency developed. I learned more about caring for the affected children, and felt a growing need to commit my practice to these children and their families. So, for the past 2½ years, I've been saying goodbye to my faithful adult patients and accepting only affected children into the practice.

My evaluations of more than 300 ASD children have demonstrated clearly that these children are physically ill, afflicted with significant problems in many organ systems. The work of treating them amounts to two basic processes, both aiming to restore balance and vigor and proper communications extending from the cellular level to the interpersonal.

The first basic process is the identification and treatment or removal of obstacles to healthy organ activity. There are many such obstacles in the worlds of ASD kids, some obvious and some subtle. Commonly encountered obstacles include allergies and food intolerances, metal and chemical toxicities, infections (fungal, viral, bacterial, parasitic, and mycoplasmal), oxidative stress (problems with electrons moving around in the body out of control), acidosis (too much acid being produced in the system, though usually not in the stomach, where it is needed), and psychosocial stress (sensory issues, confusion and frustration, difficulty recognizing and receiving love, etc.). A child may show major improvement simply by clearing an obstacle which is really troubling him, such as a food intolerance, yeast infection, or metal poisoning.



The second basic process is identifying what is weak, disrupted, or deficient in a child and working to overcome or compensate for the impairment. ASD children often have impairments or deficiencies in immune defenses (especially in cellular immunity and in the proper regulation of the immune response). They are commonly deficient in many essential nutrients due to self-restricted diets, poor digestion and absorption, nutrient wasting through cellular energy disruption, our nutrient-depleted food supply, etc. Their tissue oxygenation may be disrupted by stiff red blood cells, abnormal clotting tendencies, and acidosis. Excess acid in the system results in hyperventilation (over-breathing), which decreases brain blood flow. Deficiencies in digestive factors are extremely common, including essential enzymes (dipeptidyl peptidase IV [DPP-IV] and others), stomach acid, intestinal hormones (secretin, cholecystokinin [CCK]), bicarbonate (acid neutralizer), secretory IgA (antibody lining and protecting the mucous membranes), and beneficial flora (friendly germs). Neurotransmitter levels and activities are often weak in ASD, related to a number of factors, including disruption of vitamin B6-dependent enzymes (which are extensively involved in neurotransmitter synthesis; impairment of these enzymes may raise body requirements for B6 several hundred-fold). Weakness in detoxification functions is common in ASD. There are many aspects to this problem, salient factors being impaired synthesis of glutathione (a personal cellular "bodyguard"), disrupted activity of metallothionein (a super-potent metal chelator made in the body) activity, and depleted sulfation (a good form of sulfur) pathways. ASD children often have injuries or imbalances in thyroid and adrenal glands that need attention. Finally, these children often have obsessive tendencies and almost addictive behaviors that lead to restrictions of input in many critical areas, including balanced diet, effective play, social learning, problem solving, physical activity, language, and positive emotional feedback.

Healing happens through removing obstacles and strengthening weak systems by supplementing for physiologic deficiencies and providing corrective therapies. As Sid Baker, M.D., has said, "We seek to find out what the child needs to eliminate, and what they need to get more of—we're specialists in 'more or less' medicine. In doing so, we allow the body to return to a state of balance, restoring its incredibly intricate communication systems and repairing injured organs to the extent that is possible."



I often reflect on the fact that chronic illness is chronic because of self-perpetuating cycles of injury that the body cannot break without help. There are many such cycles in autism. For example, many autistic children exhibit elevated mercury levels. Mercury poisoning disrupts digestion, so that nutrient depletion and food sensitivities (including sensitivity to gluten and casein) develop. Opportunistic infections arise, and antibiotics further weaken the system, upsetting intestinal flora, and increasing the toxicity of mercury that is already in the system. Nutrient depletion impairs the detoxification pathways, and other toxic substances in the environment cause further injury. Toxic materials, yeasts, and other microbes injure the immune system, and autoimmunity and unregulated inflammation result. Inflammation activates clotting systems and results in reduced tissue oxygenation. The result of all these processes is tissue injury in many organ systems, and the cycles continue. Our work is to break these cycles wherever possible; and as this is accomplished, the body will regain homeostasis and self-regulation, and move toward healing. This work is often a struggle, requiring "tough love" and a clear sense of priorities.

The following are extracts of conversations I have had with moms or dads that illustrate some of the struggles we face in treating these children. "Change his diet." "*He won't eat anything but gluten, casein, and carbs.*" "Give her ½ teaspoon of cod liver oil each day." "*She vomits when I give it to her.*" "Rub the glutathione into her back each night." "*She gets hives when I put it on her skin.*" "Let's treat his intestinal worms." "*We'll have to treat the cat, too, as he's been eating the cat poop.*" "You need a break, why don't you have an overnight with your husband?" "*My son's bitten the last three babysitters we tried.*" "Make sure not to give her any more antibiotics, unless they're for a life-threatening illness." "*She had pneumonia three times last winter, is that life-threatening?*" "Hide the Nu-Thera in his juice." "*He won't drink anything but water."* "Let's turn off the television and computer." *"He tantrums and beats his head on the floor if I don't keep his video running over and over, just showing the credits."* "Please get a urine sample after the DMPS shot." *"She's pulled off the bag every time I try to do a urine collection."* "We'll sedate him for the blood draw." *"The dentist tried that; it only made him hyper and drunk."* "We have to avoid dehydration in order to succeed with EPD." *"She's refused all liquids the past 24 hours since we took away her pear juice."* "How's the GFCF diet going?" *"Fine, except when she sees grandma, who sneaks her cookies."* "We have to get all sources of aluminum out of her life." *"I've gotten rid of all the sources I can control, but she is always chewing on metal objects."* (When in my office, this child, who has severely elevated aluminum levels, chews on the metal handle of the reflex hammer and the metal knob of the blood pressure cuff, rather than the soft rubber ends of these.) "How's he responding to chelation?" *"It was going great until we added ALA, when his stimming increased and he stopped sleeping through the night."* "We need to get that amalgam filling removed." *"Her dentist refuses, and the two mercury-free dentists you recommended won't treat uncooperative children."* "I see you haven't done the organic acid urine test." *"My insurance paid for the whole workup at the University—MRI, EEG, chromosome studies, an organic acid test, and amino acid test; they were all normal. But since we've started to make progress with your treatment, they're not even paying for office visits. They say it's experimental and unproven."* "How did the colonoscopy turn out?" *"The gastroenterologist changed his mind when he saw my boy. He said it's normal for autistic children to be constipated, and wasn't concerned about the rectal bleeding or the vomiting." "The pediatrician said to immunize my younger typical son or find a different doctor."*



Following are extracts of conversations that convey some of the reasons why I continue to look forward to each day in the office. "Since his first dose of DMPS he's potty trained." "Her teacher called me to ask what I'd done; he's a different child since the secretin shot." "We took corn out of her diet, and now she sleeps through the night." "He said a three-word sentence an hour after the Epsom salts bath, and the language keeps coming. How many times a day can he have a bath?" "The constipation has cleared up since that course of Flagyl last month." "Every time I give a B12 shot, she has two great days of better focus, mood, and energy. Can I give it twice a week?" "The tantrums stopped after three days on Super Nu-Thera, and now I can take him shopping with me." "When he's on DMSA, the hyperactivity is gone! It has more impact than Ritalin." "My child is not autistic when he's on Nizoral. He's still a lot better; but a week after stopping it, he started to disconnect and do some of his quirky things again." "I got my child back when I raised the cod liver oil to one tablespoon a day; is it OK that I did that?" "The diarrhea stopped within a week on the specific carbohydrate diet, and she's starting to eat lots of new foods now." "My daughter's doctor was really impressed by her improvement. He warned me to stay away from those doctors who are doing chelation treatment, and said to keep up what I've been doing to help her." "After one dose of cod liver oil, she stopped looking at everything sidewise." "This diet is hard, but so worth it: after a month she's calmer, her language is clearer and more complex, and she's begun to play appropriately with her brother." "He stopped talking about cutting people up with chain saws after about a week on Yeast Control." "Since I started giving lemon juice with each meal the bloating and regurgitation have dropped off dramatically." "Melatonin is wonderful; it had been more than a year since she slept through the night, and she went right to sleep the first night. It's kept working all month, can we continue to use it every night?" "The zinc sulfate cream really helps reduce his stimming." "The developmental pediatrician who diagnosed him, and said that nothing can be done, told me that you're a quack. I went home and made an appointment to see you, and everybody's noticing improvement after just three months." "Thyroid has made such a difference—no more constipation, and he's so much more alert and with it." "At last I've found someone who believes me. Thank you for listening." "We've seen lots of improvements since starting NAET—best is the disappearance of aggressive behavior." "She produced a whole stream of new language on the way home from the first craniosacral treatment." "The regurgitation episodes have gone down from dozens per hour to just a few per day since we treated the yeast."



I have presented a lengthy (though not comprehensive) set of considerations to be addressed in undertaking to treat your autistic child. It can be (and often is) overwhelming to attempt to do everything possible. The important thing is to decide what to do next, and then do it properly. My perspective is that it is necessary to establish a strong collaborative relationship with your doctor and others who work with your child. For this to succeed, parents need to be willing to "step up to the plate" and shed the old view that one must simply obey the doctor. You are creating a team to treat your child, and you are in charge of the team. You hire doctors and therapists to help you understand how to better take care of your child, and also to provide treatments that you cannot do on your own.

In order to form an effective collaborative team, it is helpful to look beyond the medical perspective on illness, and instead view your child's ill-

| Conventional Medical Approach | Holistic Perspective |
|---|---|
| Illness: Bad entity | Illness: imbalance, overload |
| Statistical "they" | Anecdotal "thou" |
| ICD-9 computer code | Unique story |
| Cure | Heal |
| Treatment: fight, burn, cut, starve, suppress, devitalize | Treatment: support, listen, nurture, teach, activate, express, vitalize |
| Accident | Meaning |
| Doctors know and direct care | Doctors learn and collaborate |
| Latin, Greek | Vernacular |
| Professional, separation, hierarchical | Humanism, intimacy, equality |
| Theoretical, technological, material | Empirical, physiological, psychospiritual |
| Doctor does more → patient passive | Patient does more → person active |
| Success/failure | Unconditional |
| Diagnose, categorize | Dialogue, understand |
| Conservative, dogmatic | Open mind, discovery |



ness from a more holistic perspective. I have included a table that compares some of the philosophical differences between holism and conventional medical thinking. If you seek to understand your child's autism from a holistic perspective, it will help everyone involved in his or her treatment to "come aboard" with you.

You may find a holistic approach in unexpected areas. Some naturopathic physicians (who are all trained to think holistically) have nevertheless adopted a model of treatment that is very "allopathic" (traditional and disease-oriented) rather than holistic. And many practicing physicians who care about their patients will be able to partner with you and adopt a more holistic perspective when evaluating and treating your child.

In some conditions, such as cancer and heart disease, establishing a diagnosis is critical to effective treatment. In the case of autism, it is useful to make a diagnosis in order to become eligible for services, to have an address to go to on the Internet for researching your child's problems, and to explain your child's difficult behavior in public. But this diagnosis tends to close the door on medical treatments unless you are able to locate a physician who is willing to listen to you and move beyond the stereotype of autism as a developmental illness that has no medical treatment. If you are thinking functionally and holistically about the manifestations of your child's illness, it will help if your child's doctor joins you in learning to effectively dialogue and decipher the language of your child's illness.

Your insurance company will balk at reimbursing for any medical care if the diagnosis of autism is used (i.e., ICD-9:299). For insurance purposes, it is best to focus on the specific symptoms your child is experiencing and bill for diagnostic and therapeutic services based on those problems. For example, if your child bangs his head, it is not because he is autistic, but because his head is bothering him. If she won't eat properly, it is probably because she has digestive upset. If he eats dirt, it is likely that his minerals are out of balance. If he goes bananas after eating bananas, he is probably sensitive to phenolics and not just "autistic quirky." In each of these instances, it is appropriate to look deeper into the particular symptom, recognizing that it is meaningful and relevant to the body wisdom of your child.



In a greater sense, our society is finally beginning to look deeper into this epidemic of autism. But it is just beginning to do so, as more professionals and influential people see their own children impacted. This disorder is threatening to fiscally incapacitate our educational system and will place inconceivable burdens on the next generation if not solved. Even if the rate of increase of autism is halted now, the costs of caring for affected children growing into adulthood will be more than we can bear. It is you parents, hundreds of thousands of you in the U.S. alone, who will determine the fate of our children and, ultimately, of our society. Children need to have full access to all of the currently useful treatments. No longer can we tolerate the "head in the sand" approach of regulatory agencies to vaccines, heavy metals, environmental toxins, overuse of antibiotics, and nutrient depletion of our soils and foods, all of which are contributing to this disease. We need to demand and receive vigorous funding from the government for relevant and unbiased research into the remaining unanswered questions about causation, prevention, and treatment.

If we unite in purpose and make our voices heard, the undue burdens on our children that are causing this epidemic can be targeted and removed.

*Update for Second Edition:*

There is increasingly strong evidence that the autism epidemic, along with increases in many other childhood diseases, is related to environmental toxins (in addition to mercury). These toxins are persistent, bioaccumulative agents, which are found in food, water, and air. Some of these harmful agents include PCBs, flame retardants, plastic derivatives, pesticides and herbicides, fluorinated hydrocarbons found in Teflon, and a long list of toxic waste products that are added to fertilizer as a means of disposal. These types of chemicals produce oxidative stress (inability to protect the brain and other sensitive tissues from our own metabolic byproducts), hormone disruption (especially thyroid and sex hormones), obesity and insulin disturbances (arsenic and MSG), and impairments in neurotransmitters and cell signaling systems (pesticides, plastic derivatives, heavy metals, PCBs). The developing nervous system is particularly susceptible to disruption by toxins, and such disruptions may result in many of the symptoms of autism.

It is becoming apparent that through epigenetic mechanisms (such as the switching on or off of critical genes through effects of certain chemicals), parents may transmit to their children damage to genes acquired through environmental exposures. This may result in a syndrome that looks like a classical mutation, in that several children in a family may be affected. The critical difference is that these disturbed genes might be restored to appropriate functioning by vigorous detoxification and nutritional support of the parents before they conceive another child, thereby reducing the risk of having a subsequent special-needs child. From many perspectives, it makes very good sense to do all we can to minimize exposure of ourselves and our children to man-made chemicals. Implement the precautionary principle with regard to these substances: Assume it is unsafe until proven safe. Extending the extraordinary care you have provided for your children to yourselves and your environment will help ensure a world in which our grandchildren will have a chance to live and thrive without the specter of autism.

— Chapter 3 —

# What I Would Do If I Were a Parent of an Autistic Child: Recommendations Based on 25 Years of Research Experience

By Stephen M. Edelson, Ph.D.
Autism Research Institute, San Diego, California



In this book, you'll read the stories of dozens of families and physicians. The message of these stories is clear: *Autism is not hopeless.* The majority of autistic children can make enormous gains, and many can be cured. The battle is long, hard, and often expensive, but it is a battle that can be won—and it is being won, by thousands of parents around the world.

In the beginning, however, this battle can seem overwhelming. Learning that your child has an autism spectrum disorder is a devastating blow. At this difficult and stressful time, you are faced with a critical question: What should I do to help my child? The decision about which treatments to implement (and not to implement) will likely determine your child's prognosis.

Moreover, as you will see from the stories in this book, each autistic child is unique. A treatment that works for one child may not help a second, and may make a third child worse. Fighting autism is not like setting a broken leg or mending a heart defect. It requires research, experimentation, and the courage and perseverance to try treatment after treatment until you find the combination that will make your child better.

Fortunately, while each family of an autistic child must find its own answers, there are well-lighted paths that every parent can follow on this journey. Over the past 25 years I have been fortunate to conduct research and to collaborate with many of the leading pioneers in several areas of autism, including biomedical (Bernard Rimland), behavior/education (Ivar Lovaas), and sensory (Temple Grandin, Guy Berard, Lorna Jean King, Melvin Kaplan, Helen Irlen, Margaret Bauman). In addition, I've worked with hundreds of families, and learned from their struggles and successes. These experiences have given me an understanding of what can be done to help individuals with autism.

Here, based on that experience, are the steps that I would take if I were a parent of an autistic child.

## Action Plan

First, I would write to the Autism Research Institute (ARI) and request their free parent packet. Much of this information is on the ARI website: www.AutismResearchInstitute.com. The packet contains a wealth of information that describes ways to understand and treat many problems associated with autism. It includes a sample issue of the quarterly ARI newsletter, the *Autism Research Review International (ARRI).* Subscribing to the ARRI is the best way to keep informed.

I would also contact the local chapter of the Autism Society of America (ASA). The autism chapter will likely provide valuable resources and contact numbers in the community and throughout the state. In addition, I would attend at least one parent support group meeting to see what I could learn from other parents' experiences and expertise. ASA maintains a listing of most autism chapters throughout the country (800-3-AUTISM).



Important note: Before contacting my health insurance carrier, I would first read the policy. Many policies do not cover treatment services for autistic individuals. These insurance companies may reimburse therapies if the therapy is not specifically aimed at treating autism *and* if the insurance company is not aware that the child has autism. For example, if the child has gastrointestinal problems, the insurance company may pay for the testing.

## Intervention

When selecting treatments, there are three major approaches that I would pursue simultaneously. The earlier these interventions are started, the better the prognosis is for an autistic child. I would then pursue other recognized interventions, which are also listed below, if there are any lingering problems.

**The first approach is biomedical.** It initially involves determining whether the child has health problems. These problems may include a critical need for essential vitamins and minerals (e.g., vitamin B6 with magnesium, DMG, vitamins A and C), gastrointestinal problems (e.g., leaky gut, yeast overgrowth, viral infection), high levels of heavy metals and other toxins (e.g., mercury, lead), food sensitivities and allergies, and more. The majority of autistic individuals have one or more of these problems. Many of the stories in this book describe how parents were able to recognize such problems and how they treated them.

The Defeat Autism Now! (DAN!) approach to autism addresses these biomedical issues. ARI distributes a diagnostic and treatment manual titled *Autism: Effective Biomedical Treatments.* A list of practitioners who understand and know how to treat autism spectrum disorders may be obtained by writing to ARI or visiting their website. Of the many treatments described in the protocol, I would first give my child vitamin B6 with magnesium, then dimethylglycine (DMG), and then I would implement the gluten-free, casein-free (GFCF) diet.

*Comment on drugs.* Some pediatricians prescribe drugs to autistic children even though the FDA (the U.S. Food and Drug Administration) has not approved any drugs for treating autism. Additionally, almost every drug has harmful side effects. I sometimes hear reports of some benefits from using Risperidal, Prozac, and Ritalin. However, it is very likely that even greater improvements will occur following other, non-drug, biomedical treatments (see ARI's publication, "Parent Ratings of Behavioral Effects of Biomedical Interventions," on page 381).



If my child talked very little or not at all, I would have the child tested to see if he or she might be having seizures. Seizure activity may affect speech production. An EEG (electroencephalogram) measures brain wave activity, and it may be able to detect seizure activity. If the EEG showed evidence of seizures, I would first try nontoxic nutritional supplements to treat the seizures, such as vitamin B6 and DMG.

**The second approach is behavior/education.** Applied behavior analysis (ABA) is a well-documented and effective teaching method for many autistic children. This method involves one-on-one instructional sessions using educational tasks developed specifically for autism. *Teaching Individuals with Developmental Delays: Basic Intervention Techniques,* written by O. Ivar Lovaas, is an excellent resource and describes in detail how to implement this method.

**The third major approach would involve sensory interventions.** Many autistic individuals suffer from a hypersensitive or hyposensitive sensory system. These problems may involve hearing (e.g., sound sensitivity, apparent deafness), vision (e.g., light sensitivity, visual attention problems), tactile (e.g., sensitivity to touch, insensitivity to pain), vestibular (e.g., craves or resists certain movements, such as swinging), proprioceptive (e.g., excessive jumping), smell (e.g., sensitivity or insensitivity to odors), and taste (e.g., picky eater, pica behavior). There are several interventions that can reduce or eliminate many of these problems, such as auditory integration training (hearing), vision training and the Irlen lenses (vision), and sensory integration (vestibular/tactile/proprioceptive).

The three treatment approaches outlined above complement one another. Autistic individuals often become more attentive and more motivated to learn soon after their biomedical and sensory problems are treated. A child may do well with only one of these approaches, but the combination can lead to amazing results, and even recovery for some children.

## Other Interventions

It is also worth looking into other effective interventions for autism, such as structured teaching, social stories, the Greenspan "Floor Time" method, the Picture Exchange Communication System, sign language (e.g., "simultaneous communication"), and Grodin's relaxation/visual imagery techniques.



## Evaluation

To improve my chances of success as I developed a treatment plan, I would formulate a strategy that allowed me to accurately determine which approaches worked for my child and which did not. To do this, I would follow these general guidelines.

1. As a rule, I would try a treatment for about two months before beginning a new one. This would make it easier to determine which treatments were truly responsible for positive or negative changes. However, if it became clear after the first week or two that my child improved as the result of a treatment, I would feel comfortable adding a new intervention.

2. I would complete the Autism Treatment Evaluation Checklist (ATEC) once or twice a month for a few months prior to beginning an intervention, and then monthly after starting the intervention. The ATEC was designed specifically to evaluate treatment effectiveness. If improvement occurs simply because a child is maturing, then the ATEC will typically show gradual improvement over time. However, if there is marked improvement after the intervention is started, then the treatment may be helping. You can find a copy of the ATEC in Appendix C. Alternately, the checklist can be completed on the Internet at www.ARI-ATEC.com or paper copies may be obtained by writing to the Autism Research Institute (4182 Adams

Ave., San Diego, CA 92116; fax: 619-563-6840). There is no charge for use of the ATEC.

3. If at all possible, I would tell no one when my child started a new treatment. This would include teachers, friends, neighbors, and relatives. If a noteworthy change occurred in my child, these people would most likely mention it. I would refrain from asking, "Have you noticed any changes in my child?" because spontaneous comments would be more objective.

4. I would ask any people who did know that my child was receiving a specific treatment to independently compile lists of any changes they noticed. After a month or two, I would compare their observations. If different people noticed similar changes, this would be good evidence that these changes were real. I would ask these people to write down their observations, to ensure that their recollections of my child's previous behavior were valid.



5. I would note in writing when my child's behavior "surprised" me. If a child is improving or worsening as a result of an intervention, it's likely that he or she will act differently than before. These "surprises," good or bad, can reveal a great deal about a treatment's effects.

Some people suggest that parents give their children only treatments for which there is strong supporting research. However, when a new treatment is introduced, there often is little or no research on its effectiveness. It takes, on average, five to 10 years to complete enough research to support or refute an intervention's efficacy. Additionally, chances are fairly good that even after 10 years, the results will be mixed, because researchers often use different populations and assess changes using different measures. However, I would be leery of any treatment that has been around for ten or more years and has no research studies to support its effectiveness. For example, Ritalin is one of the most frequently prescribed treatments for autism, but we are not aware of any published studies supporting its effectiveness with this population.

Before trying a new treatment, I would learn as much as possible about the treatment. Rather than focusing only on positive reports, I would seek out criticisms of the treatment as well. When evaluating conflicting claims, I would consider the nature of the studies and their methodologies, being careful not to give poorly conducted studies the same credence as methodologically sound research.

## Family Issues

Raising an autistic child can be very stressful to the entire family. Siblings or spouses sometimes feel ignored because so much attention is directed toward the autistic child. Additionally, relatives and close friends may distance themselves. It is important to be aware of these potential problems and address them if they should occur.

## Conclusion



Finally, if I were the parent of an autistic child, I would be a strong advocate for my child. Many professionals are aware of the symptoms associated with autism. However, they do not know how to treat them. Information is a powerful tool. I would keep all of my child's documents and diagnostic test results in one well-organized folder. Whenever possible, I would provide relevant articles and other information to therapists and other professionals working with my child. Like many other parents of autistic children, I would likely wind up teaching professionals how to work with my child. I would also take advantage of the many resources available to aid parents in identifying and implementing treatments, such as books, newsletters, Internet websites, and conferences.

Most important of all, I would refuse to listen to doctors or other professionals who told me that autism is "hopeless," that it cannot be treated, or that I was unrealistic to expect significant improvement. It is crucial to realize that autism is treatable, that nearly all autistic children can improve and many can recover fully, and that the drugs-and-institutionalization mentality of many doctors is outdated and dangerous.

As the stories you are about to read will prove, autism can be fought successfully. It will take all of your strength and persistence, but the end result will be a better future for your child. Find doctors and other professionals who share your determination to achieve this goal, and—as so many parents will tell you in this book—never, never give up.

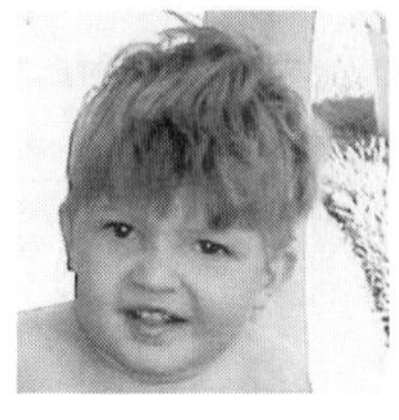

# PART II

# PARENTS REPORT THEIR EXPERIENCES



Thirty-one families share their personal struggles with autism and report the results of their use of biomedical treatment for their children. Some of these children have recovered from autism; other children appear to be on the road to recovery.

Each family who contributed to this book represents a different perspective, and the severity of their child's disorder varies considerably. This diversity will help readers broaden their understanding of the concepts and practical issues involved in treating autistic children.

Each chapter concludes with brief updates on the child(ren)'s progress written just before the first printing in May 2003 and before the printing of the second edition in summer 2006.

Several of the authors or their spouses are also medical doctors. These include: Claire Burrell-Stella, M.D., Amy Holmes, M.D., Nancy Jelen, Bryan Jepson, M.D., Carolyn Lewis, Natasha Campbell-McBride, M.D., Jaquelyn McCandless, M.D., and George Young, M.D. Many of the strongest advocates of the DAN! approach are parents who are also physicians.

Several of our authors have written books about autism. These include: Lynn Hamilton (*Facing Autism: Giving Parents Reason for Hope and Guidance for Help*), Karyn Seroussi (*Unraveling the Mystery of Autism and Pervasive Developmental Disorder: A Mother's Story of Research and Recovery*), Jaquelyn McCandless, M.D. (*Children with Starving Brains: A Medical Treatment Guide for Autism Spectrum Disorder*), Amy Lansky, Ph.D. *(Impossible Cure: The Promise of Homeopathy)*, and Natasha Campbell-McBride, M.D. *(Gut and Psychology Syndrome: Natural Treatment for Autism, ADHD, ADD, Dyslexia, Dyspraxia, Depression and Schizophrenia)*.

The chapters in Part II appear in alphabetical order, based on surname of the authors.

*The parents who contributed chapters to this book were asked to indicate the symptoms their children exhibited prior to initiating the biomedical treatments. The Autism Symptom Profile below is designed to help readers identify children described in this book who are most similar (match the profile) to their own children.*

| | Barnhart | Bayliss | Bezalel | Blanco (Ryan) | Blanco (Stacy) | Burrell-Stella | Campbell-McBride | Corcoran | Doggett | Duffield (Jessica) | Duffield (Michael) | Hamilton | Helmick | Hoffiz | Holmes | Jelen (Betsy) | Jelen (Jerry) |
|---|---|---|---|---|---|---|---|---|---|---|---|---|---|---|---|---|---|
| Aggressive toward others | ○ | ○ | ○ | ◍ | ◍ | ○ | | | | | ◍ | ● | | | | | ○ |
| Anxious/fearful | ○ | | ◍ | ◍ | ◍ | ○ | | ○ | | ● | ● | ◍ | | ○ | | ● | ○ |
| Constipation | | | | ● | ● | | ● | ● | | | | ◍ | | | | | |
| Destructive of things | | | ○ | ◍ | ◍ | | ● | | ○ | ● | ● | ○ | | | | ◍ | ● |
| Diarrhea | ◍ | ◍ | | ● | ● | ● | ● | | | ◍ | ● | ◍ | ○ | ◍ | ● | ● | ◍ |
| Did not point | ● | ● | ● | ● | ● | ● | ● | ● | ● | ● | ● | ● | ● | ● | ● | | |
| Feeding/eating (self-limited) | ● | ○ | ● | ● | ● | ● | ● | ● | ◍ | ○ | ● | ● | | ○ | ● | ○ | |
| Vaccine reaction within 24 hrs: | | | | | | | | | | | | | | | | | |
| DPT | | ◍ | | ● | ● | | | ○ | ◍ | | ● | ○ | | | | ○ | |
| MMR | | ◍ | | ● | ● | | | ○ | ◍ | | ● | | | | | ◍ | |
| Hep B | | | | | | | | | | ● | | | | | | | |
| Head banging | | ◍ | ○ | | | ○ | ● | | | ○ | ● | | | ○ | | | |
| High pain threshold | ● | ◍ | ● | | | ◍ | ● | | ● | ◍ | ● | | | ○ | ◍ | ● | ○ |
| Hyperactive | | ◍ | ● | ○ | ○ | ○ | ● | ◍ | ● | ○ | ◍ | ◍ | ● | | ◍ | | ● |
| Inattentive | ● | ◍ | ● | ○ | ○ | ● | ● | ● | ● | ◍ | ● | ● | ◍ | ● | ● | ● | ● |
| Intolerant of changes | ● | ◍ | ● | ◍ | ◍ | ◍ | ○ | ◍ | ○ | ● | ◍ | ● | ○ | ● | | ● | ○ |
| Normal then regressed in 2nd yr* | E | L | L | L | L | L | L | L | L | L | L | L | E | E | L | L | L |
| Poor eye contact | ● | ◍ | ● | ● | ● | ● | ● | ● | ● | ● | ● | ● | ● | ● | ● | ● | ● |
| Repeated courses of antibiotics | ◍ | ● | ● | | | | ● | ● | ● | | ● | ● | | ● | ● | ● | ◍ |
| Repeated ear infections | ◍ | ● | ● | | | | ◍ | ● | ● | | ● | ● | | ● | ● | ● | ● |
| Rocking | | ◍ | ● | | | | ● | | | ● | ● | ◍ | | ● | | | |
| Self-injurious | | | ○ | ● | ● | ● | | | | ○ | ● | | | ○ | | | |
| Sleep difficulties | ◍ | ◍ | ● | ◍ | ◍ | ● | ● | ◍ | ● | ◍ | ● | ● | ○ | | ● | ● | ◍ |
| Sound sensitive | ◍ | ○ | ● | ◍ | ◍ | ○ | ● | ○ | ◍ | ● | ● | ○ | ○ | ◍ | ● | ● | ● |
| Stimming: | | | | | | | | | | | | | | | | | |
| hand-flapping | ● | ● | ● | ◍ | ◍ | | | | | ● | ○ | | ○ | ● | ○ | | |
| spinning | ○ | | ● | ● | ● | | ● | ◍ | ◍ | ○ | ○ | | ◍ | | ○ | | |
| other | | ● | | | | | ● | | | ● | ● | | | ● | | | |
| Tantrums | ● | ◍ | ◍ | ◍ | ◍ | ○ | ○ | ◍ | | ● | ● | ● | ◍ | ○ | | ◍ | ◍ |
| Toe-walking | | ◍ | | | | | ● | ◍ | | ○ | ◍ | | | ○ | ● | ◍ | ○ |
| Toilet training problems | ● | ● | ● | | | ● | | ● | ○ | ● | ● | ● | ◍ | ● | ● | ◍ | ◍ |
| Unaware of danger | ● | ◍ | ● | ● | ● | ● | ● | ◍ | ● | ○ | ● | ◍ | | ● | ● | ● | ● |

**RATING KEY FOR THE AUTISM SYMPTOM PROFILE**

Blank – Not a problem
○ – Mild problem
◍ – Moderate problem
● – Severe problem

*E – Early-onset autism
*L – Late-onset autism

| | Jepson | Kitt | Lansky | Lewis | McCandless | Mead | Mendenhall | Miller | Parrott | Petrie | Rowe | Savage | Schlapfer | Seroussi | Sytsema | Vest | Young |
|---|---|---|---|---|---|---|---|---|---|---|---|---|---|---|---|---|---|
| Aggressive toward others | | ● | | ◍ | | ○ | | | | | ● | ○ | ● | | | ○ | |
| Anxious/fearful | | ◍ | ○ | ● | | ○ | ○ | ● | ○ | ● | ◍ | ◍ | | ◍ | ○ | ● | ◍ |
| Constipation | | | | ○ | | | ● | | ○ | ◍ | ◍ | | ◍ | ● | | ● | ● |
| Destructive of things | | ◍ | | ◍ | ○ | | | | | | ○ | ○ | ● | | ○ | ◍ | |
| Diarrhea | ● | | ◍ | ● | | ● | | ● | | | ◍ | ● | ◍ | ● | ● | ● | |
| Did not point | ● | ● | ◍ | ● | ● | ● | ● | ◍ | | ● | ◍ | ● | ○ | ● | ● | ● | ● |
| Feeding/eating (self-limited) | ● | | | ● | ● | ● | ● | ○ | ◍ | ● | ○ | | ○ | ● | ● | ● | ◍ |
| Vaccine reaction within 24 hrs: | ○ | | | | | | | | | | | | | | | | |
| DPT | | | | ○ | | ● | | ● | | | | | ◍ | ● | ● | ● | ● |
| MMR | | | | ○ | | ● | | ● | | | | ○ | ◍ | | ○ | | ● |
| Hep B | | | | | | | | | | | | | | | | | ● |
| Head banging | ○ | ○ | ○ | | | | ○ | | ● | | ◍ | | ◍ | | | ● | |
| High pain threshold | ◍ | | | | ● | ● | ● | ◍ | ○ | ◍ | ◍ | | ○ | | ◍ | ● | ● |
| Hyperactive | ◍ | ◍ | ◍ | | ● | ● | ○ | ○ | | ● | ◍ | ● | ● | | ◍ | ● | ● |
| Inattentive | ● | | ● | ● | ● | ● | ● | ◍ | ◍ | ● | ● | ● | ● | ● | ● | ● | ● |
| Intolerant of changes | ○ | ● | ○ | ● | ◍ | ◍ | ● | ● | | ● | ● | ● | ● | ◍ | | ● | ◍ |
| Normal then regressed in 2nd yr* | L | E | L | E | E | L | L | L | L | L | L | L | L | L | E | L | L |
| Poor eye contact | ● | ◍ | ◍ | ● | ○ | ● | ● | ● | ○ | ● | ● | ● | ◍ | ● | ● | ◍ | ● |
| Repeated courses of antibiotics | | | | ◍ | ● | ● | ● | | ○ | | ● | ● | ◍ | ● | ● | ● | ◍ |
| Repeated ear infections | | | | ● | ● | ● | ● | | | | ● | ● | ● | ● | ● | ● | ◍ |
| Rocking | | ◍ | ○ | | | | | | | ◍ | ◍ | ○ | | | ○ | ● | |
| Self-injurious | ○ | ● | | | | | ○ | | ◍ | | ● | ○ | | | | ● | |
| Sleep difficulties | ● | ● | ○ | ● | ◍ | ● | ● | ◍ | ● | ● | ◍ | ● | ◍ | ● | ● | ● | ● |
| Sound sensitive | ◍ | ● | ○ | ◍ | ◍ | ● | ◍ | ◍ | ○ | ● | ● | ● | ● | ◍ | ● | ● | ● |
| Stimming: | | | | | ● | | ◍ | | | | | | | | | | |
| hand-flapping | ○ | | | ◍ | | ● | | ○ | | | ○ | ◍ | ◍ | | ◍ | ○ | |
| spinning | ● | | ○ | | | ● | | ◍ | | | ○ | ● | | | | ● | ◍ |
| other | ● | | | | | | | | | | | | | | | ● | |
| Tantrums | | ◍ | | ● | | ◍ | ◍ | ◍ | ● | ● | ● | ● | ● | ● | ○ | ● | ○ |
| Toe-walking | ◍ | | ○ | ◍ | | ◍ | ◍ | ◍ | | | | ● | ○ | ◍ | ○ | ◍ | ○ |
| Toilet training problems | ◍ | | ○ | ◍ | | ● | ● | ● | ◍ | ● | | ○ | ◍ | | ● | | |
| Unaware of danger | ● | ● | ◍ | | ● | ● | ● | ◍ | ○ | ● | ● | ● | ● | ● | ○ | ● | ● |

# — Chapter 4 —
# Jackson's Story
By Kristin Barnhart

*Kristin and Dan Barnhart live in Portland, Oregon with their son, Jackson, who was born in April 1996, and two other young children. This story was written in March 2002.*

This is the story of Jackson Barnhart. Jackson was born in the spring of 1996, the brother of Lydia, who is 18 months older. We were thrilled to have two lovely children. In the winter of 2000, Miranda was born into our family and completed the picture.



Jackson was an early walker and tried to keep up physically with his older sister. From his early days he liked toys with wheels, and he would make the wheels of anything spin around. If he saw a big truck in a parking lot, he would stroke its wheels. He loved to be in the company of men. He was turning out to be quite a boy's boy.

When he was two years old, we commented to each other about how physically precocious he was. He seemed able to do everything his older sister could. However, there were other milestones he wasn't hitting. He had very few language skills, and no interest in other children. Friends and family reassured us that he was a typical boy, and told us not to compare him to his older sister who was very verbal and social. "He'll catch up," everyone comforted us. But over the next few months there were nagging questions about our sunny little boy. Why couldn't he make a transition without breaking down into a major tantrum? He would cry on the way from the house to the van, from the van to the store, from the store back to the van. That wasn't normal. We also thought it was odd that at age 2½ he could name all of the characters on the "Thomas the Tank Engine" videos but never had said "mama" or "daddy." His pediatrician wasn't too worried but suggested we might have his hearing tested to see if there was a problem.

A speech pathologist at Oregon Health Sciences University (OHSU) referred us to the early intervention program that our state has set up to help little guys like Jackson catch up before starting regular schooling. Jackson met with an intake coordinator from the early intervention program here in Portland, and she agreed that he had some issues requiring attention. She also mentioned we might want to screen him for autism. We agreed, figuring there was no way our cuddly little snuggle pumpkin could be autistic, but that we should have it ruled out so the experts could figure out what was really wrong.

The school team that evaluated Jackson determined that he did fit the criteria for autism spectrum disorder (ASD), a diagnosis that has subsequently been confirmed by several medical professionals. At first we did not agree with the diagnosis. We didn't know much about autism, but Jackson was not "Rain Man"—he didn't have odd physical behaviors and he responded lovingly to his family. However, as we read more about autism, we became aware of many behavioral deficits we had never noticed before: Jackson never pointed at things; he completely ignored other children; he did not make eye contact as frequently as most children do; he didn't ask for things; he would play for hours by himself with his wood train set. So many of these things we had considered the blessing of having an easygoing child.



We started researching how we could help our little boy. This was the confusing part. The teacher in Jackson's early intervention program told us to enjoy playing with him and just let him be himself at home, and let the school work with his behaviors during the 10 hours a week he was in class. Dr. Ivar Lovaas's research told us that we needed to deal aggressively with the autism by implementing an intense one-on-one behavioral therapy program. Then we read some weird stuff about eliminating dairy and wheat products from Jackson's diet and supplementing his diet with megadoses of certain vitamins and other supplements.

We easily understood the scientific research that Dr. Lovaas had done at UCLA and the anecdotal reports, such as Catherine Maurice's book *Let Me Hear Your Voice*, supporting behavioral therapy. It just made sense. We quickly placed Jackson in school 25 hours a week and had a private therapist in our home 10 hours a week. It went well, and we started to see results immediately. We were still interested in looking at the biomedical interventions we had read about but were very wary about them. It really seemed like it could be quackery.

The more we read about autism and the health issues of autistic children, however, the more we started to have concerns about Jackson's physical well being. He has always been a pale child, but I am also rather pale, so we didn't think much about it. He had black circles under his eyes, which had never concerned us much since he had erratic sleep patterns. About six weeks after Jackson's autism diagnosis, we took him to a DAN! (Defeat Autism Now!) doctor and a behavioral pediatrician. The DAN! doctor recommended that we immediately start the gluten-free, casein-free (GFCF) diet as well as some nutritional supplements such as Super Nu-Thera and cod liver oil. He also ordered some blood work and allergy testing. The behavioral pediatrician told us the diet and other supplements were quackery, and that we should instead focus on letting the school do its work. We were conservative people and wanted to agree with the mainstream behavioral pediatrician, but we could tell that Jackson had health issues that the mainstream doctors were ignoring.

It seemed to us if we did try the GFCF diet and vitamin supplements, they couldn't hurt Jackson. We would investigate these approaches with the idea that they probably wouldn't do anything for him, but at least we would have tried. A few weeks after starting the GFCF diet, Jackson's eye contact improved. It was impossible to attribute this to the behavioral intervention since the improvement was consistent no matter what he was doing, whether there was a reward or not. He has been on the diet now for over a year, and we are convinced that it has helped.



Jackson's blood tests revealed that he had parasites in his intestines. We treated those with a drug prescribed by the DAN! doctor. This helped his bowels. Under the doctor's care, we also treated a yeast overgrowth in his bowels. We started with nystatin, a fairly mild drug that combats the yeast that kills off the helpful bacteria necessary for a healthy gastrointestinal (GI) tract. The initial results were terrifying. Jackson's behavior, which had always been reasonably calm, became wild. He sat in our backyard eating dirt. He would spin around and around. His tantrums were now frequent and loud. We learned that this was a sign that the drug was doing something, and the "die-off effect" was a result of the poisons working their way out of his body. After about one week the behaviors stopped. We have subsequently used a few other yeast-controlling drugs, but none with such dramatic results.

We have been cautious about the supplements we give Jackson. It is hard to treat your beloved child as a chemistry experiment. However, in the year that we have been giving Jackson supplements, we have seen a dramatic turnaround in his health. He is more lucid and has lost the dark circles under his eyes, and his skin is a healthier hue. His sleep pattern is completely normal. He is rarely ill. The supplements that we have continued using include the mega B-vitamin mix (Super Nu-Thera), cod liver oil, evening primrose oil, essential fatty acids, probiotics to promote healthy gut flora, zinc and various other minerals, and colostrum.

The other major biomedical intervention we have pursued is heavy metal chelation. Again, it was not an easy decision for us to pursue this course.

With Jackson, we did not notice the horrible reactions after immunizations that some parents notice and which may indicate mercury poisoning from the vaccines. The blood, urine, and hair tests did not show the elevated levels of mercury seen in so many autistic children. However, they did show that he had plenty of other metals in dangerously high amounts, such as lead, antimony, and aluminum. We have treated this using the DAN! Protocol as our guide, under the care of our physician.

Initially, we gave Jackson the prescription drug DMSA (meso 2,3 dimercaptosuccinic acid) to get the toxic metals out of his body. After three days on the drug, he was taken off for eleven days before we started the next round. The first few rounds of chelation left Jackson tired and dehydrated, but his verbal output was very encouraging: he spoke more, and he spoke more clearly. We did routine blood tests to make sure the drugs did not adversely affect his liver. Recently, we added alpha lipoic acid (ALA) to the chelation schedule. The ALA seemed to release some toxins into his body, similar to the yeast die-off we saw with nystatin. However, his verbal output again was fantastic. His teachers at school, unaware of the chelation schedule, remarked both times he had a course of ALA how well he was doing with his programs at school.



A year ago, Jackson was effectively nonverbal and unaware of most of his environment. Today, at almost four years of age, he can ask for what he wants, tell us what he's doing, and describe the world around him. He loves to play with his two sisters and is starting to pay attention to other children. He has a long way to go, but has come so far. We are so happy we were able to find a caring doctor who could help us look into these alternative treatments. If we had stuck with mainstream medicine there is no doubt Jackson would have progressed with the behavioral therapy. But he is making far greater progress with the help of alternative therapies, because he is a healthier child.

*Update (March 2003):*

Jackson is now almost five years old. He is continuing to make progress in all areas of his life. His speech, while not quite at a five-year-old level, is becoming more conversational and we are working with a wonderful speech and language pathologist to help his intonation and speech patterns.

Socially, Jackson shows a desire to play with peers and plays appropriately with his sisters, who are 18 and 21 months younger than him. He relates better to younger children, in general. His play skills have always been one of his strong suits. He loves to tease and has a good, silly sense of humor.

Academically, Jackson is reading and doing simple addition equations. This is his strongest area, as it is with many ASD children. It was a long and arduous task teaching him to write with a tripod grasp, but now he draws pictures of things like boats on the sea and a house with a lawn. His behavioral therapists help him to write and illustrate his own stories.

Jackson does not stim anymore. (This was never a huge behavior problem for him, but we did see some hand flapping.) His body movement is awkward and he still has issues with bilateral movements. This is something we would like to address, but our insurance doesn't cover it and there are too few occupational therapists working with the kids at our early intervention program.



Jackson enjoys generally good health. His skin is pale and does not tan; we don't know what to make of this. He has been potty trained for about a year, but refuses to use the toilet for bowel movements; this is currently one of our main areas of focus. His diet has remained self-restricted to a few favored foods, but he has recently started eating apples, pears, and applesauce.

What a great kid! We couldn't love him more.

*Update for Second Edition (February 2006):*

Jackson is now almost eight years old and in the second grade. He was mainstreamed into public school in first grade, which initially did not go smoothly. He has an aide and is in the class three-fourths of the time and pulled out for help with reading and math. His speech skills are improving more and more every year (perhaps thanks to his two sisters). We removed supplements from his diet when he was six, and now he just takes a multivitamin and calcium. We are weaning him off the GFCF diet currently. He is a happy child and fun to have around. Toileting and finicky eating are still issues for him, but every year we see encouraging improvements. He has made one close friend in school and gets along well with his classmates. This past month he was the narrator in a school play.

# — Chapter 5 —
# Dillon's Story

By Debbie Bayliss

*Debbie Bayliss lives in Virginia with her son, Dillon, who was born in August 1992. This story was written in March 2002.*



My name is Debbie Bayliss and I am a single mother of a nine-year-old boy named Dillon, who has autism. He is the light of my life.

Dillon was not diagnosed with autism until just before his fourth birthday. He had developed normally, but after he turned three we started noticing that things just weren't right. I often think back and realize that if I had read more books about child development, I would have recognized the behavior that was right in front of my eyes. He'd had quite a few ear infections, beginning at six months of age, and he had numerous bowel movements each day, usually quite soft in consistency. He also was allergic to pollen—little did I know then that it was much more than that. In addition, he was quite a picky eater, and got pickier with age; I can remember when he was under two years old, he would try new foods off my plate, eager to taste something new. That didn't last long.

After his diagnosis, Dillon started in a half-day special needs preschool program in public school, and continued the next year in all-day kindergarten. He was doing all right in school, but he had lots of behavioral problems. He often dropped to the floor instead of doing tasks they wanted him to do. He had some anger issues, but was never violent toward anyone, although he was known to kick.

By the following year, when he was six, I decided to look into some medication to help Dillon's behavior. His teacher had mentioned more than once that maybe "meds" would help Dillon learn, and that the younger he was, the better he might absorb information. Our family doctor referred me to a pediatric neurologist, who ran some tests. Dillon's video electroencephalogram (EEG) showed activity in the brain that the neurologist believed could indicate the possibility of seizures in the future. He wrote a prescription for Tegretol, which he thought might help Dillon's speech and behavioral problems. But I just didn't feel right giving Dillon a medicine used to treat seizures, when he wasn't having seizures.

The day after we saw the neurologist, the library called to say that they'd received a book that I had been waiting to read, *Special Diets for Special Kids*, by Lisa Lewis. It is one of the best books I have ever read about autism. Around this time I met Sue Wells, a classmate's mother, who provided so much help and support during these hard decisions. After reading Lewis's book and talking with Sue, I decided not to put Dillon on Tegretol. It was one of the best decisions I ever made. Instead, I started my long journey into changing Dillon's diet.

Dillon was a very picky eater—we called him the "sandwich man" because he would eat only sandwiches. He loved peanut butter, so I switched him to soy nut butter to get him away from peanuts. By May 2000 I had found a rice-flour bread recipe that Dillon liked. I noticed that after we stopped using gluten, Dillon started eating a wider variety of foods. But I had no idea what food allergies or intolerances he had.



In August 2000, Dillon was given the Great Plains Laboratory Comprehensive Food Panel to test for allergies. It was a real help to me. It showed that Dillon did have problems with dairy and peanuts, but that egg whites were even more of a problem, and soy was the worst. I had to get rid of that soy nut butter and many other products I had been using in his diet.

It took me months to figure out what to substitute for the four eggs in Dillon's rice bread. First, I used only egg yolks, then started cutting back on how many I used. Eventually, I changed the recipe to light buckwheat flour instead of rice flour. Finally, I discovered flax seed powder: in place of eggs I use one tablespoon in three tablespoons of hot water. The bread comes out perfectly and Dillon loves it!

When parents are overwhelmed at the thought of changing their child's diet, I just tell them to take it one step at a time. That is what I did—I didn't figure it all out overnight. I experiment all the time with Dillon's diet; sometimes it turns out OK, sometimes not. Miss Roben's special recipes have been a great help (www.MissRoben.com).

I was lucky enough to find another friend, Jennifer Stevens, who shared with me what she had learned about other treatments for autism, and whose son had been fighting "yeast overgrowth" for a long time. I decided to ask my doctor to test Dillon for yeast overgrowth. Dillon had always had bowel problems, including loose bowels and quite a few bowel movements per day. And, of course, there had been all those antibiotics for his ear infections. The test results showed that he did indeed have a yeast overgrowth problem, which we started treating with nystatin.

We also tried vitamin supplements. One thing I learned is that it really makes a difference where you get your supplements. Dillon would not always have positive results when I got supplements from the drug store, or even from natural foods stores; either he would get no noticeable results, or he would have a negative reaction. I hesitated to try Kirkman's product when Sue recommended it, because I figured it wasn't going to help Dillon either. I was wrong—really, really wrong! I experimented first with sample doses of Super Nu-Thera, and then moved Dillon to regular doses twice a day. I also started experimenting with magnesium and vitamin B6.

I started treating Dillon with cod liver oil, a natural form of vitamin A, based on the research of Dr. Mary Megson. After two months we added the prescription drug bethanechol. Dillon continues to do well on both; when he takes bethanechol, he listens and cooperates better.



During the summer of 2001, my doctor tested Dillon for mercury toxicity. Dillon's mercury and aluminum were high on a hair analysis test. We also did liver function tests, and other evaluations, following the DAN! paper on mercury detoxification.

Since that time I have been considering chelation for Dillon. In order to prepare him for chelation, to strengthen his system, and for his general health, I started to add more supplements from Kirkman Labs in May 2001. Dillon was already taking Super Nu-Thera with P5P and without vitamins A and D, a tablespoon a day of flax oil, vitamin C, and Culturelle. I added Yeast Control, Pro-Bio Gold, magnesium, and vitamin E. In June I added zinc liquid, Colostrum Gold, EnzymAid, calcium powder, L-glutamine, TMG (trimethylglicine) with folic acid and B12, and cranberry capsules. In August I added B complex with CoEnzyme capsules, selenium, and CoQ10 capsules. By October I had added Epsom salt cream to Dillon's regimen. In November I added taurine, Beta Glucan, and Amino Support. In December I added Idebenone and buffered vitamin C powder. In January 2002 I started using EnZym-Complete. I also use Kirkman's Melatonin Plus if I have trouble getting Dillon to wind down—he is asleep within 30 minutes.

I made the mistake of taking Dillon off nystatin, and the yeast came back with a vengeance. His anaerobic bacterial level (DHPPA analog) was up to 396 (the normal range is 0-150). I decided to ask my doctor if we could treat with Flagyl. He agreed, and it was a good decision—the last organic acid test (OAT) showed that his bacterial level was completely under control. The yeast is still a problem, but we are almost there. I have even added Biocidin from Emerson Ecologics. To help with the yeast die-off this time around, I started off with activated charcoal, but then switched to bentonite clay (which comes in a liquid form and is organic) after reading Kirkman Labs' book *Guide to Intestinal Health In Autism Spectrum Disorder*. Dillon takes it only once a day, but when he misses a few days he gets stomachaches and starts to wake in the middle of the night itching all over. It has been so much help to him.

I am quite strict with Dillon's diet. The meats I purchase for Dillon are antibiotic-free, and are fed organic feed. He eats beef, chicken, buffalo, turkey and pork. I just try my best to keep him away from the foods that bother him. The digestive enzymes have really helped. His teacher has been very cooperative with me, giving him his digestive enzymes before he eats anything at school. She has been great! I make Dillon's buckwheat bread, and cook and freeze all of his individual meals in one-serving containers. He eats BBQ with a homemade sauce sweetened with molasses and honey, spaghetti, beef stew, chili with beans, chicken and rice with veggies, and anything else I think he might try. For lunch I use ham, chicken, and roast beef ground up in a food processor (he won't eat meat if it is a chewy consistency), then add mayo and maybe a little mustard. He loves cashew nut butter and jelly for breakfast and snacks. I finally found this delicious chocolate shortbread cookie that not only is gluten-free but also has no eggs.



Since the beginning of the current school year, we've had some miraculous breakthroughs. Dillon had been talking, but not a lot. He could spell his name, but his writing was almost illegible because of his weak fine motor skills. On his third day of school his teacher, Pam Snow, tried "hand-over-hand" assistance to see if he could write the alphabet and he wrote the whole thing. She then asked him to write his numbers—he wrote 1-18 for her. We were ecstatic.

Things only got better. I had noticed that he was spelling—without my help—what I told him to write, but we wondered if he could read, or form thoughts of his own. On December 14th his teacher asked him to write his own thoughts. Well, he did! He wrote that he wanted lots of presents for Christmas, particularly Matchbox cars. The next day she decided to see if he could read. She wrote a sentence to him and he wrote back. She even tried to fool him and wrote in cursive, but he read that with no problem. The following day we decided to see if he could add and subtract. He could, without any problem. That afternoon Mrs. Snow tried multiplication and division. Again he could do both. I was beyond being a proud mother. They did number patterns, and Dillon did them with ease.

Dillon can spell anything, and I mean anything. He listens to the news and is able to write about current events. When he was writing to his teacher about the tragedy in New York and about bin Laden, I was blown away; I had no idea he even understood what was going on. When his teacher asked him what it feels like to be autistic, he answered, "Nobody knows what you are thinking and nobody knows what you are like." He doesn't want to be autistic, something he has written several times. He even wrote a prayer for the secretary of his school when her son Andrew was killed in a car accident on his way home from college. She said that Dillon's prayer and words helped her through many long nights.

I want to end this by saying that my strong area with Dillon isn't working one-on-one with him. We do homework together, but a few years ago when Dillon would get really angry, I couldn't even get through that with enough patience. My strongest area with Dillon is his diet and supplements. I teach him everyday living tasks, but I have read books about parents who spend hours a day teaching their children. I have not been able to do anything like that, but I keep trying to do what I can, five minutes here, 10 minutes there. Just do the best you can, and please don't give up!!!



*Update (March 2003):*

Dillon's yeast overgrowth finally cleared up, and we began chelation in December. He's doing well, talking more, and is much more curious about things than he used to be. He also seems to be more confident. This weekend we're adding lipoic acid to the chelation, and I'm looking forward to the results.

When Dillon began experiencing some anger and frustration that affected his work at school, Dr. Mary Megson, our DAN! doctor, put him on Clonidine (a very low dose). But Dillon was just mean when he took it, and he would have a terrible time almost every night, until we finally realized that he was one of the 2% of people who have night terrors while on Clonidine. In addition, he continued to have trouble at school, so we switched him to a low dose of Risperdal instead, and he is doing wonderfully—he no longer has that anger and he is able to attend to his work with a smile.

He is doing very well in school. His quality of life is much better.

*Update for Second Edition (November 2005):*

We are still chelating. Dr. Mary Megson tested Dillon to see how high his testosterone levels are (apparently, when testosterone levels are high, the body holds in the mercury that we are trying to chelate out). Dillon's levels are very high, so Dr. Megson prescribed a monthly shot of pediatric lupron to decrease levels. Then we will chelate more aggressively to get rid of the mercury that isn't coming out now. The shot is very expensive, and I have been waiting over a month for our insurance company to approve (or deny) the prescription. Dr. Megson has two other patients who have used lupron and are now talking. I am so excited about this new treatment. I feel strongly that this will do the trick and get the mercury out. I am going to borrow my brother's video camera to document Dillon's progress when he starts the shots. I think it would be worth getting on tape, especially if my insurance doesn't approve it and I have to pay out of pocket for it.

Dillon is in seventh grade now. He switched schools two years in a row, which shut down his written communication. With new people, he pretends that he can't write at all. In the past it took him a year before he opened up to the teacher and assistants. He is in his second year at middle school and he's just starting to write with the assistant, Ms. Susan. I actually had to go into school and show them how he writes hand over hand with another person. He is in a good place now.

I hope to have great news about the new treatment in the next update.

## — Chapter 6 —
# I Am Sam

By Cheryl and Ike Bezalel

*Says Cheryl Bezalel, "We are an average family of four, and we live in Canada. I work in a bank, one week full-time and one week job-sharing with another woman. Ike is self-employed. Ike and I decided that Sam needed a lot of care, attention and work, so that is why we work the way we do. Sam's brother Daniel had attention deficit disorder (ADD), and it has been a big challenge to deal with both Sam and Daniel. Not all days are smooth sailing, and sometimes Ike is dealing with one child while I am dealing with the other. Fortunately, it is usually only one or the other who is 'going off the deep end,' not both at the same time!" Sam was born in May 1986. This story was written in March 2002.*



Sam. We had already named him before he was born. Legally it was Sassoon, but we did not want to burden him with a name that could be cause for teasing when he started school. Little did we know that he was already burdened with something much bigger than a name: autism. We did know before he was diagnosed at the age of four that something was not right with Sam. He was delayed in almost every aspect of childhood development. He had to be taught how to sit up, crawl, and roll over—not in the everyday sense of "taught"—we had to physically move him into position, hold him in that position, and then move him the way he should move to perform the activity. For example, crawling: his father put Sam on his stomach, then put his knees and hands under him, then moved his hands and knees to show him how to crawl. This was the case for each milestone that Sam had to master.

Sam was also a very demanding baby. When he wanted to be fed it had to be done immediately. He would scream in his high-pitched screech until he was fed. I remember driving down the highway about five minutes from home one day when Sam decided that he needed feeding. He started the screech (it's the only way to describe his cry), but I thought he could wait until we got home, and that he would stop crying if I didn't feed him right away. Not Sam—he screamed right up until the last second before I started feeding him. A lot of these little things led up to our belief that something was not right with our son.

At two years of age Sam had very delayed speech and was quite wild. It was as if he were on uppers most of the time. He was constantly in motion. Once he learned how to walk, he took off at a run and never stopped. Looking back at home videos, we can also see that he was self-stimming from a very early age. When I watch the videotape of his first birthday, I can now see that his hands were flapping and his feet were in constant motion while he was sitting in his highchair.

When Sam was three we were very concerned about his speech, and so we talked to our doctor. He suggested that we have Sam's hearing tested at the Children's Hospital. From that testing it was clear that Sam actually had exceptional hearing but very delayed speech. The specialist recommended speech therapy at our local health unit. Unfortunately, the speech therapist had quit and had not been replaced, so we waited about six months before a new one arrived. Finally, Sam was assessed by the new speech therapist, and he started treatment.



The funny part of this story is that I had seen a show about autism on television. A couple of weeks after that, when we went to pick up Sam from his speech therapy, the therapist looked at us and said, "Have you heard about . . ." I just knew what she was going to say, and we said "autism" at the same time. She suggested that we get Sam in for an assessment at the Children's Hospital. On June 7, 1990, Sam was assessed and diagnosed with autism. When the doctor told us the results I remember letting out a big whoosh of air from my lungs and looking over at my husband. Then we both said, "Well, what do we do for this child?" There was no denial, no anger, no tears—just relief that we were not the bad parents that we were beginning to think we were. Sam was uncontrollable and we knew that we had to do something very soon to help him. The doctor recommended that we place him in an integrated preschool program for special needs children, and that we get on the waiting list for behavior therapy.

And so at a stage when most parents are looking forward to their child going off for the first year of school, we were having meetings with the preschool board and attempting to convince them that Sam would be a good candidate for their program. We got a crash course on how to get services for this child: yell loud because "the squeaky wheel gets the grease." My husband is the person who gets all the credit for getting Sam the help that he needed. Ike made sure that if there was help out there, Sam was going to get it.

Being self-employed, Ike could adjust his schedule so he could attend all meetings regarding Sam. He has not missed one of Sam's individual education plan meetings. He has been a very big advocate for Sam and ensures that he gets the help he needs in every situation. Not to say that I do not contribute, but Ike has been the driving force behind Sam's success.

In June of 1993, three years after his diagnosis, Sam finally started behavior therapy. Many of Sam's behaviors were a result of his trying to do things the best way he knew how. As a result, we had to stop all of the bad habits and start over with new good habits. Topic perseveration, improper voice modulation, poor social skills, aggression, prompt dependence, lack of eating skills and table manners, difficulty remaining seated and keeping still, running, insistence on sameness/inability to deal with change, and self-stimulatory behavior were all issues that had to be retaught or changed. Behavior therapy never stops, and, eventually, the parent must become the therapist. This is what this therapy has taught us to do, and I still use many of these techniques today with my children. The therapist worked with us for two years. She would come by once or twice a week to see how we were implementing the strategies that were set out for us in Sam's behavior plan. The behavior therapy was a good start down a long road. It made a difference for Sam. If he had not received this treatment, Sam would not be in the position he is now.



After the speech and behavior therapy, Ike and I started exploring other kinds of treatments. We had heard about a nutritional therapy, B6 and magnesium, and started to look into this. We found some reading material on the subject and then contacted the local Autism Society chapter. They suggested we get a video by Dr. Bernard Rimland. After we received the video from the Autism Research Institute, we had an "information night" at a local autism organization and showed the video to a group of parents.

We decided to try the B6 and magnesium, and ordered it from Kirkman Labs. The first form of this vitamin was an orange powder that we tried to put into yogurt, shakes, pudding—anything to get Sam to take it. Unfortunately, it was grainy and did not dissolve well. We did get Sam to take it for a while and then decided to switch to the pill form. We spent a week or two teaching Sam how to swallow pills (he was about seven or eight years old at this time), and he has been taking the vitamins ever since.

On the advice of Dr. Steve Edelson, we did not tell anyone that we had started the vitamins. This allowed us to see if the vitamin formula really did make a difference. The first thing that his teachers noticed was that Sam was less distracted. Normally if a fire truck, ambulance, or police car went by with a siren on or a plane flew overhead, Sam would jump from his desk and run to the window. The teacher noticed that he was less attentive to these distractions. If another student dropped a pencil on the floor, he would have to get up or turn around and look, thus losing his concentration on the task he was doing. Now he was less fidgety and less hyper and he was able to sit at his desk for longer periods of time. He was also calmer. Sitting at the dinner table was always a big challenge for Sam—now he seemed to be able to stay seated and finish his meal. Sam used to have chronic ear, nose, and throat infections; but once we started the vitamins, these problems seemed to go away. Sam has had antibiotics only a few times since he has been on the Kirkman vitamins, which is about eight years now. In addition to the Super Nu-Thera formula we added dimethylglycine (DMG) to Sam's therapy and again his behavior improved.

Around the beginning of 1994 we heard that Dr. Edelson was going to be in Canada and offer auditory integration training (AIT) at Gateway. We were very interested in this treatment, as we always knew that Sam had what I call "Super Hearing." This child could be in his room with the door closed with me in the living room watching TV, and as soon as a McDonald's commercial came on he would shoot out of his room and be there to see that commercial. He also had a problem with certain noises. I had a blender I could not use in his presence as he would scream, "Stop, stop, stop!" at the top of his lungs. The same would happen with one of our vacuum cleaners. We were always puzzled about his ability to hear planes and sirens before we could hear them. I remember driving in the car with Sam and hearing him say, "Police car, police car." I kept looking around for the police car and sure enough, a few seconds later I could hear the siren. Sam also had a very high-pitched voice. We were concerned about this, as we knew he probably would be teased about it later on in school when the children were not so accepting of his behaviors.

With all of this in mind we were very interested to try AIT and see what the effect would be. So in August of 1994, Sam participated in AIT under the direction of Dr. Edelson. After the treatment, we immediately noticed that his high-pitched voice was a little better. But about a week later we noticed that his sensitivity to sounds increased. We were very concerned about this and were just beginning to think we had made a big mistake when suddenly his hearing settled down and the pitch of his voice became much better. The next big thing that happened was when Sam came up to his Dad after riding his bike and said, "This is a girl's bike." The bike was light purple and had not seemed to bother Sam before, but now it was a problem. We felt that someone at the school must have told Sam he had a girl's bike. Before the AIT Sam was not really aware of these types of things and didn't care about the way other people saw or thought of him. Now, suddenly, he paid attention, cared, and understood. This was a big step not only for Sam, but for us. Sam was more aware of what was going on around him, and he was aware of the teasing.

Vision therapy was the next treatment that Sam received, from the summer of 1997 to the summer of 1998. This program involved the wearing of prism lenses and a series of exercises. Dr. Melvin Kaplan did the assessment and decided which prism lenses would be appropriate. A one-year exercise program went along with wearing the glasses and a new exercise was done each week. During the course of the year, we did notice that Sam became more aware of things around him. For example, at this time he was playing soccer. When the ball was passed to Sam it was difficult for him to judge where it was coming from, because he always had his head turned downward. All of a sudden he was able to keep his head up and receive the ball. Subsequently his soccer skills improved to the point where he was asked to play on a more advanced team. Sam's gross motor skills improved greatly after this treatment. He also became more sensitive to teasing, and to the nuances of people's voices. He was starting to understand how the tone of people's voices could change the meaning of what they were saying. He also started to understand sarcasm, which before had gone completely over his head.



During 1998, we removed all food colorings from our children's diet. As a result their behavior improved. One day Ike bought vitamin C that contained red and yellow food dyes. The boys had been off the food colorings for about six months. We were visiting my sister, and she noticed that the boys seemed more calm and relaxed. Within half an hour of taking the vitamin C with the food colorings they were both grouchy and fighting with each other. My sister couldn't believe how their behavior changed so quickly. It was a very good test to see if the food colorings made a difference in their behavior. In about four to five hours they calmed down and became more agreeable.

In January of 1999, we had Sam tested for food allergies and found that he was allergic to milk products. We immediately took Sam off all dairy products: no cheese, milk, or dairy products of any kind. With the removal of the dairy from his diet, we also saw a change in his behavior for the better. He became less sensitive to teasing and less emotional, and we were able to reason with him more.

Sam has come a long way. He is now attending the local high school with some support and is an "A" and "B" student. He was on the Honor

Roll first term and has a 3.5 grade point average. He plays basketball on our local Junior Grizzlies, belongs to the Shotokan Karate Club, and will be going for his yellow belt in April of 2002. He has friends and has decided he would like to be a pharmacist. His teachers all like him and enjoy having him in their classrooms. His social studies teacher said to us the other day, "He is so intelligent that he says things that just go over the other students' heads."

Sam's brother, Daniel, who had ADD, is 13 years old and attending grade eight in the same high school as Sam (our high school is grades 8-12). Daniel is also on nutrient therapy, namely B6, magnesium, and omega-3 fatty acids. We saw some improvement with the B6 and magnesium, but so far the greatest improvement has been with the omega-3. Daniel is also off all food colorings, which helped improve his attitude.



We know that all the treatment and therapy that Sam has received has played a big part in his being where he is today. Each one of these treatments has made a difference; even if it is only a little, they have all added up to make a big difference. We have a long way to go, but we see the light at the end of the tunnel and know that Sam will be a productive, contributing member of society and enjoy a good quality of life. I always look back to when Sam was in kindergarten and we were told, "Don't expect too much, he's autistic." Our response was "Why not!"

*Update (February 2003):*

Sam is progressing well in both school and karate. He is in grade 11 and has quite a heavy course load this year because he wants to attend Simon Fraser University after he graduates. He has an orange belt in karate and has attended several tournaments, where he's won numerous medals.

Sam is still taking the Kirkman vitamins and staying off dairy and food colors. We have not introduced any new treatment at this time but have noticed that Sam has matured yet again. There are still many challenges ahead, but with the right support Sam will be able to achieve his goals.

*Update for Second Edition (October 2005):*

Sam is now officially an adult, at least in Canada. Sam turned 19 years old this year; how the time flies, and they grow up so fast. I remember when Sam was diagnosed at the age of four and I was asked, "When your son is 18 where do you see him in his life?" My answer was, "I want him to be a productive, contributing member of society." I can honestly say that I believe that Sam has accomplished this. He is starting his second year at Simon Fraser University in the Faculty of Science. When he started at SFU he wanted to become a pharmacist, but I think he may change his mind. He has now become interested in human kinetics, diet and exercise. Sam has continued with his karate and is now a brown belt and is looking forward to becoming a black belt. Sam works six hours a week at our local library shelving books. He is involved in the Hillel group (Jewish student group) at the university and has made many friends. Sam is commuting up to the university by bus every day and it has been difficult to allow him to do this on his own, but we knew that this was an important part of his growth and maturity.



Daniel, Sam's brother, is in his last year of high school and will be graduating in the spring of 2006. Sam and his brother are very good friends and spend a lot of time together. They play video games, listen to music, and talk to each other a lot.

Sam is still on his Super Nu-Thera vitamins and DMG. We still keep a watch on his diet, and he is also taking more interest in his diet because of the classes he is taking at school.

Of course, we have ups and downs and Sam still has some meltdown days, as we call them. He did not do well in his recent midterm physics exam and was quite distraught about it but was able to hold it together until he got home. He still gets emotional in times of stress, but we are working with the university on coping strategies for him.

Overall, we are very proud of Sam's accomplishments and feel that we can handle most problems that will crop up. Next up: Dating! I'm not sure how we will deal with that, but I do know we are up for the challenge.

## — Chapter 7 —

# Story of Ryan and Stacy Blanco

By Kathy Blanco

*Kathy Blanco and her husband have four children, two of whom—Ryan and Stacy—are diagnosed with autism spectrum disorders. Currently, Kathy is focusing much of her attention on facilitating a project designed to identify children who may be genetically vulnerable to vaccine damage (www.ChildScreen.org). Ryan was born in September 1981 and Stacy was born in October 1987. This story was written in February 2002.*



It seems as if I am living this life over and over again, in an endless case of déjà vu. Along the way I've encountered many pitfalls and experienced many triumphs, and I hope that the lessons I've learned will benefit others.

My son, Ryan, is now 20 years old and has a dual diagnosis of epilepsy and autism. The first signs of trouble were so obvious that I cannot deny, nor can his doctors, that he experienced an excruciating entry into the world of autism.

While carrying Ryan I was working full-time in a high-stress job. I would come home so tired, and wonder if it was good for me to do this to the baby. Yet I persevered as long as I could. I was married only one month before I became pregnant—whoops. Before the pregnancy I lost a lot of weight—you know, the typical I-want-to-look-good-in-my-wedding-dress sort of thing, and dang, I did look good!

Before we got our marriage license I received a titer check, and was told that I did not seem to have adequate MMR (measles/mumps/rubella) titers. So they gave me a quick shot and sent me on my way. Nothing to fear, nothing to even give me an inkling of future trouble. My life seemed to be following a new, happy course.

During the pregnancy I came down with a mild sore throat but just passed it off. At the same time, however, I discovered some rather scary information about the well water in the area where I worked, in Silicon Valley—an area in which there appears to be a cluster of autism.

I distinctly remember feeling so exhausted at this time that I would lock the front door of the office and go to sleep on the carpet in the back room at lunchtime. I didn't know what to make of it. The sore throat became worse, so I made an appointment to see the doctor. He did a swab test and found that I had mononucleosis. Scared, I asked him, "Won't this hurt the baby?" He said, "I want you to quit work for a month, get off your feet, and get bed rest." I was so sick for two weeks that I thought I was going to die—fevers, trembling in my bed—hoping and praying that nothing would harm the baby. About five days short of the due date, Ryan James Blanco was born, with no complications, and an Apgar score of nine.

He was a beautiful baby, a blend of Castilian Spanish and Irish. I remember distinctly that a good friend, a nurse at the hospital, told me they'd fought over who was going to bring the baby to me! This is consistent with the common observation that many autistic children enter the world with beautiful faces.

Ryan was a good eater, and as a new mom I had no complaints. In hindsight, however, I remember that he reacted more negatively to each succeeding vaccination. I heard the usual line from the doctor each time: "Give him Tylenol."



When Ryan was six months old I remember thinking, why is he not sitting up? He did, but then when he did, he would fall to one side. Years later I learned that this is a clear sign of mercury poisoning (in his case, we now believe, as a result of his childhood vaccines). He also began to have sleep problems. On the other hand, he said plenty of words—"mama," "dada," "baba," "juju," "doggie," "cat"—and signed and cooed and made good eye contact. I really had no suspicions.

Feeding was a problem with Ryan, and I have a film of me hanging over his chair, begging him to eat. Worried about his health, I breast-fed him as long as possible. He was plump and happy, and walked at around 13 months. I did notice a slight hand flap here and there, but I just thought, oh, he's being cute and excited. When he was around 14 months old, I began to notice other slight things, but nothing to worry me unduly. I was concerned, but I got pregnant again (another whoops) and was distracted by the fact that I had another baby on the way.

When Ryan was around 18 months of age and received a polio/DPT (diphtheria/pertussis/tetanus) vaccine at his well-baby visit, I again gave him Tylenol to assure an easier time. Around that time, news programs were airing reports that the pertussis part of the DPT shots was cause for concern. I remember begging for more information on this, and asking my pediatrician if we should give Ryan a shot excluding pertussis. He brushed it all off as if serious reactions never occurred, at least to children like Ryan, and he said it would be fine.

Fine? Eleven days after Ryan's DPT he had a sudden, rapidly rising fever (to 105°) and a stiff neck and body. He screamed and pitched for 24 hours, having convulsions, his eyes rolling. We took him to the after-hours doctor, who gave him phenobarbital. Later I took him to the emergency room for a spinal tap, to make sure he didn't have meningitis. I clearly remember sitting in tepid baths with Ryan the whole night. One of the interns said that he was going to record that it was a vaccine reaction, even though if he did that, he would be putting himself in harm's way. I was thankful for his bravery and perseverance. After we were sent home, with other doctors saying that Ryan's reaction must have been a "viral illness," I held the release paper in my hand and told myself, I need to put this away for safekeeping.

We had no son for a week. He lay in his bed listless and tired and feverish. Then he seemed to pop out of it, but into something else.



His appetite grew even worse. I would take him on little walks with my daughter and notice that he would do things over and over. When I took him to the church nursery, he would stay in the corner, not paying attention, staring out the window. I took him to his pediatrician again and mentioned how he couldn't even push the pedals on his tricycle, and how his speech was stagnating and sometimes there were no words at all.

The pediatrician referred me to a speech pathologist who mentioned autism to me for the first time. I didn't even know what the word meant. I spent hours at the library, poring over books and pouring plenty of tears. I put Ryan in an early intervention program, but he continued to regress or, at best, developed a few splinter skills. We went to several neurologists and had numerous tests done. When Ryan was around four, I noticed other problems such as muscle wasting and bouts of what I call "movement disorders," in which his legs twitched and writhed when he got up in the morning. The doctors didn't know what that was all about. We then took him to see Bryna Siegal at the Stanford Autism Research Center. She diagnosed him with PDD-NOS (pervasive developmental disorder—not otherwise specified).

While we were discussing Ryan's diagnosis, I had my fourth child, Stacy, on my lap (yes, I was a very busy mom!). By then, I think my heart was a little hardened, or perhaps I was in shock that this had become my life. Four children under the age of 6½!

Later, when we got Dr. Siegal's written report on Ryan, I noticed one line that shocked me: "Stacy seems to have some movements that I recognize as the beginnings of autism." Back then, we didn't have a lot to go on, a little Lovaas here or there, the first inklings about milk being bad for autistic children, and that was about it. No mention of a vaccine connection. Also, with my two kids after Ryan, there had been no problems with the vaccines, so I thought, gee, it must have been a fluke. I had, however, eliminated pertussis vaccinations for Ryan's three younger siblings. I thought I had my bases covered ... NOT. Sure enough, as I looked back I could see that as Stacy had gotten older, the signs of autism had slowly crept in. On one occasion Stacy became quite ill after her MMR, and within two weeks she was throwing up and had diarrhea from hell. I remember telling the doctor there was something strange about this. Stacy also had funny rashes all over her bottom, with actual welts. She had other telltale signs: not sleeping, losing her language, and even bouts of extreme anger. I remember one report commented, "Mother was tolerant during our interview while the baby was pulling her hair." With all the knowledge I had gathered for Ryan, even I, a savvy mom, had not recognized until our meeting with Dr. Siegal that another child was following the same pattern.



I put Stacy into early intervention at 11 months of age, based upon Dr. Siegel's report. The early intervention was a lifesaver, providing us with many referrals to good doctors and many ideas for interventions not only for Stacy but also for Ryan. We worked on the GFCF diet extensively, and were probably the first parents to figure out that our children had rampant *Candida* and seek the advice of an immunologist (who put them on nystatin). This was a big breakthrough for both of them, particularly Stacy. We also put them on the Feingold diet, in which we avoided colored foods and dyes, and phenolic foods. This was another positive step.

During this time, Ryan began to have facial seizures. We took him to the neurologist, who put him on a ketogenic diet. This really helped him for a time. The neurologist also put Ryan on a mitochondrial cocktail because extensive tests showed that he'd built up too much pyruvate and lactic acid, which are waste products of the Krebs cycle. Later, I found out this was also a sign of mercury poisoning.

As the years went by, the seizures escalated into something I call pubescent HELLO-OO. At around 13 years of age, Ryan began to have grand mal seizures. We put him on everything we could think of, pharmacologically speaking. Some improvements occurred, here and there, but nothing that made us say AHA! I then put him on glycomannans and sterolins, as well as on various other supplements such as good fatty acids, homeopathic hGH, zinc sulfate, and tons of B-complex vitamins. This (along with other approaches to "healing the gut," which would in turn "heal the seizures") really seemed to stave off the seizures. Don't get me wrong: there is still work left to do, but for the most part it's better than when Ryan was having one or two grand mals a week.

As for Stacy, during this time she really started making gains under the same protocol, with some additions to address her own deficiencies. We also recognized how PST-deficient she was. (Children deficient in phenol-sulfo transferase, or PST, accumulate excess amounts of potentially damaging phenolic compounds.)

At her three-year evaluation, Stacy was declassified as autistic, but diagnosed with Asperger syndrome. She has a keen sense of humor, and can joke and laugh and make friends, but she has some social "issues." She reads at around a second or third grade level, and requires no aide in her modified classroom of learning-disabled children.

The journey doesn't end here, because we found new information that answered even more of our questions. As a mom, I was tired all the time, and had signs of chronic fatigue syndrome. Then I learned that my mother had multiple myeloma, cancer of the blood and immune system. This was devastating. Her prognosis is good, however, compared to the prognosis of someone who has lesions or tumors at the outset. She is also on the protocol I have outlined to treat my children's autoimmune problems.



While researching treatments for my mother, I discovered that not only her cancer but also my chronic fatigue could be connected to autism. I came across the website of the Center for Complex Infectious Diseases (CCID), www.ccid.org, which I had seen before while researching autism. I searched for the terms "autism" and "multiple myeloma," and it was there that I read a report by Dr. Brian Durie describing how he often saw complex neurological conditions within a family. He even mentioned the case of a mom with two kids with autism! I nearly fell off my chair. I called CCID, and asked if they would like to test our family. "Would we!" they said. I sent in blood samples from the entire family: my mother, my father, my sister, her children, and my family in total (four kids, my husband and myself). *All of us* tested positive for stealth virus infection. Those with obvious neurological conditions were strongly positive, and those with moderate or unnoticeable signs were moderately positive. This was an answer I had been seeking. You may be asking, doesn't this mean that stealth viruses are a cause of autism? I don't know. But I do know that the standard PCR (polymerase chain reaction) and Western blot tests were used to look at our blood, and we cannot deny what we saw. The virus detected in our family, SV-40 (a monkey virus), was contained in polio vaccines given to the general population in the 1950s and early '60s (the good old sugar cube). It is also implicated in frank cancers.

This, along with mercury poisoning, is a very interesting explanation not only for multiple myeloma, chronic fatigue syndrome, and autism, but also for fibromyalgia, tics, bipolar disorder, schizophrenia, drug/alcohol problems, dyslexia, ADD, and depression. I am sure that many families with autistic members also have histories of these problems.

We are about to enter the world of chelation therapy, as soon as we get the children's mineral stores up. Both children show telltale signs of poisoning: low minerals, such as selenium and even lithium and manganese. These are all signatures of mercury poisoning.

Since we have two kids with autism, I also have had many genetic C4B allele tests and have participated in multiple studies. One of the most interesting involved the major histocompatibility complex. This cluster of genes is responsible for handling viruses, toxins, and fungals, all implicated as contributors to symptoms in children who became autistic following vaccinations. What the study showed was that expression of these proteins was so low in the children that any vaccines would be harmful for them; had I known that they had incompetent immune systems, I would never have vaccinated them. We are working closely with CCID, and are about to begin taking antivirals such as Valtrex, Biaxin, Acyclovir, and Ganciclovir. We also have done dark field microscopy and have still found invasive fungus and *Candida*, so that's something to work on. It looks as though I may also have *Mycoplasma* infections, which could also be "stealthy." I am currently on Biaxin, said to lower chemokine and cytokine production. Ryan's blood work almost made the technician lose her cool, when she saw what she thought was the oddest form of cells she had ever seen, filling the whole screen. It screamed STEALTH to me. (What I have learned since is that these were virally infected cells called "giant cells.")



So you see, I've had some successes here and there, and I've gained much knowledge, but I have a lot more to think about. We just received test results showing that the kids have antibodies to almost all of their brain proteins and neurotransmitters. They have antibodies to myelin, serotonin and receptor sites, catecholamines and neural axon filament proteins. You cannot tell me that these children are just psychologically involved; they are *systemically ill.* They have many gut issues that I keep in check with probiotics, enzymes, fatty acids, glycomannans, and everything else I can find that heals the gut. Typically, we spend about $1,000 per month out-of-pocket for nutraceuticals and supplements. Yes, it is unfair—but it has made me strong.

I await more news on whether I should have endoscopies performed on my children, as well as other tests that may provide further clues. Biomedically these kids are so challenged that one small twist or turn or change in their diets can set them off, or make them regress. This became clear when I found out the kids were more allergic to corn than to the gluten in wheat. In my opinion, performing enzyme-linked immunosorbent assays (ELISA tests) and other targeted treatment tests is advisable.

This I can tell you: I am absolutely resolved that if we prescreen our newborns, we may find more than a few who cannot handle vaccines. I am currently working on a project to have such prescreening done, as a simple needle stick or phenylketonuria (PKU) test is done, and will offer my insights as I progress. I hope this idea can be put forth to DAN! doctors, who may be able to form a consensus as to which alleles of the immunogenetic system will stamp a child "DO NOT DISTURB." My hope and prayer is that I will help to squelch this epidemic, and possibly save another child from the life my children have had to endure.



My motto as a parent: "Knowledge is power."

*Update (February 2003):*

We continue to investigate new treatments for Ryan and Stacy. IV glutathione, Primal Defense, and Houston enzymes have revealed interesting clues about our kids. We will add metallothionein (MT) promotion therapy soon. We have scoped Ryan for autistic enterocolitis (Stacy is next). We as a family have an iron disorder, which I believe is also a cause of autism, and in addition we all have the stealth virus. Unique to us? Oh, no. All of these are of concern not only to me, but also to the researchers with whom I have been so blessed to work.

Both Ryan and Stacy went through chelation. Their mercury was off the charts and their mineral levels were abnormal as well. We detected a kryptopyrrole problem as mentioned by Dr. McGinnis, and we are awaiting results on this. Also, my daughter had a low lithium level, so we began giving her natural lithium and found that many of her mood changes, which had been so noticeable before, were eliminated. Also, we added boron to the children's protocol, as well as niacinimide (1000 mg helps kryptopyrrole children). I am now looking into tetrahydrobiopterin ($BH_4$) deficiency, which may affect autistic children.

I have also formed a think tank called Childscreen (www.ChildScreen.org), whose members are developing standards to write into resolution and pass into law, mandating that children must be tested to rule out immune system problems before they are vaccinated like pincushions. Another of our goals is to change preconceptual care practices and birthing procedures that also produce autism. It would behoove every parent to read our website carefully, and learn why our children are, in my estimation, THE SITTING DUCK CHILDREN. My own children's lives are an example of how TRUST creates autism. The biologics we push into our children, the birthing procedures to which they are subjected, the foods we feed them, and the environment to which we expose them have all changed dramatically since the first diagnosis of autism in the 1940s. The more we look away from these obvious things, the farther we are from solving the puzzle of autism.

*Update for Second Edition (September 2005):*



We are currently still on the protocol, and have done numerous adjuncts. First, we found out Stacy and Ryan have WA-1 *Babesia* (a strain of *Babesia* found in Washington State, where we lived for eight years). *Babesia* are protozoa that infect red blood cells. Protozoa are nasty creatures, probably worse than bacteria. It has been reported that many symptoms of autism are found in people with *Babesia*: epilepsy, sweating profusely, ataxia and limb movements, all part of my son's scenario. If you don't get rid of this, the Lyme remains in the body untouched. So we are doing Mepron/Zithromax, and at times Cipro. We have used Rocephin as well. Keep in mind, this is not just an autism disease, we are talking about our *whole family* being infected. Recently, the website www.ilads.org described the co-occurrence of Lyme with autism or other DSM diagnoses. This is not to say I believe it is the whole reason, or the trigger, or THE infection; I am saying it is among the more important findings.

Now, we have had backslides. For instance, you have to be quite careful with antibiotics, and make sure the Culturelle and enzymes are coming. We have also decided to use Virastop (proteolytic enzymes). We had a month where my son could not make it to the bathroom and had even more seizures than before. At times when something exacerbates autism symptoms, it makes you wonder if you are doing the right thing. No wonder parents were scared off antibiotics! But one must remember: no infection, no autism; infection equals autism. My problem is getting the autism community to accept that one more thing is wrong with our kids. There probably are more infectious agents than I can imagine that are causing autism, including *Chlamydia pneumoniae* or even Borna! The latter is often found in parents of autistic children with family histories of heart problems and autoimmune diseases, including MS.

We have also done UVBI, which is a treatment that was used before penicillin became available in the 1940s. The treatment involves removing a small amount of blood from the body and exposing it to UV light before re-infusing it into the patient. The exposure to UV light activates processes that enhance the immune system's ability to kill bacteria and viruses. Back then they used it for septicemia, syphilis, and even measles and mumps. We feel this is a viable option along with the antibiotic therapies. Most naturopaths versed in this therapy can buy a machine or rent one and make a nice profit on it. We convinced our ACAM/LLMD doctor to do such, and it has been very interesting for his practice, which consists mainly of people with MS, mercury poisoning, heart problems, and Parkinson's. The machine is being used for cancer patients/research by Dr. Brian Druker, the maker of Gleevac for lymphoma, at OHSU in Portland.



Along with this we continue to do vitamin and mineral IVs with glutathione. We also use UVBI treatment (not with glutathione, as the UVBI is an oxidative therapy and cannot be used in conjunction with glutathione). The UVBI is 10 weeks of therapy, 10 weeks off, and 10 weeks on again. The UVBI helps the body re-trip the immune system. I feel this is very important to address in autism. This also has some effect on detoxification and liver function, so mercury can also be excreted. The light itself helps the red blood cells, which are usually depleted in our kids, become energized via biophotonic energy. Before the Lyme therapy we made sure we reduced mercury through DMPS IVs, and now that is down to 2, according to Doctor's Data. If mercury is not addressed before Lyme therapy, the Lyme will remain in the body. However, I have also come to realize through research by Dr. Vera Stejskal that mercury can be chelated with antibiotics (they have mercury chelative qualities).

I truly feel most of the bacterial dysbiosis, fungus, and yeast is exacerbated by Lyme infections. We also have used cat's claw, which is said to be the basis of Lyme antibiotics, but is herbal. Artesiminin is also very good for malarial protozoa like *Babesia*. It was interesting for me to learn that the highest incidence of epilepsy per capita is in the African nations where malaria exists. Could it be that *Babesia* is causing seizures in our kids (along with mercury)? I also think that something about gliadin/gluten and casein exacerbates all these microorganisms by compromising intestinal barrier functions, thus wiping out the gut systemically. All the neurotoxins from Lyme and mercury, combined with antibodies, would make a sane man mad.

Unfortunately, traditional medicine treats Lyme disease as a fad, and

Lyme-literate doctors are often taken to the mat for giving their patients long-term antibiotics. I estimate this information won't be out for another 20 years, as autism still continues to ravage the population via congenitally based mechanisms of infection.

As for my kids, it will be a long journey to bring them back from this abyss. They were sick for a very long time, and it will take a long time to make them better.

# — Chapter 8 —
# James

By Claire Burrell-Stella, M.D.
[M.B.B.S., M.R.C.G.P., D.R.C.O.G., D.F.F.P., T.(G.P.)]

*Dr. Burrell-Stella, a General Practitioner, lives in northern England with her triplets, one of whom is autistic (they were born in February 1998). The children's father, Marcello Stella, is a plastic surgeon who now lives in Italy. This story was written in May 2002.*

James is the second of triplets born on February 20, 1998. He is severely autistic, but has two normal sisters.



We knew the risks of a multiple pregnancy, but as the weeks went by before my delivery my hopes soared because fortnightly scans consistently revealed three structurally normal babies who were all growing equally well. Furthermore, I had absolutely no medical complications, and my blood pressure remained low throughout the pregnancy. I fussed to make sure I was given oral steroids to assist fetal lung maturation in case of a premature delivery, but I was lucky and underwent an elective (planned) cesarean section at exactly 36 weeks gestation.

I anxiously waited to hear each of my babies cry spontaneously after birth, and each one obliged perfectly. However, 25 minutes after delivery, while I was still being stitched, a midwife most apologetically said she had rung for one of the pediatricians to return to the room because James was having some respiratory difficulty. She asked if I would like to hold him until the pediatrician arrived. Of course I wanted to; until then no one had even thought to let me see my children. What I saw horrified me, because James was definitely cyanotic (blue from shortage of oxygen). The panicking mother in me wanted to say, "Run with my son to the Special Care Baby Unit (S.C.B.U.)—don't waste any more time," because it was clear too much time had already been lost. But to my shame, my "oh so English" diffidence won, and I did not want to "make a fuss" in front of my colleagues, so I did not say a word. That is a decision that will haunt me for the rest of my life. I have come to believe/hope/pray that perhaps it was James's underlying autism—with its associated enzyme deficiencies—that caused his respiratory disorders and not the hypoxia that caused the autism. Certainly James's blood gases were never as bad as those of some babies who go on to develop normally.

I still feel resentful that even after the three pediatricians had left the room initially, because the babies were doing fine, none of the remaining personnel had noticed what was happening to James. After all, there was a very experienced anesthesiologist accustomed to obstetric work, two distinguished professors of fetal medicine, a plastic surgeon (my husband), three midwives, and several theatre nurses. The neonatologist told us afterward that it had been a very close call as to whether James was going to need artificial ventilation, and he seemed somewhat shocked when my husband's first question had been whether James was brain damaged. But he allayed our fears by saying that James handled normally throughout his four days on S.C.B.U. James weighed 4 lbs., 14 oz. at birth, while his sisters weighed 5 lbs., 5 oz. and 5 lbs., 12 oz., respectively.



Perhaps I have dwelled too long on what cannot be undone, but I feel it is important to point out that even in so-called "centers of excellence," care is often far from optimal.

I know I am enormously lucky to have two normal daughters from the same pregnancy. I guess it makes it much easier for me not to blame myself for any imagined thing I may or may not have done in the pregnancy, which is a fear that I know haunts many mothers who give birth to a handicapped child. I am sure James is a "victim" of a genetic flaw that lies within my family, which contains an astonishing number of atopic (allergic) individuals. I, myself, suffered from a devastating autoimmune condition called Stevens-Johnson syndrome at age seven, which has left me with severe corneal damage in both eyes.

After James left S.C.B.U., I was struck immediately by how different he was from his sisters. He seemed somehow more "distant," more passive, and more self-contained, and he opened his eyes less. It is not just with hindsight that I have realized these differences. They registered with me immediately, but did not particularly worry me because he learned to breastfeed much more easily than his sisters, and physically blossomed. I am ashamed to say that I attributed his differences to the trauma after his birth and the time spent apart from us on S.C.B.U., and to the fact that he was a boy. Heaven forgive me!

These were the first of a number of delusions under which I lived for more than eighteen months. Even if I had voiced my concerns about James being somehow different at birth, I know my colleagues would have brushed them away as simply being a result of postnatal depression on my part.

It became an affectionate standing joke that often while feeding, James would avert his eyes as though to look over his shoulder to see who was going to come to steal his milk—we assumed he suspected his sisters!

I was also puzzled as to why only James would occasionally have a projectile vomit containing quite a lot of mucus after bottle-feeding, but it didn't happen often so I did not dwell on it. As the weeks passed, I puzzled over why James had a perpetually stuffy nose and a very distended, swollen abdomen. With triplets it is very difficult to find time to think about anything other than surviving the next few hours, but I did consult a professor of pediatrics. He, like me (until much later—too late), had obviously never heard of milk allergy causing a blocked nose; and because James was growing so well, the abdominal distension was dismissed. I guess James continued to thrive because 50% of his feeds were breast milk. I find writing these words incredibly painful because if only I had known then what I know today, how much better a position James would be in.



As it happens, James took matters into his own hands at about the time of his first birthday, and started refusing milk except in the form of yogurt or cheese.

Right from birth James would have about five dirty nappies (diapers) in 24 hours, and this continued until a year ago when, in addition to having implemented a casein- and gluten-free diet, I introduced digestive enzymes, probiotics, and herbal remedies. (I will return to this later.) James initially suffered abdominal colic like his sisters, but his abdominal pain did not seem to be associated with his abdominal distension.

My initial or residual worries were allayed because James reached all of his developmental milestones on time until he was 14 months old. The three children used to "play" with each other when they were in their baby walkers, continually chasing each other round and round. In retrospect, the only inkling I could have had about James's underlying autism was the fact that he very occasionally would become terrified of some normal situation such as our next-door neighbor suddenly saying hello to him in the garden. In fact, it was my very dear next-door neighbor who inadvertently hit the nail on the head when she said, "James will not look me in the eye." He was then about six months old, but she entirely blamed herself for having scared him that day in the garden. Poor Eriza, how guilty she felt.

Everyone used to comment on how "good" James was as a baby, so much more placid than his two sisters. While he loved cuddles, he did not demand them. He was a dreadful sleeper, but his sisters were, and still are, worse!

While I can berate myself for missing these telltale signs, I also know they were missed by the two mother's helpers we employed. Giovannella, who worked with me in the mornings, had 30 years' experience working with children; and Catia had three normal daughters of her own and helped me in the afternoons. Neither of them ever noticed anything amiss.

Charlotte walked on her first birthday, and Sophie and James learned to walk within a few hours of each other at 13 months; but ironically, it was then that the great gap opened up between James and the girls. Until then, James and Sophie had been inseparable, but that bond was broken from the moment they walked. I foolishly thought that even at the tender age of 14 months the girls must have developed different interests. In reality, it was almost certainly due to the MMR vaccinations they all had within a couple of weeks of learning to walk.



My attitude toward immunizations has undergone a radical overhaul since I became the mother of an autistic son. Previously as a doctor, I had always assured parents that vaccinations were completely safe, and that it would be criminally negligent not to have their children immunized. I now feel deeply uncomfortable giving advice about immunizations. I am certain James was autistic from birth, but I do feel that probably each vaccination he received further damaged his immune system and increased the severity of his symptoms.

In Italy, where we lived at the time, babies are routinely given the triple hepatitis B injections at the same time as their other routine vaccinations. While I frowned a little at the idea of giving such tiny babies Hep B, I decided to go along with the practice, believing at least it was one less lethal disease to potentially threaten them as they grew up. Only much later did I discover that it was the worst decision I could have made for James, because blood sulfate levels fall even in normal, healthy adults after Hep B immunization, and we all now know about Rosemary Waring's findings on low sulfate levels in autistic subjects. However, it was the meningitis C injection, given at 20 months of age, that proved the final straw and catapulted James from a gradual descent into autism into a frenzied free-fall. Yet while I deeply regret that James received his immunizations, the corollary is that I am enormously thankful that the girls have been vaccinated. They have the best of both worlds, having been unscathed by the vaccinations and being protected from a number of potentially lethal diseases. They will receive their boosters and James will not. If I had known what I know now about diagnosing autism, James would never have been vaccinated.

It was agonizing to watch James withdrawing into a world of his own. Once a beaming, happy little boy, he stopped smiling; and his once healthy, glowing face became pale, with panda shadows around his eyes. He began tearing at the skin on his arms and upper chest; and he would become agitated and claw his face, resulting in ugly scratch marks. He started pulling his hair out. He lost the few words he had learned, stopped humming his favorite tune and making clip-clop noises for a horse. He stopped making eye contact and finger pointing. While in retrospect his play had previously been very repetitive, he suddenly stopped playing altogether. He would spend long periods lying on the floor, or running backward and forward, and jumping. He continually opened and shut cupboard doors.

The penny only clicked when I saw an isolated example of him lining his vehicles up in a semicircle around him. For an instant, my heart leapt for joy because I thought he had started to play again with his toys, but a second later the awful reality dawned. He didn't repeat this exercise, so my hopes rose a little, only to be dashed when I saw him hand-gazing and starting to mouth objects again.



James suddenly went from having an excellent appetite, and being a joy to feed, to eating only about five different foods. He ate bread, biscuits (cookies), apples, cake, and dried fruit, washed down with about 14 bottles a day of diluted blackcurrant juice. Worse still, he no longer sat at the table to eat. He would only eat his food off the floor. It was physically impossible to hang onto him and get him to eat at the table. Mealtimes were a nightmare.

He also started to suffer from the most appalling nappy rash, which was so severe it would have had any normal child writhing about in agony. But James was much more stoic, due to his high pain threshold. That was another delusion I always had about James: I had thought what a brave little boy he was—if he fell over and hurt himself he hardly cried at all. Another dream shattered, when I realized that a high pain threshold was yet another feature of autism. Instead of rejoicing in having a son who was courageous like my husband, I realized that I had to bite the bullet and do what I should have done months earlier—obtain an official diagnosis of autism so that we could move forward.

It may seem ludicrous, but my training actually delayed me from seeking a diagnosis. Because I knew how little hope was offered to autistic children and their parents in England, I truly believed it was a diagnosis without hope, as at that time I had never heard about Dr. Bernard Rimland, Dr. Paul Shattock, or Dr. Ivar Lovaas.

My worst fears were confirmed when an eminently kind pediatrician diagnosed James as autistic and could only advise me to "enjoy" my son. Her only other suggestion was that she could put me in contact with another family in our area with an autistic child for "mutual support." Even the Professor of Child Psychiatry whose main research interest is autism could not advise me on any specific treatment other than attending a Hanen More Than Words course to help me to find ways to communicate better with my child. I did not find the experience beneficial for either of us. It only increased my sense of anger and frustration, and my belief that there must be a better way to help my son.

At this point, as fate would have it, I had the immense good fortune to encounter a casual acquaintance whom I hadn't seen for some time, and who asked how the triplets were. She was the very first person to whom I confided my worst fears about James's probable autism. For some reason at the beginning I could talk to comparative strangers about James's condition, but not to family and friends. Anyway, without batting an eyelid, Deborah said, oh, yes, her nephew had just been diagnosed as autistic and had already started a gluten- and casein-free (GFCF) diet and applied behavior analysis (ABA) therapy. She kindly put me straight away in contact with her sister-in-law, who was enormously helpful in giving me useful contact numbers and advice.



It was from Elaine that I first heard of Paul Shattock and the Sunderland Autism Research Unit, which he runs with his colleague, Paul Whiting. I must say an enormous "thank you" to them both for spending so much time explaining the background and implementation of a GFCF diet to me. I shall always be immensely grateful to Paul Shattock because in addition to giving me a welter of invaluable information, he was also the first person to give me a glimmer of hope for James's future. Room for improvement was something I had hardly dared hope for. It is scandalous that the Sunderland Autism Research Unit receives no funding from Government or the pharmaceutical industry.

While the thought of implementing a GFCF diet was daunting, I had no choice. James was deteriorating rapidly. He was scratching his chest and arms until they bled, and he now had two or three bald patches at the back of his head. His eyes were lackluster, and his five dirty nappies a day were indescribable. The perineal candidiasis was getting even worse; and when I gave him paracetamol (acetaminophen) for a fever at New Year 2000/2001, he became very aggressive toward us all, biting and scratching and hitting his head repeatedly against the wall.

It now seemed easy to try removing milk from his diet for three weeks as recommended, because we were only getting milk into James by feeding him porridge. By this stage he couldn't even eat the porridge because he would begin retching and vomiting small amounts of mucus if he saw it at breakfast time.

The worst of the aggressiveness and self-injurious behavior had stopped as soon as I discontinued paracetamol. It was Paul Shattock who explained to me that some autistic people cannot tolerate paracetamol because they have difficulty breaking it down and excreting it, possibly due to problems with their sulfate metabolism.

However, a further dramatic improvement occurred the moment I excluded casein from James's diet. Overnight he looked healthier; he stopped retching; he looked happier and seemed calmer.

After three days of this amazing transformation I began to realize that some of the improvement was probably due to inadvertently removing the porridge oats themselves. I could not contain my enthusiasm any longer, and I removed gluten too from James's diet. I well remember feeling so panic-stricken every time James ate something he shouldn't. I felt as though even a single biscuit would ruin everything we had achieved with the implementation of the diet and the commencement of ABA therapy. I think if we had not embarked on the diet and vitamin and mineral supplementation, we would have made little progress with ABA.



Within a couple of weeks, James's face no longer bore any scratch marks, and he stopped tearing at his skin. It took about five months, though, for his hair-pulling to disappear altogether. There were only two disappointments with the diet. The first was that his range of "acceptable" foods did not broaden within a few months as most commentators suggested it would. If anything the reverse happened, which, given how little he would accept to begin with, was hardly conceivable. However, after 15 months on the diet he is at last starting to broaden his range of foods just a little bit. On the positive side, James never seemed to suffer a withdrawal reaction when I removed gluten from his diet.

The second disappointment with the diet was that it did not sort out his bowel problems. So I set about tackling the problem, which I have no doubt was due to candidiasis, by removing all dried fruit from James's diet (this was very traumatic for us all); and I started digestive enzyme supplementation, probiotics (Bio-Kult from Cambridge Probiotics and Culturelle from Kirkman Laboratories), and fructooligosaccharide liquid (Fructolite from Biocare) to nourish the beneficial bacteria in Bio-Kult and Culturelle. This sweet-tasting liquid was also useful for disguising the strange bitter taste of an herbal product called Biocidin from Bio-Botanical Research Institute. The results were dramatic. James has never again suffered from candidiasis (at least clinically), and his bowels now open only once per day. I had followed the instructions of the Bio-Kult suppliers and gradually built up to a dose of five Bio-Kult capsules per day for two months, and then gradually reduced the number of capsules back down to a maintenance dose of two capsules per day. James had only a month of Culturelle; and after a couple of months I had to discontinue Biocidin, which had had such a dramatic effect when I introduced it. The reason I had to discontinue it was because James again became pale with panda eyes, and he was more agitated. As soon as I stopped he looked healthier again, and calmed down, and his bowels remained stable. In retrospect, I wish I had given James milk thistle when I introduced Biocidin because I suspect Biocidin was upsetting his phase-1 liver functions.



For the first time I had a comprehensive stool and parasitology analysis done by Great Smokies Diagnostic Laboratory last month, and I was delighted that they found no evidence of yeast infection or pathogenic bacteria.

At the same time that I implemented the GFCF diet, I added a multivitamin and mineral preparation and Super Nu-Thera, followed by dimethylglycine (DMG), trimethylglycine (TMG), L-glutamine, 5-hydroxytryptophan, evening primrose oil, cod liver oil, beta-glucose, Ambrotose, PhytAloe, Seacure, broad spectrum amino acids, taurine, CoQ10, lecithin, lipoic acid, vitamin C, N-acetyl cysteine and homeopathic secretin. Initially, I added methylsulfonylmethane (MSM), in addition to half a cupful of magnesium sulfate, in his bathwater. I have always added James's oral supplements to his juice in an opaque beaker with a lid on it, and he has been angelic and drunk whatever I have given him.

Yes, I spent a fortune and still spend a lot of money on these supplements, but it is so worthwhile. Which of these supplements helped the most? Super Nu-Thera and DMG have both helped greatly. James had better eye contact and was calmer, more focused, more verbal and more sociable. Recently I decided to experiment a little and see if I noticed any difference if I withdrew the DMG. I will not do that again! James started crying again with minimal provocation and for prolonged periods. I am sure it is no placebo effect.

Although the benefits of introducing TMG were less clear-cut, I would be reluctant to stop it as the recent stool analysis showed that the acidity was at the lower end of normal. (TMG raises the acidity of the stomach, aiding digestion and reducing the risk of infections.)

James's skin improved when I added evening primrose oil. Also, 5-hydroxytryptophan helped a little at a dose of 25 mg, but seemed to make a significant improvement at a dose of 50 mg daily.

The introduction of cod liver oil seems to have led to marked cognitive improvement and sociability. I spent a long time needlessly worrying about how to get James to accept the taste, because he kept rejecting all the various flavors I purchased. Then, to my astonishment, I found that he quite happily takes plain cod liver oil off a spoon.

I am still ambivalent about the other supplements, and periodically add them in with the exception of N-acetyl cysteine, lipoic acid, and homeopathic secretin, which all seemed to worsen James's symptoms. In due course I will experiment again even with these.

Very soon after I implemented the diet, James started sleeping better and no longer squealed, babbled or giggled like the maniac Bertha Mason in Charlotte Brontë's novel *Jane Eyre*. Or at least if he did, it meant he had eaten something that he should not have had.



When implementing the diet it is not enough simply to see "gluten-free" on the packet because such things as barley enzymes sometimes get sneaked in. James reacts badly to soya (soy) too.

The next hurdle to tackle was the blackcurrant juice. Impossible, I thought. "Essential," said Paul Shattock. Feasible, thought my mother, and she and Paul were right. My mother had the brainwave to substitute ordinary blackcurrant juice for the aspartame-rich "tooth-kind" blackcurrant juice to which James was addicted. The results were astonishing. Within 24 hours, James was no longer addicted. Quite literally overnight he went from craving bottle after bottle to actively rejecting it in favor of plain water, drunk in normal amounts and from a normal glass, not a bottle.

Again, I was very lucky because I saw no adverse withdrawal effects, only an immediate interruption to the cycle of polydipsia (excessive liquid intake) and polyuria (excessive urine output). I think while he was visually receiving the message that he was still drinking the same juice, his brain was no longer receiving a "kick" from the aspartame, so he lost interest in it.

The addition of magnesium sulfate to the bath helped with profuse head sweating and panda eyes, but the problem didn't resolve completely even with oral methylsulfonylmethane until he started homeopathic silica. Recently the homeopath suggested I try stopping it, but within five days the head sweats had returned. Needless to say, I recommenced it and have had no further problems.

After all my glowing recommendations for following a GFCF diet, multivitamins, probiotics, and enzyme supplementation, perhaps one would think that James must be just about cured. Sadly not. James remains severely handicapped by autism, but the quality of his life and, therefore, our own lives has undoubtedly improved beyond measure. It has given me enough space to go on hoping, searching, and praying for a "magic bullet." And to return to my previous comment, without these biological interventions James could not have embarked so successfully on his ABA program.

The attitude of the medical profession in England, even among those who claim to be experts in the field of autism, remains arrogant, ignorant, and, above all, negative. It is a sad irony that most parents, when they are most vulnerable and desperate to help their autistic children after a diagnosis is obtained, will never hear about biological interventions or ABA from the mainstream medical profession.

A diagnosis of autism is a lonely and isolating experience. Even close friends unintentionally say the stupidest and most hurtful things. A simple rule should be: if you don't know what to say to a grieving parent, then at least say "sorry" and "how awful it must be for you!"



You also have to endure through gritted teeth parents of normal children bemoaning the difficulty of raising their children. They should try rearing an autistic child!

I cannot finish my article without mentioning how beneficial I have found both osteopathy and homeopathy for James. Most of my colleagues would want to have me struck off the medical register for voicing such heretical beliefs! To avoid wasting time and money, choose only alternative practitioners who have had previous experience treating autistic children.

Lastly, as a mother of an autistic son, I owe Bernard Rimland an enormous debt of personal gratitude for sparing me the dreadful burden of being labeled as a cold, dysfunctional mother who had caused her son's autism. It is a sobering thought that prior to his groundbreaking work 40 years ago, that would have been the accusation leveled at me. It must have taken enormous personal courage to overturn the perceived wisdom of the etiology of autism.

The challenge facing all parents with autistic children demands that same quality of courage displayed by Bernard Rimland, Paul Shattock, and so many others.

*Update (March 2003):*

For the three months prior to Christmas 2002, I was rejoicing because James was making excellent progress. Then, for the third year running at

Christmas, James had an upper respiratory tract infection associated with a fever and, as usual after a fever, it has taken a full six weeks for him to "lift the curtain" that always seems to fall after these infections. He becomes "absent" somehow and more irritable and starts to refuse his Super Nu-Thera.

However, I am glad to report that he is "with us" again. Probably this is partly a result of resuming Super Nu-Thera, but I don't think this is the full explanation. It seems as though the fever throws a "switch" in James's brain that takes ages to correct itself. I continue to feel cranial osteopathy benefits James at these crisis points and the young man himself seems to agree. He visibly relishes the session with the osteopath.

Alas, the triplets' fifth birthday fell during the agonizing six weeks when I felt I was not getting through to James. It is so sad to see how birthdays mean nothing to him. He has no interest in opening his presents or cards, and he had to be taken home early from their birthday party by my parents because he cried so much at the noise and commotion from the other children. It was sad to see his birthday cake standing with its unlit candles, when the girls were eager to blow out the candles on their cakes. Such is the grief that all parents of autistic children must experience, I suppose.



Everyone does describe James as a most gentle and affectionate child, and I am lucky that he is not at all destructive. Unlike a normal five-year-old boy, he carefully steps around the towering edifices that his sisters build with wooden blocks and he is mortified if one gets knocked down, which occurs very rarely as he has cat-like powers of negotiating spaces—not your usual autistic picture.

James has virtually age-appropriate gross and fine motor skills and he is very affectionate with reasonable eye contact, much of the time. However, he is nonverbal and flatly "refusing" any attempts at toilet training at present.

The speech analysis done recently showed that James is following a "normal" pattern of development, and that the range of sounds that he can now produce should, ultimately, combine to form speech. The toilet training also should happen, as 14 months ago he did, on one occasion, actually request to sit on the toilet and did urinate appropriately. If he can do it once I hold onto the belief that it will eventually recur.

My biggest disappointment is that despite being on the GFCF diet for two years, James remains as fussy an eater as ever. Everyone else seems to say how well the children start to eat—or at least how their tastes broaden once the offending food items are removed and adequate zinc supplements are given. Forget it with James!

I fully believe that James's supplements are worthwhile and have been responsible for allowing me to again have an affectionate, happy little boy who is calm enough to benefit from ABA. And, while I cannot prove it, I genuinely believe that osteopathy and homeopathy do produce beneficial effects.

I am so very fortunate to have the most devoted and committed parents and sister, who are a tower of strength to me and the children.

*Update for Second Edition (October 2005):*

I stopped giving James any supplements shortly after I wrote the last update (March 2003), partly because it was getting impossible to get him to take any and partly because my asthma was becoming awful as a result of my exposure to the various powdered supplements. The result has been that I have not needed to use an inhaler since; James is a lot happier; he is eating better; and he continues to make painfully slow progress. I have also abandoned the gluten- and casein-free diet, and he is now eating very well and a fairly broad range of foods. I wish he could be persuaded to continue taking DMG, Super Nu-Thera and omega-3 and -6; but he will not, and I cannot face the battle on my own; however, how much difference it would make, I do not know.



James still cannot say a single word, he is still not toilet-trained, and his inability to go to sleep is incredible (it is 12:30 a.m. and he is still awake). But on the positive side, he is very affectionate and beautifully calm (no tantrums or self-injury). He was angelic three weeks ago at my sister's wedding. His routine was invaded from 8 a.m. until 1 a.m. the next morning and he behaved impeccably, including sitting silently in church and sitting at a table of 10 people in a room full of 160 strangers—just incredible. The next day, 50 people came to our home for a follow-up celebration and again he took it all in his stride.

# — Chapter 9 —
# My Son

By Natasha Campbell-McBride, M.D.

*Dr. Campbell-McBride, a neurologist who also holds a Master's degree in nutrition, lives in Cambridge, UK, with her husband and her autistic son, who was born in the autumn of 1992. Her clinic treats autistic children from around the world, and she is currently working on a book on effective autism treatments. This story was written in February 2003.*



My son is 10 years old. He is in a mainstream school, doing well. His academic achievements are within normal range for 10-year-olds, although math is not his strong point. He can be clumsy as far as social skills are concerned, but he has friends, and children generally like him. He can be naïve and hyperactive at times, but amazingly mature at other times. His language is excellent with a wider-than-usual vocabulary, and he likes to write poetry and short stories. He is learning to play piano and is doing very well, particularly at composing his own music. No one would suspect what this child and his parents have been through. Nobody who meets him now would ever think of autism in connection with this boy. All this is now. I have been asked to look into the past and describe how we got here.

It is always painful for a mother to recall those years of desperation and hard work with an autistic child. It is particularly painful to realize all the things you were doing wrong. If only we knew then what we know now! If only we had done this and that, when he was smaller, he may have developed very differently.

However, I do not regret for a moment the mind-blowing educational journey my son took me through. When he was born, I was an M.D. trained in neurology with seven years' working experience. But as they say, doctors make the worst patients. When it comes to your own child, you are just as prone to denial and blindness as any other parent. Apart from that, as all the parents of autistic children discover, doctors know very little about autism. They are taught how to diagnose it, but when it comes to treatment, official medicine has nothing to offer. On the contrary, it is hell bent on convincing you that there is nothing you can do and that any other opinion is quackery. So, being a doctor has given me no advantage at all.

Our son was diagnosed autistic at the age of three. After the initial shock and grieving my husband and I started to learn as much as we could about autism. In those days there wasn't as much information available on the subject as there is now, but at least there was something offering our son hope. I remember that somebody gave us a phone number for Dr. Rimland in California. We had a long conversation with him and as a result our son was on an ABA program by the age of $3\frac{1}{2}$. At the same time he started taking DMG. This conversation with Dr. Rimland was like a ray of sunshine in our lives. Here was a person who knew so much about autism and who was prepared to share his knowledge with us and help us. Here was a parent who did not accept the official position on autism and who had devoted his life to changing that position. I am sure that there are thousands of families around the world forever grateful to this man. I want to add my family to that list.



From the very beginning the ABA program was performing absolute miracles with our boy. I will never forget our first workshop with our excellent ABA consultant, who had flown to us from the U.S. At the end of an exhausting two days of training, she said that in three months' time she expected our son to speak in small sentences. All of us, including our five therapists, thought that she was dreaming, because our boy had no speech and his understanding of language was very questionable. But to our huge surprise, she was right! We have meticulously recorded that period in our son's life on video. In three months' time we were able to have quite a sensible conversation with him.

As our son was moving through his ABA program I devoted my time to learning as much as possible about biology, biochemistry, and nutrition in autism. It was clear to me that our son's extreme fussiness with food—and as a result, very poor diet—had a lot to do with his autism. I went back to university and took a master of sciences degree in human nutrition. I devoted particular attention to studying the digestive system's pathology and how to treat it by natural means. The reason for my interest was the fact that our son's digestive system almost never functioned normally. Beginning the day we introduced solids into his diet, he went through a period of severe constipation, which eventually turned into constant diarrhea. Again, consulting with official medicine was a complete disappointment. Apart from symptomatic drugs with lots of side effects, it could offer our boy nothing to help with his digestive problems, constant fungal nappy rash or tremendous feeding difficulties. At the same time it was clear to me that his immune system was in disarray due to his poor nutrition. Like many autistic children he went through ear infections, chest infections, impetigo, and fungal thrush. And of course, all my medical colleagues offered were antibiotics and more antibiotics.

Based on my newly acquired knowledge I changed his diet dramatically. Our ABA consultant helped us work out a system of introducing foods into our son's diet. Without that system it would have been impossible to change his diet, as he was so finicky with food. Having examined diets that have been successful for children with severe digestive problems, such as ulcerative colitis, Crohn's disease, and chronic malnutrition, I realized that just introducing a gluten- and casein-free (GFCF) diet would not be enough for my son. So I have worked on a far more natural and focused approach, which also excludes gluten and casein. The result was amazing, as if somebody had lifted a toxic fog off his brain. He was much calmer, much more able to learn. His eye contact improved on its own and a lot of self-stimulation disappeared.



At the same time we introduced a strong therapeutic probiotic. There was no doubt that his gut flora was abnormal. From early on I have tried to give him various probiotics, available on the market, with no particular results, until I found a formula that worked. It was powerful enough to heal his digestive system to such an extent that we could cheat on the diet on an occasional basis without any problems. At the same time it gave his immune system such a boost that I don't remember now when he last had a cold. Now he looks a picture of health with rosy cheeks and bright eyes and he is full of energy. Since then I have developed my own probiotic formula, which works very well for autistic children and people with digestive and immune disorders.

It is impossible to overestimate the role of the family in the struggle against autism. I have seen quite a few very sad situations, where one parent is trying to help a child without the support of the other parent. Treating an autistic child is a huge undertaking and united families usually succeed much better. I would like to say that what we have achieved with our son, my husband and I have achieved together. Without my husband's constant support, intellect, and organizational skills I would not have been able to do half of what I have done in these years. Our son is very lucky to have an excellent dad, of whom he is very fond.

A great part of the successful treatment of autism is the fact that parents of autistic children all talk to each other. This is where we get our strength and inspiration to carry on. Our success became an inspiration for many other families, who were calling me and who were willing to try what we did.

That is how my clinic for autistic children started. Having seen hundreds of families from many different countries, I never cease to admire their determination and strength in trying to help their children. I have learned a lot from them and their experiences.

A few months ago at the end of a consultation, one of the parents looked at me and asked in a stern voice, "Why haven't you written a book yet?!" That was followed by a number of other parents telling me that I must write a book on autism. I am working on it now. I feel that it is my duty to share the knowledge and clinical experience that I have accumulated over the years thanks to my son and the many families of autistic children I have met. I hope, too, that my experience will help others to avoid the mistakes that we have made. We all eventually learn by our mistakes, but time is precious for our children. The earlier we start helping them in the right way, the better chance they get to recover from autism. I believe that every autistic child has a chance, given appropriate help.



And do not let anybody tell you that autism is incurable!

*Update for Second Edition (November 2005):*

It is hard to believe that more than two and a half years have passed since our story was published in 2003. My son just turned 13. He is tall and handsome and he is a delight.

In my previous story I mentioned that I was writing a book. Well, the book has been out for a year now and is very successful; a third print was done a month ago. It is called *"Gut And Psychology Syndrome. Natural treatment for autism, ADHD, ADD, dyslexia, dyspraxia, depression and schizophrenia"* (www.MedInform.co.uk). The book describes in detail how these conditions develop and how to treat them using a solid nutritional protocol. It has a large recipe section to help people start on the diet, as well as chapters on how to deal naturally with ear infections, constipation, toxicity, fussy feeding habits, and other issues.

My son was very proud to contribute to my book—he has written a beautiful poem, which is published at the beginning of the book. We still have not told him about what happened to him in his younger years; we decided to wait until he is older. There are no traces of autism in him now and he is leading a normal life. He is doing well at school and started playing rugby on his school team. His digestive system works like a clock now, though we still adhere to the diet, which I have described in detail in my book. The good news is that my son can have anything now on an occasional basis without it causing problems. However, the whole family is on this diet as it is very healthy and can prevent many health problems (such as weight gain, heart disease, cancer, diabetes, autoimmune problems, osteoporosis, and allergies) in all members of the family. When we go on holiday we eat what is available, but when we come back home we go back to our diet because it is good for us. Both our children have a considerable knowledge of nutrition now and we often hear them lecturing their friends on what is good for them to eat and what is not.

I hope that our story can be an inspiration for parents of autistic children. Never give up on your child, and your child will reward you!

## — Chapter 10 —

# For the Love of Jake

By Londa Corcoran

*Londa Corcoran and her husband, Jerry, are the parents of Jake, who was born in November 1997, and his younger sister, Olivia. They live outside Portland, Oregon. This story was written in July 2002.*



This is a story of intense love for our child—no different from the love felt by other parents we have met on this journey to save our children. It is a story of unbelievable challenge and of extreme, even excruciating pain. But it is also a story of incredible joy at the seemingly smallest accomplishments. It is a story of despair and of willed hope, of confusion, and often chaos. But most of all it is a story of love—the most intense, driving love that has empowered us beyond any previous experience, love that won't let us stop pushing, and searching, and trying, and believing. It is a story of love that refuses—God forbid—to give up. This is the story of many hurdles overcome, with many victories yet to accomplish. All for the love of Jake.

Jacob William Corcoran was born on November 30, 1997, and was a perfect baby: tested 10-10-10 on the Apgar scale—no drugs for mom, because he came so fast—full-term, nine pounds, and gorgeous. My husband, Jerry, and I used to laugh at pictures of infants because they look like aliens when they are first born. But not Jacob. He was perfect.

The first year seemed to be marked by typical milestones and accomplishments. Smiles, laughter, sitting, and walking were all right on schedule. So were the vaccinations. He received the full load of vaccines between two weeks of age and 15 months. He cried a lot for two or three days after each one, but there were no infections or other signs of concern.

At about 15 months, Jake started to say a few words, like "uh" while lifting his hands in the air to be picked up, and "mama" and "dada." He waved and said "bye." We questioned our pediatrician at Jake's 15-month checkup about his speech; she assured us that he was coming along just fine, that boys are usually later talkers than girls. We began to worry when his speech didn't continue, and when, in fact, he lost the few words he had been saying. He didn't appear to understand the things he should. At Jake's two-year checkup his pediatrician suggested that it was time for a hearing evaluation (which was normal), and one for speech. The speech evaluation indicated that he was in the first percentile for both expressive and receptive language, meaning 99% of children his age tested higher than he did. This was the equivalent level of a 10-month-old, and he was over two years old. It was Christmas Eve, 1999. It was a bad Christmas.

We started our journey that day and continue on it still. I sometimes wonder if it will ever end, but I know that it does get better—much better. We started speech lessons immediately, which led to our county education services. They offered us 1½ hours per week of services after their evaluation also indicated that our son had skills equivalent to an eight- to 15-month-old in most critical areas (he was now two years and four months old). After two months of these weekly classes, and continuing speech therapy, people started telling us about the "autism spectrum." And the more we researched, the more confused we became. Our son was clearly not the classic example of autism. He loved to cuddle and often had great eye contact. He didn't sit in a corner rocking back and forth. Yet he was in his own world most of the time, didn't respond to his name or seem to understand most of what we said to him ... or to care. He had never pointed to show us anything. He began to tantrum and became obsessive about carrying objects in each of his hands. He would bounce his chosen items up and down in front of his face for hours and could not leave the house without them. He communicated his wants and needs to us by guiding our hands to what he wanted, looking at our hands and not our faces. We began to search for a diagnosis for these disturbing characteristics.



The first behavioral pediatrician we attempted to see was "not taking new patients," but we were referred to a new kid on the block. On June 15, 2000, we saw a child psychiatrist who spent an hour with our family and wrapped up the last five minutes of our session by telling us that our son was definitely autistic. Jerry asked him about the prognosis. He said that there was a chance, with a lot of work and intervention, that Jake might speak but only enough to ask for food or for other highly desired items. He might be able to hold down a simple job one day, but would not have normal relationships with us or anyone else. Then he told us our time was up. We walked to the car in a daze. I felt as if I had been kicked in the stomach. We were numb. No emotion during the hour-long car ride home. Just numb. Jerry and I couldn't speak or look at each other. We went through our evening routine with Jake and his six-month-old sister, Olivia. After they went to bed we cried. I remember I wailed. We hugged and cried some more. We sat up almost all night talking, and it got better. We found hope.

Hope in each other, in our commitment to our son, and in our belief that God would be there guiding us and giving us the strength we were afraid we would need.

In the days to come we searched for answers to the many questions we had about Jake's future and our family's. Unfortunately, for quite some time the search for answers only turned up more questions. Hundreds of them. We learned about biological issues, potential causes, and the unbelievable number of things that could be "wrong" with our son. This included speech disorder, sensory integration dysfunction, motor planning difficulties, immune system dysfunction, permeable gut, malabsorption, food allergies and intolerances, heavy metal toxicity, and brain damage, to name a few. We also learned about the theories about excessive antibiotics, vaccines, and the mercury used as a preservative in many vaccines.



I realized that this was going to take an immense amount of research and decision-making; but time was of the essence, so I took a leave of absence from our family business where I had been working afternoons. I still went into the office and used the computer and phone for six hours a day, seven days a week, for three months. I devoured books, searched intensively on the Internet, called the best autism schools around the country, talked to parents of recovering and recovered children, and joined groups. I had to find out what had happened to our little boy, what options we had for his future, and what decisions we were faced with, based on all of the information I gathered. I look back on this time as sort of a blur—extremely painful, emotionally charged with energy to keep going, even though I slept very little, night after night after night. This was the same summer that we started an addition on our home, something that we had been planning for and dreaming about for 10 years. Now, the daily intrusion of contract workers and the constant noise were a chaotic nightmare, instead of the joy that we had anticipated for so long.

We saw every professional we had heard of in the Portland area who might shed some light on our son's current situation and future outlook. I think Jake had over 10 evaluations of some sort that summer. Four pediatric specialists confirmed the autism diagnosis. We were learning about biomedical interventions, but none of these pediatricians could give us any information or recommendations about these approaches due to lack of research. So we had to find these answers ourselves.

One week after Jake's first diagnosis that fateful day in June, a relative forwarded a magazine article by Karyn Seroussi *[Editors' note: A chapter by Karyn Seroussi is included in this book]* about curing her son's autism through dietary intervention. The way she described her son's strange behaviors before she removed dairy and gluten from his diet seemed very similar to what we were seeing in Jake. We had noticed him giggling to himself, sometimes uncontrollably, seeming to leave our world and acting as if he were high on drugs. It was horrifying. I ran to my husband's office to show him the article. He agreed that it sounded like what we were seeing, and that we should give the dietary changes a try.

We eliminated gluten and casein right away. In fact, we put our son through withdrawals by going "cold turkey," which, in retrospect, we shouldn't have done. But we were desperate and a little frantic. We made a few rash decisions back then—it was hard not to. The first week on the diet Jake wanted to be held all the time; he was emotional; there was very little strange giggling. After five or six days, we gave in to our son at the grocery store where he saw some fish crackers. We foolishly thought, "What can it hurt? He's been through so much!" He devoured them like a lost love. Shortly after we got home, I noticed Jake rolling on the ground, shaking his head back and forth, and laughing so crazily that he couldn't stop. He was gone. I yelled to my husband, who came running and witnessed what I did, and stared at me in disbelief. We then knew we were on to something, and that there was to be no more gluten in our son's diet. (We have never challenged the dairy, even to this day.)



Our Internet research intensified, particularly in the area of biomedical interventions. The fifth DAN! conference was scheduled for the fall, and we registered immediately. We ordered tapes and transcripts from the prior year. We got the DAN! Protocol and tried to understand it. We were going to follow it, no matter what it took, because our research led us to believe that our son was clearly a candidate for recovery if we could "fix" his damaged systems.

We liked our pediatrician, although she was woefully ill-informed about autism and had no clue about the tests and treatments we were describing for our son. She agreed to order some of the preliminary tests as outlined in the protocol—not without reservation, however—and warned us not to be "misled" by our frantic emotions. I think she pitied us for what we were going through and felt that we were illogically and desperately seeking answers. We were grateful that she honored our requests to order the tests. But we knew that we needed to find a new doctor to go down this road with us. We needed a DAN! doctor.

There were no DAN! doctors listed in Oregon at the time. But we heard through a couple of other families that there was a sympathetic doctor of environmental medicine, an M.D. who practiced in our hometown suburb of Portland. He was not taking new patients but was seeing some other autistic children with some of the same biological symptoms, so I decided to write a letter. I had learned before not to accept the phrase "currently not taking new patients"—I would write letters; and we would become patients, usually quite quickly.

Within a few days, the receptionist called and said Dr. John Green would like to see us. We scheduled the first available appointment, which was a month away. We also asked to be called in the event of a cancellation, since we lived less than a mile away. The cancellation happened within a week. We were elated. And we were on our way. This was August 2000. Jake was now two years, nine months old.



I'll never forget the feeling we had when we first met Dr. Green. He was such a warm and loving man. Clearly he had compassion for our son and for our family, and seemed very knowledgeable about what was going on. Dr. Green asked to borrow the tapes from the DAN! conference, and listened to them over and over. Shortly after, he announced his decision to change his entire practice to treat only those children with environmentally induced autism or related disorders. His practice went from a handful of autistic children to hundreds in just a few months. The only DAN! doctor in Oregon was one mile from our house. We were ecstatic.

At this point, our story becomes one of incredible challenges, lots of miracles, accomplishments, disillusionment, and hope. We prayed every day that summer as we learned about this new life into which we had been catapulted. We prayed and believed that God would guide us through this confusing maze of decisions that needed to be made. My husband said something astounding the first night we received Jake's diagnosis, and many times since then. He said he was so grateful that God gave us Jake. If he were in another home, he might not have been given the kind of love, care, resources, or opportunities that we could give him. We also believed, from the beginning, that we were being given an opportunity to rise above this challenge and become a stronger couple, family, and even a stronger Jake. (We still have visions of his giving the commencement speech at his graduating class at Harvard.)

Then we learned about the developmental treatments: applied behavior analysis (ABA), Greenspan's Floor Time, county educational services (ESD), and speech and occupational therapies, to name a few. We put Jake's name on a waiting list for behavioral therapy, which our research led us to believe was the most promising developmental treatment. This was an extremely frustrating experience for us. We were assigned a terrific lead therapist who moved to Washington a month later. At first, we couldn't get any more than 2½ hours of services a week, and we wanted 30. So we met with our "assigned" ESD team in late summer to talk about what services our son was entitled to receive from the state. We couldn't afford the ABA therapy anyway, so we were looking for another miracle.

We were blessed with a most unbelievable and rare ESD team headed by a 30-year veteran, specializing in autism. She recognized our intensity, which mirrored her own for all of "her" children, and she respected our desire for immediate and intensive services. She agreed to collaborate with the private professionals whom we would hire along the way. She fell in love with our little boy, said he would go very far—she had no doubt that Jake would enter a regular kindergarten. We were sure she was a gift from heaven. The ESD team agreed to 20 hours a week of one-on-one services to start, which quickly increased to 30. Within two months our son said his first words and began building sentences. This was just before his third birthday. What incredible joy it was to hear his first words, "I want sucker!"



Jake's exposure to other children at school showed us just how compromised our son's immune system was. He was sick every other week. I kept a journal and logged his symptoms and treatments. He would be well for less than a week, before coming down with another virus. This went on for six months. Then it became bacterial infections. We battled nine ear infections, with the dreaded antibiotics, from March through June. One of these led to pneumonia. But throughout this first treatment year we were seeing the good doctor once or twice a month, taking all kinds of lab tests, and trying all sorts of supplements and treatments to help Jake's immune system and clear up the "bugs" in his gut. We may never know which treatment helped the most, probably a synergistic combination, but his system got stronger and he quit getting sick. At least he quit getting colds. The ear infections required tubes, but ever since they were placed (nearly a year ago), he has not had another infection.

Jake's lab tests indicated typical patterns that Dr. Green and other DAN! doctors were seeing with this group of children. His gluten and casein antibodies were approximately 4,000, when normal levels are around 100. His various tests revealed severe intestinal dysbiosis, including yeast overgrowth; food allergies; severe deficiencies in amino acids, most vitamins and minerals, and essential fatty acids; and the list goes on. The doctor developed a supplement schedule based on Jake's test results. Many of the supplements that he needed he couldn't tolerate. He would become hyperactive, and sleepless, and generally exhibit more autistic-like symptoms. This was horribly frustrating. Keeping the journal was, and still is, important. Jake had terrible constipation about the time we started treatment the first year, another typical symptom of the overall state of his gut. The treatments for yeast and bacterial infections did wonders for this.

Fall of 2001 began the second year of both medical and developmental treatments for Jake. We decided that we couldn't postpone chelation any longer. Jake's initial toxic metal tests, which included hair, blood, urine, and stool, indicated some high levels of toxic metals. At one point we looked into Jake's vaccine schedule—dates and lot numbers—and determined that Jake had received the "disaster load" of mercury in his vaccines. This was just before the FDA decided that mercury shouldn't be used as a preservative any more. This revelation is one reason why we will never give up fighting to recover our son. He didn't ask to be vaccinated. He didn't ask to be ill in so many ways. He didn't ask to be autistic. This is why we fight so hard to give him back his ability to make a choice: because on the days of his vaccinations, he didn't have that choice.



The first year, we tried oral chelation twice but Jake became very ill—not from the chelation itself, but from viruses that his body couldn't fight, as the chelation process seemed to compromise his ability to fight illness even further. We decided to wait until we cleared up his gut and strengthened his immune system before continuing with the chelation. After a year of following Dr. Green's advice, Jake's immune system was much stronger and he had only slight dysbiosis of the gut. We were very anxious to try it again—we had heard that the rates of recovery through chelation therapy were much higher in younger children. Jake was going to be four years old in three months. Time was wasting.

Over a period of nine months, we did eight rounds of oral chelation (DMSA) and seven rounds of intravenous chelation (DMPS). The interesting thing is the tests. Before chelation, we got low mercury readings. Subsequent testing throughout the chelation process revealed more and more mercury, until we finally saw "severely elevated" levels. But both processes of chelation, oral and intravenous, led to significant intestinal problems, including yeast and bacteria. So we have stopped chelating to give our son's gut a chance to heal, but we may revisit it again sometime in the future. We believe there are some promising chelating agents on the horizon that won't be so hard on the children. They are promising because their aim is to build up the child's own system and ability to rid itself of toxins naturally.

We are currently going through a noninvasive allergy elimination process, called NAET, which has done wonders for some children. It is based on the principles of Chinese medicine, chiropractic, and acupuncture. It is a stretch for most "Western" minds, but if a child becomes healthier and more open to learning, with no risk of harm, we have learned to listen, consider, and often try. Ask me in a few months.

Occupational therapy has truly helped our child. Jake couldn't run or jump. He was terrified to balance on a large ball or swing on a swing. After just a few months of OT, he is doing all of these things; and what's more important, he's loving it. We have done "listening therapy," the therapeutic use of music to stimulate brain processing, an approach that can treat specific symptoms and behaviors. The therapy may have contributed to his overall improvement in balance, motor planning, and processing issues, resulting in his learning to jump, swing, climb, and hop.



Jake's speech therapy has been going on for a year and a half, and again we have been blessed with an amazing speech-language pathologist who drives to our house because she believes that the child learns best in his own "comfort zone." She has battled our insurance company personally, and won for us. That's dedication.

Jake's growth also has been guided by a developmental pediatrician who has taken a special interest in Jerry and me, and instilled in us the value of keeping "connected" to our son by promoting his internal desire to be in our world. This doctor has encouraged and trained us to practice daily "Floor Time" concepts, developed by Dr. Stanley Greenspan, in order to balance out the intensive, goal-driven developmental therapies our son has received and is still receiving. We feel this has been key to the incredible moments we experience most evenings when we are completely joined together with our son in a common world of shared laughter, typical eye contact, and persistent requests to play.

After a year, we felt it was important for ABA to play a more intensive role in Jake's rehabilitation. We felt very comfortable with a modified approach called "Verbal Behavior" and have seen lots of great changes, particularly at typical preschool. A wonderful behavior group entered our lives last fall. The lead therapist has practically become a member of our family and loves Jake as if he were her own child. She believes in him and his future as strongly as we do. Together we have chosen a program tailored specifically to our son's individual needs and designed to help him become more communicative and social with other children. She understands the biomedical treatments we are doing and is extra-sensitive on days when he may be having difficulty with a new treatment.

Our greatest miracle besides the gift of our son is his little sister, Olivia. God blessed us with a second child when I was nearly 40 years old. I think He knew Jake was going to need a joyful, loving, and extremely verbal and social little person in his life. Olivia finds ways to include Jake in play, whether he likes it or not. She has brought such great joy, amidst the heartaches, into our lives the past two years and has given us visions of the days when they will play together like "typical" siblings. We even look forward to the rivalry.

Jake is now 4½ years old. He has beautiful blue eyes and a gorgeous smile. He tries so hard in all of his therapies to please and to succeed, even when he doesn't feel good. In his first typical preschool class last fall he made his first girlfriend, Sarah. She likes Jake so much because of his gentle and sweet spirit. He was "shy," like her. Even though school is over, she continues to come to our house for play dates.



At 2½ Jake was a nonverbal child who couldn't follow simple directions or even respond to his name. He was usually lost in a world of inappropriate laughter that was not to be shared. He now has an extensive vocabulary and is beginning to be conversational. He tells us how he feels, and he says, "I love you, Mommy and Daddy." Jake has gone from a diagnosis of severe dyspraxia of speech to moderate dyspraxia, and he is continuing to improve. The autism diagnosis was recently "upgraded" to pervasive developmental disorder (PDD) by his behavioral pediatrician. Jake was a child who felt sick and lethargic most of the time, and now is a little boy who loves to jump and climb and laugh and play. He still has days when he is "off," particularly when he is experiencing side effects of treatments that sometime seem never-ending. We struggle to keep the big picture, and not get discouraged by the regressions, which can come and go with no apparent reason.

Our hopes are for no less than a complete recovery, although we will be there for Jake in any way that God plans for us to be. There are many promising treatments and therapies we have yet to try, and many more being developed all the time. We have never seen "wonder" results from any one treatment, but overall we have seen great improvements, undoubtedly due to the combined effects of many of the therapies we have tried. We are eternally grateful to God for giving us the grace to persevere and the wisdom to make decisions through this most difficult trial of our lives, and most of all … for the Love of Jake.

*Update (February 2003):*

Jake is now five years old. He absolutely loves going to preschool where he sings and plays games with his friends. He reads, writes, and follows the routines better than most of his classmates. His biggest challenges continue to be social and communication skills. We are currently redirecting our developmental therapies to focus intensely on these deficits. RDI (Relationship Development Intervention), founded by Dr. Steven Gutstein, is a wonderful curriculum for play-based learning designed to help our children understand and develop deep, long-lasting, typical relationships. We will be attending our first workshop next month. The efforts we have been making to incorporate RDI principles into our daily interactions and therapy sessions have already resulted in more playful, interactive, and enjoyable times together.



Jake's gut still has significant dysbiosis and needs further healing. We have been intensely researching diet change options beyond removing gluten and casein to speed up the healing process. We are very excited about what we have heard from many families who are using digestive enzymes. They are used to help digest food properly, absorb nutrients, and heal the gut. We are following the guidance of a group of parents and professionals who have seen significant improvement in their children, including a reduction of food allergies and intolerances, sometimes leading to the return to completely normal menus (including gluten and dairy). We are clearly seeing more benefits and positive changes since beginning the use of enzymes than we have seen with any other single therapy or treatment in such a short amount of time. Language, eye contact, and social interaction are significantly improved. Jake is the happiest we have ever seen him, with an emerging sense of humor. He has a big appetite, and is trying new foods. We are very hopeful about the long-term outlook for this treatment.

Our personal prognosis for our child is another year or two of hard work, treatments, and therapies. By the time our son enters first grade we have every reason to believe that he will be a happy, healthy, typical little boy with an entire lifetime of love, learning, heartaches, and joys to look forward to. Never give up the dreams you have for your child. Love is an unbelievably powerful force that can accomplish miracles.

*Update for Second Edition (October 2005):*

Jake is almost eight years old now. He goes to first grade at our local public school in the afternoons, and gets private academic instruction in the mornings. He does great in both settings. Academically, he is at grade level in most areas, and a couple of years ahead in reading. He still lags behind in language and social skills, but makes progress every year. He loves to play with his best friend and sister, Olivia, and keeps us all laughing as he acts out scenes from his favorite movies and stories. He just joined a gymnastics class with his sister, and follows the routines and instructions just like the others, with no assistance. We recently came back from our second trip to Disneyland, where we had a wonderful time going on the rides, watching parades, and even waiting in lines. On the plane ride home, he and his sister sat across the aisle from mom and dad. Very independent, indeed!

We are chelating again, with a topical cream, TD-DMPS, and it seems to be a gentle and effective way to get rid of the mercury. Overall, Jake's progress has been remarkable. It's not been an easy road, and we are not fully recovered yet, but we expect to be one day. In the meantime, we are enjoying every day with our children, who have both been incredible blessings on our journey, "for the love of Jake."

# — Chapter 11 —
# A Very Tough Kid

By Dianne Doggett

*Dianne Doggett and Gary Fagelman now live in Lake Oswego, Oregon, where they moved to enable their autistic son Augie—born in 1997—to attend Project P.A.C.E., an intensive applied behavior analysis program. This story was written in May 2002.*

We knew being older parents would be challenging. We just didn't know it would be this challenging. My name is Dianne. I was 43, and my husband, Gary, was 44, when Augie was born.



At the time, we were living in Austin, Texas. I was working as an attorney, and Gary was working as a real estate appraiser and investor. After three years of trying to get pregnant on our own, months of unsuccessful fertility treatments, and almost adopting a child (the birth parents decided to keep the child), I then quit a very stressful job, and much to our amazement, I became pregnant. We were so excited we didn't know what to do.

I was very careful during my pregnancy—no caffeine, alcohol, or cigarettes (I had never smoked). I watched my diet carefully, trying to eat all the right food groups, and taking prenatal vitamins religiously. I developed high blood pressure, but other than that had a fairly uneventful pregnancy. Early in the third trimester, my doctor gave me a RhoGAM injection because of the difference between my blood type and Gary's. Later we found out that the RhoGAM contained a large amount of mercury.

Labor was induced using Pitocin, a drug whose use has been correlated with increased rates of autism. I was on intravenous antibiotics during labor because I had been diagnosed with mitral valve prolapse, a heart condition in which infection can be very dangerous. I developed preeclampsia during labor. Nonetheless, Augie was born a healthy boy, at seven pounds even, in October 1997.

Right after Augie was delivered, I hemorrhaged, lost half my blood, and was rushed into emergency surgery. The surgery successfully stopped the bleeding, but I had to spend Augie's first night in intensive care, without Augie. Gary fed him formula in my absence. After a transfusion the next day, I was able to be with Augie, but I was unable to breastfeed him.

In the midst of my medical crisis, on the day he was born, Augie received his first vaccination, for hepatitis B. We were not aware that he was not at risk for contracting hepatitis, which is primarily spread through sexual contact and contaminated needles, and that the vaccination lasts only five years. Later we found out that the vaccine contained mercury. Right after the shot, Augie began to have trouble maintaining his body temperature, and he had to be put in a warmer from time to time. Augie and I stayed in the hospital for five days.

Finally, we all got to go home. I stayed home with Augie and published a legal newsletter from our house. Gary went back to work. Our beautiful baby boy seemed pretty healthy, but something was not quite right. Toys with electronic music bothered him. Once a lightweight polymer mirror fell on him, and he laughed out loud for the first time. He didn't want to be held very much, and at times cried inconsolably. We had to "bounce" him vigorously in our arms to help him fall asleep, carrying him up and down the hall. Even the tiniest bit of light seemed to keep him awake, and the tiniest bit of noise would wake him up. He seemed to get upset right after feeding.



The pediatrician said he was just getting used to being outside the womb, and that there was nothing to worry about. He told us we could switch to a "hypoallergenic" formula that contained casein hydrolysate, which we did. This helped little, if at all. But we had no experience with babies, and we put our trust in our pediatrician.

Augie was an early walker; when he was about a year old, we started taking him to Gymboree (a play program) and the local children's museum. There he came into contact with other infants, and the colds, ear infections, and sinus infections began, one after another. His immune system seemed totally incapable of fighting off anything. The pediatrician prescribed round after round of antibiotics. Eventually, we learned that it is not uncommon for autistic children to have a history of repeated courses of antibiotics. Later we had tubes inserted in his ears to help with the ear infections.

Augie loved going to Gymboree, yet he often wanted to escape to the foyer, probably because he was unable to cope with the amount of noise and activity in the big room. He was very hyperactive, and even parents with children the same age would comment to us about how very active he was. Gary talked for weeks about the day he came home and found Augie sitting still on my lap, watching an alphabet video. We were exhausted. Just about the only time he sat still was when I read books to him.

Despite his hyperactivity, at that time Augie was still very interested in other children, hugging and tackling them. One day parents at Gymboree were very impressed with his "sharing" skills, as he passed out toys to the other children. He tried to get them to play chase with him at the bookstore and at the mall.

By about a year and a half, he was beginning to say some words, including "toe," "towel," and "Julian," his best friend's name. He could do some of the gestures to songs like "The Wheels on the Bus." At the park, he liked to climb and go down the slide. But he was still a very challenging child, constantly on the go, and wearing me out. So at about that time, Gary quit his job to help me at home.

Then Augie seemed to lose the few words he had learned. He began to shake his head for no apparent reason. He was spinning in circles. We asked the pediatrician about this. He said that he had also noticed that Augie was hyperactive, had poor eye contact, and lacked "connectiveness." He referred us to a neurologist for an evaluation.



We were dumbstruck. Terrified. There couldn't be anything wrong enough with our little boy to justify a trip to a neurologist. OK. Maybe he had ADD (attention deficit disorder) or ADHD (attention deficit hyperactivity disorder). We knew he was hyperactive. A lot of kids were. But no way were we going to put him on Ritalin at this age. We steeled ourselves for an ADHD diagnosis.

While we were waiting for the day of our appointment with the neurologist, Augie started attending a Montessori preschool that we had chosen for him months before. We warned the staff that Augie was very active, but they assured us that all children that age were very active. They told us they had worked with children with special needs before and not to worry. They had never turned away a child in 13 years.

After two weeks, the Montessori school asked us to find another preschool for Augie. They said he responded to no instruction, not even his own name. He climbed on everything, and they were afraid he would climb over their fence. He would not stay on his mat at naptime. He would not stay in the circle during circle time. We quickly found a very unstructured preschool for Augie, where the children were given virtually unlimited freedom to do whatever they wanted. Now we know that this kind of unstructured program was not the best thing for Augie, but at the time we had no idea.

We had to wait several agonizing weeks to see the neurologist. On the day of our appointment, we waited over an hour in his waiting room, while his staff attempted to verify our insurance coverage. Finally, we met with the neurologist. He asked us a lot of questions, and briefly examined a very tired

Augie. He told us Augie had delayed speech, with "some autistic features." "But Augie is so smart," we told the neurologist, "and already learning the alphabet." "Yes," he said, "that is typical of autistic kids." He noted Augie's poor eye contact, his spinning in circles, and the low muscle tone in his hands. Augie was 22 months old at the time of his diagnosis.

We asked the neurologist what we should do. He told us that other kids could play alone, but that we should attempt to engage Augie in interaction with us at every possible moment. That was probably the most valuable advice he gave us, and we really tried to do this. As a result, Augie never lost awareness of us and always sought out our company. The neurologist told us not to let Augie spin too much. He recommended speech therapy and a barrage of medical tests, including a hearing test, an MRI, an EEG, and blood tests for fragile X syndrome, lead poisoning, and thyroid problems. All of these tests eventually came out negative.



We were devastated. I had worked with a severely autistic child once, and Augie was nothing like that boy. I was very resistant to the idea that Augie was autistic, but I was determined to do whatever it took to get him over whatever he was going through. Gary felt as though he had lost his little boy for good. He was angry at me for being in denial about the situation and was furious at the world in general. We had no idea why this had happened to our precious little boy, and we blamed ourselves for letting him watch too many videos. We were truly a family in crisis, and we didn't know where to turn.

Augie began speech therapy and later occupational therapy. It was clear that neither therapy was going to resolve Augie's problems in short order. In his first five months of speech therapy he made over a year's worth of progress; but at 26 months old, he was still only communicating at the level of a 16-month-old child. He was not talking, and we were terrified that he might never talk.

The speech therapist didn't think Augie was autistic, because he was so emotionally attached to us, but the occupational therapist thought he was. We went back and forth with each other about whether he was autistic.

We took a Hanen Program course for parents that the speech therapist recommended. There we learned to get down on the floor with Augie, imitate his actions and verbalizations, label things and actions for him, and talk very simply to him in one- or two-word phrases. It helped us get his attention, but he still wasn't talking or looking us in the eye.

When Augie was 27 months old, we moved to a neighborhood where there were more children, as if spending more time with other children would solve the problem. We chose a neighborhood in a school district with a really good special education program, just in case he wasn't over this by the time he started school. We had no clue what the future held for us.

The occupational therapist recommended a book about sensory integration dysfunction called *The Out-of-Sync Child*, by Carol Stock Kranowitz. It was pretty clear that Augie had this problem. His brain was distorting the information he was taking in through his senses. We began to understand what Augie was going through and the depth of his problems.

We realized that his sense of touch was compromised, and that he was virtually incapable of feeling pain. Once we had found a bad burn on his hand, but he had not cried or showed it to us when it had happened. He stood in fire ant nests and was repeatedly bitten and never whimpered or cried. He was a bit of a daredevil and a fearless climber. He didn't care whether he fell down, walked into a wall, or walked barefoot on plants with stickers. On the other hand, his mouth seemed unusually sensitive; I had to wrestle him to the floor, holding him down with one of my legs across his body, just to brush his teeth.



We had not understood that Augie had sensory problems before this. One day when Gary went to pick Augie up from preschool, Augie's teacher confided to him, "You have one very tough kid." Falls that made other children cry would only get a whine out of him. At the time Gary thought, "This is great." If only we had known.

The occupational therapist told us to let Augie spin and swing as much as he wanted, and that this would help him. By now, all he wanted to do at the park was swing, swing, swing, for long periods of time. We put up a hammock swing on the porch at our new house. We tried to provide a variety of sensory experiences. We started the Wilbarger Protocol, brushing his skin with a special brush and compressing his joints every two hours. This seemed to help some.

The speech therapist loaned us a book called *The Sound of a Miracle: A Child's Triumph over Autism*, by Annabel Stehli. It's about a girl who recovered from autism through Auditory Integration Training. Apparently the hearing of autistic children can be quite distorted, with some sound frequencies registering so loud as to be painful. We knew that Augie was quite sensitive to some sounds. A toilet flushed anywhere in the house during the night had always awakened him, even as a baby. If we spoke in a normal tone of voice near him as he awoke from a nap, he would sob uncontrollably. We began to lower our voices around him, and this seemed to help.

His ability to understand or tolerate language was very limited. He would let us read only one or two words from each page in his books. If we talked with each other very much in his presence, he would get upset.

In the midst of this, Augie came down with still another ear infection. Gary took him to the pediatrician. In frustration, Gary cornered the doctor and asked, "Why is my kid always sick?" The doctor said Augie had an immature immune system. Gary asked him if drinking milk could be making his colds worse, as a good friend had suggested. "That's nonsense," said the doctor, "an old wives' tale not grounded in science." That was a turning point for Gary, and when he got home, he told me, "He'll never get better with that guy."

While Augie was on antibiotics for the ear infection, I took him to a birthday party at Gymboree. While the other children happily chased after bubbles floating in the air, Augie stood in the middle of the parachute in a daze, staring into space. His speech had regressed to a single syllable: da da da da da.



So we made an appointment with a doctor recommended to us by Augie's speech therapist. Dr. Philip Zbylot was an M.D. with a preventative, alternative approach to the practice of medicine. We met with him for the first time when Augie was 28 months old. He told us not only that he could help with the infections, but also that Augie could recover from autism through a biomedical approach. The neurologist had not told us about any medical or dietary treatments. We were skeptical and afraid of getting our hopes up, but we were willing to try just about anything.

Dr. Zbylot explained that there was something called autism spectrum disorder, and that the spectrum went all the way from attention deficit disorder to severe autism. He said that Augie was clearly somewhere on the spectrum, and that from a medical perspective, it didn't really matter where. He told us that Augie was his first patient on the spectrum, and that we would need to educate ourselves about what was going on in his body and work together to find the answers. He tried to explain to us what he thought was happening on a cellular level, and gave us a big sheaf of photocopied materials to read about the biology of autism. We had never before met a doctor who truly wanted us to be partners in our son's treatment.

Dr. Zbylot told us to take Augie off wheat and dairy products. We were to give him only organic fruits and vegetables, and only antibiotic-free, hormone-free meat. We were to avoid all preservatives, artificial colors, artificial sweeteners, and hydrogenated oils. Because autistic children are prone to yeast infections, we were to put him on a low-sugar, anti-yeast diet. We were to give him digestive enzymes, probiotics (beneficial bacteria), essential fatty acids, and B vitamins. Within a couple of weeks, we saw results that were nothing short of a miracle.

Augie's sense of touch returned. He started wanting to wear shoes outside, because the plants with stickers hurt his feet. He began to be careful not to step in puddles barefoot, because he didn't like the way the water felt, or at least was unfamiliar with the feeling. He began to be much more careful about running into things, and in general about where he put his body. When he did fall down or run into something, he'd look surprised and sometimes even cry.

At the park, he started climbing on the play structure and going down the slide, as he had before his regression. He stopped spinning in circles. His hyperactivity abated considerably, and he could sit down long enough to read a book or do a puzzle. He quit running through the house uncontrollably.



His sensitivity to sound greatly normalized, and we no longer had to lower our voices around him. His ability to understand or at least tolerate language improved noticeably; we began to use longer phrases with him. One day he let me read the entire book, "The Three Bears," to him. He started to comply with simple verbal requests for the first time.

His fine motor skills improved dramatically, and he began to scribble for the first time. One evening he spent a good half hour pinching Tub Tint color pellets between his thumb and forefinger and putting them in the bathroom sink, one at a time, practicing his newfound abilities.

And, last but not least, Augie didn't have another serious cold for over two years.

Not long after this, my hairdresser showed me Karyn Seroussi's article in the February 2000 issue of *Parents Magazine* entitled, "We Cured Our Son's Autism," about the gluten-free, casein-free (GFCF) diet. [*Editors' note: A chapter by Karyn Seroussi is included in this book*] We subscribed to the *ANDI* (Autism Network for Dietary Intervention) *News*, and found their website. We bought Lisa Lewis's book, *Special Diets for Special Kids*. Later we found the GFCF diet website (www.gfcfDiet.com). We learned about the theory that gluten and casein were not fully digested by autistic children and traveled to their brains in the form of "opioids," which had an opium-like effect on them. We began to realize that other parents were finding some of the same answers we were, and this was very reassuring.

We also began to understand what Dr. Zbylot had told us about educating ourselves. We couldn't just rely on him to tell us what to do; we had to help him figure it out. We realized that despite Augie's incredible recent progress, we had made some mistakes. Gluten was found not only in wheat, but also in rye, oats, barley, and even in the spelt rolls we had been giving Augie. Goat milk and whey powder had casein in them, and even ghee (similar to clarified butter) was too risky. From what we read, even the tiniest bits of gluten or casein could distort Augie's senses for days, and it could take up to a year for casein to leave his body. We became fanatics about cleansing his system of these substances.

Going to the grocery store became a research-oriented and time-consuming activity. We had to read every ingredient in everything we bought. We tried all sorts of new foods, few of which Augie would eat. We started shopping at health food stores. We had to cook virtually all of Augie's food from scratch. Eating at restaurants became very tricky, involving taking food with us or lengthy discussions with wait staff about how food would be prepared. But we were determined. We hired an aide to "shadow" Augie at preschool, making sure he didn't eat anything inappropriate.



We sent a sample of Augie's urine to the Great Plains Laboratory for an organic acid test, and as we understood it, to look for signs of a yeast infection. Then we got the results: *yes, there was yeast.* We were so excited. Here was something we could fix, and then Augie would be cured. But later, after Augie had been on the antifungal drug nystatin for months, he was still autistic. This was not going to be as simple as we had hoped.

Gary found Kirkman Laboratories, a vitamin company that specializes in vitamins for autistic children, on the Internet. We placed our first order, and over time became devoted customers. Dr. Zbylot was delighted with our discovery.

We had two three-way telephone consultations with Dr. Zbylot and Dr. William Shaw, Director of the Great Plains Laboratory. Dr. Zbylot asked Dr. Shaw if there was a clinician who worked in the field of autism with whom he could consult. Dr. Shaw recommended Dr. Jeffrey Bradstreet in Palm Bay, Florida, and steered us to his website (www.gnd.org). We filled out the application on the website, and submitted it. Dr. Bradstreet's office told us that he had a long waiting list, but that we could make an appointment to talk by phone with his new partner, Dr. Jerry Kartzinel.

While we were waiting to talk with Dr. Kartzinel, we got some shocking news. Going shopping was so confusing that we had scheduled a visit with a nutritionist in Dr. Zbylot's office to see what was safe for Augie to eat. We were also concerned that he was eating gravel at the park. The nutritionist ordered a hair test to see how Augie was metabolizing minerals. The test results showed that Augie's mercury level was literally "off the chart," and that he also had some aluminum in him. Both are toxic heavy metals. Dr.

Zbylot said he had never seen anyone with such a high mercury level.

Dr. Zbylot told us to stop cooking on aluminum foil and aluminum pans and to quit using baking powder containing aluminum. He told us that mercury can be removed from the body by a process called chelation. In chelation, the patient is given a drug that binds with the mercury, which then comes out in the urine. Dr. Zbylot said he did not do chelation, but he referred us to a doctor of osteopathy who did. We met with the D.O., and he said that he would have to consult with a doctor in Atlanta, Georgia to determine how to chelate mercury from such a young child. When we got impatient for him to get back to us, Gary got on the Internet and started researching mercury poisoning. Dr. Zbylot then gave us the name of another doctor who specialized in chelation, and that doctor started Augie on a very low dose of DMSA. Augie remained on DMSA in varying doses for a year and a half. Each time we gave it to him, we thought we saw him take a little developmental jump forward.



When Augie was 32 months old, we had our first consultation with Dr. Jerry Kartzinel. It was truly a watershed event for us. For the first time, we felt that we were in experienced hands. Although Dr. Zbylot was very capable, he had no experience with autism. Dr. Kartzinel and Dr. Bradstreet did nothing but treat autistic children from all over the world. Not only did Dr. Kartzinel know what we should do for Augie, but also he had an autistic son of his own, and he knew what we were going through. Plus, what we thought was going to be a onetime consultation with him turned out to be only the beginning of a long doctor/patient relationship. We offered to come to Florida for him to examine Augie, but he said that this would not be necessary. Instead, we could talk on the phone, he could call in prescriptions to our pharmacy, and he would send us lab kits so we could send urine, blood, and stool samples to labs around the country. We were incredibly relieved and excited.

Later that same day, my brother called to say that my elderly mother had fallen in her home in Houston early that morning and was in the hospital. She passed away five days later. We had been so consumed with Augie's autism that we hadn't seen my mother for far too long, and now she was gone. I focused on Augie as a way of avoiding my grief.

At Dr. Kartzinel's suggestion, we started giving Augie cod liver oil from Kirkman Laboratories. It has vitamin A in the *cis* form and is supposed to help with eye contact by reconnecting the retinoid receptors in the brain. We had read about this theory on the Autism Research Institute website. The result was simply amazing. Augie started looking at our faces as if he were seeing them for the first time! He was so excited about it, and we were too. He would pull on our noses and poke at our eyes. We began to play eye contact "games." He would run away until I recited a favorite line from one of his books, then he would turn and look me in the eye, giggling. After Augie had taken cod liver oil for a month, we started him on a drug called bethanechol, which works with the cod liver oil.

We had told Dr. Kartzinel about Augie's mercury, and he said that they were finding high levels of toxic heavy metals in nearly all of their autistic patients. He told us to increase Augie's DMSA dosage threefold. We later found out that most, if not all, of the vaccines Augie had been given literally since the day he was born contained thimerosal, which is about 50% mercury.



About this time, Augie began to have severe diarrhea, to which he was not prone, and tested positive for the parasite *Cryptosporidium*. After trying alternative therapies, Dr. Kartzinel put Augie on the antibiotic Zithromax. Dr. Kartzinel explained that autistic children should avoid antibiotics when at all possible; when antibiotics are necessary, they should be given with a course of an antifungal drug (such as nystatin) and a large quantity of probiotics, to prevent yeast and pathogenic bacteria from taking over the gastrointestinal tract. This is what we did.

Augie began to thrive. He began to play chase with us, and even had a fight with another boy over a poster at speech therapy! We were delighted. He began to respond to his own name at preschool. He started jumping with two feet together for the very first time, and we let him jump on our bed as much as he wanted. He was more interactive, but he was still autistic.

From what we were reading, it seemed that the children who recovered from autism not only had biomedical intervention, but also had extensive behavior therapy (applied behavior analysis). An article appeared in the Austin newspaper about people moving from all over the country to put their autistic children in an ABA program at Princeton University. We began to wonder whether Augie would need ABA, and whether we would need to move to get it.

In Austin there was an ABA consultant who trained therapists, but we would have to find the therapists (probably local college students), hire them, and manage them. We just didn't think we could do it effectively. Gary's father had seen a television interview with Lynn Hamilton, author of *Facing Autism [Editors' note: Lynn Hamilton's story is included in this book]*. He told us about the book, and we rushed right out and bought it. In an appendix, Hamilton lists ABA programs around the country. We found an

ABA clinic in Portland, Oregon called Project P.A.C.E. Project P.A.C.E. hired and trained its own therapists and could manage Augie's entire ABA program for us. There was nothing like it in Texas.

We flew out to Oregon to check out Project P.A.C.E., attend a meeting of the local parent support group, and rent a house. We were impressed with Project P.A.C.E.'s low-key, play-oriented version of ABA. When we returned to Austin, I sold my business, we sold our house, and we moved to Oregon, all in a matter of two months. I was reluctant to move so far away from my brother in Texas and my sister in Kansas, so soon after my mother's death. (My father had passed away years earlier, and Gary's family was already far away, in Boston.) We knew we would miss our friends in Austin. But we just didn't see how we could manage Augie's ABA program effectively in Texas, and we knew that early intervention was important. Augie was just 35 months old when we moved to Oregon.



Within several weeks of our move, we had Augie on a full schedule of ABA and speech therapy at Project P.A.C.E., totaling nearly 40 hours each week. It was a demanding schedule. He worked hard, and got tired, but generally liked his program and his therapists.

We began attending meetings of the local parent support group. It was formed by a dedicated mother of an autistic boy and has been a wonderful all-purpose support group for parents of autistic children. The group discusses the GFCF diet, the latest biomedical interventions, ABA, OT, and every other topic of mutual interest. It has really helped us to know other people who are going through the same things we are.

About the time we moved to Oregon, we found out that Augie's myelin basic protein (MBP) autoantibodies blood count was 29. The reference range for the test is 0-10. This apparently meant that Augie's immune system was trying to attack the myelin sheathing on his neurons. This made him a good candidate for intravenous immunoglobulin (IVIg) treatment. A month after moving to Oregon, we began flying to California every six weeks for four-hour IVIg treatments from Dr. Sudhir Gupta. We made the trip five times before the treatments became available in the Portland area from a wonderful doctor named Dr. John Green, who has dedicated his practice to treating autistic children. Eventually Augie's MBP count dropped to 7, then to 4. We thought we saw progress from each treatment.

When Augie was 43 months old, he started back in occupational therapy. We had thought that perhaps he didn't need OT, but we were wrong. Our new occupational therapist told us that Augie lacked upper body strength, among other problems. Gary started working with Augie at the park on hanging from the monkey bars. Slowly his arms have become stronger, but he is still not as strong as other kids his age. His ability to hug and be hugged has progressed from very brief encounters, to more relaxed and prolonged affection.

About the same time, when Augie was 3½, we contacted our local Education Service District. By federal law, states have to provide educational services to children of any age with disabilities. Augie began attending ESD preschool one morning each week in the summer, and then two mornings each week during the school year. He has a wonderful teacher and supporting staff, and he really seems to benefit from the program. He loves going and even stays in the circle at circle time.

We started Augie on the Feingold diet, after consulting the Feingold website. The Feingold diet removes artificial colors, artificial flavors, certain preservatives, and natural foods high in salicylates from the diet. It was developed 25 years ago to help children with ADD and ADHD, but the diet also helps other children on the autism spectrum. Augie was essentially already on the diet, except that we were giving him strawberries and organic cherry juice, which are high in salicylates. When we removed these from his diet, his tension level went way down and his ABA therapists noticed an increase in his ability to understand and use language.



About the time Augie turned four years old, we started him on intravenous secretin and glutathione infusions. The day he had his first secretin infusion, he started telling us when he needed to poop, which he hadn't been doing. His ESD teacher and ABA therapists began to report progress on emotional issues: more "appropriate happiness" and more "shared affect." His language seemed to blossom, and his fine motor skills really picked up.

We continue to try new biomedical treatments and nutritional supplements all the time. Some of them help, and some don't, and sometimes it's hard to tell. But we keep pushing forward, and Augie keeps getting healthier, happier, and more normal. He continues on a full schedule of speech therapy, ABA, OT, and ESD preschool.

When we got to Oregon, when he was three years old, Augie had no words that he used regularly. Now at 4½, he is a regular chatterbox. He can say every letter of the alphabet, count to 29, name about 12 colors and which colors you mix to make them, and tell you what sounds animals make. He learns new nouns easily and speaks in four- and five-word sentences. He tells us what he wants, responds to questions, calls us Mom and Dad, and says, "I love you."

When we got to Oregon, Augie could not imitate the simplest of gestures, such as waving bye-bye. Now he can imitate fairly difficult gestures, and can even do gestures to songs—not quickly, but he can do them. He is learning to ride a tricycle. He plays with toys appropriately, and even engages in pretend play. He is potty trained, though sometimes we still have to remind him to go to the bathroom. He can dress himself with assistance.

His ESD teacher and his ABA therapists tell us that he will have no problem with academics, and that he has good cognitive skills. He's still about two years behind other kids his age in language and social skills, but he's making rapid progress. His ESD teacher thinks that if we start him in kindergarten a year late, at almost age seven, he may be able to go to school without an aide.

We are relieved and happy to report that Augie has turned into an affectionate, playful, sociable, and very smart little boy. We could not have done it without the support of our family and friends, and the courage of the parents who went before us, and we are grateful to them. While we are still distressed about Augie's autism, we have hope that someday he will fully recover and be a normal child. We feel that this is the start of a long trip, and that ultimately we will reach our destination.



*Update (March 2003):*

Augie is now 5½ years old, and a lot has happened in the last year.

We took Augie to Mary Bolles at the Sensory Learning Institute in Boulder, Colorado, for two weeks of intensive sensory integration therapy. Mary simultaneously combines vestibular motion, auditory integration training (AIT), and vision therapy. Augie lay on a special table in a dark room for half an hour, twice a day. The table moved in a circular motion, either from side to side, or head to foot. While he was on the table, Mary put earphones on him for AIT. While this was going on, a light box above Augie's head showed him colored lights, one color at a time, slowing pulsing from bright to dim and back to bright. Mary gave him glow-in-the-dark toys to play with so he would not be bored or sleepy, and Gary and I massaged him and encouraged him. He seemed to tolerate it well.

Before the sensory learning therapy, Augie was extremely hesitant to go very far into the McDonald's play structures. Halfway into the therapy, we took him to a McDonald's, and he scrambled all over the play structure without any hesitation. This effect has lasted, and when we returned to Oregon his occupational therapists commented on how much more sure of himself he was on climbing structures. Before the therapy, Augie was riding a large tricycle with some assistance. Within a month or so after the therapy, he started riding a two-wheel bike with training wheels, and can now ride it with very little assistance.

Also before sensory learning therapy, Augie showed virtually no interest in the large animals at the zoo, although he was otherwise very interested in animals. During his first visit to the zoo following the therapy, he was really excited about the large animals, running from pen to pen, and asking for specific animals. I really think he couldn't see them before the therapy.

At Dr. Kartzinel's suggestion, we had a SPECT scan done. As I understand it, the scan measured blood flow in Augie's brain. The scan showed low blood flow in parts of his frontal and temporal lobes, and "hot spots" of too much blood flow in other areas. Dr. Kartzinel first prescribed Trental, often prescribed for circulation problems, to help the red blood cells get to the areas of low blood flow. A month later he prescribed Tenex, often prescribed for high blood pressure, to reduce pressure on the hot spots.



Our perception was that the Trental made Augie more emotional, which makes sense, since the frontal lobes control the emotions. I read a book called *Smart Moves*, by Carla Hannaford, Ph.D., in which she says that there is no learning without emotion. Augie seemed to begin to take more pride in his accomplishments. One day he surprised us by dressing himself without any prompting or assistance, from choosing his clothes to putting them on, even though he was unsure of some of the steps.

The Tenex really seemed to take the edge off his tension, which had always been a problem for him. He used to jump up and down and say "eeeeeeeeeeee," when he was even just a little bit excited. After he started on the Tenex, the keening stopped, and he seemed calmer and more able to concentrate.

Augie is still going to Project P.A.C.E. for behavioral therapy. However, P.A.C.E. has changed the direction of its program, and has adopted Relationship Development Intervention (RDI) as its primary focus. RDI was developed by Dr. Steven Gutstein of the Connections Center in Houston, Texas. It focuses on the autistic individual's ability to form relationships with other people, including the ability to understand subtle social cues. It takes the autistic individual through the steps a normal child goes through to learn how to relate to other people. We are very pleased with the changes we have seen in Augie since he started receiving this therapy. We recently visited the Connections Center to have Augie evaluated, and to have a treatment plan formulated for him.

We still have a lot of challenges ahead of us. Augie is by no means normal, but we still have hope that one day he will be. As he continues to improve, we take joy in each of his accomplishments.

*Update for Second Edition (October 2005):*

Augie turns eight years old this month. It's been two and a half years since my last update.

In the summer of 2003, we tried neurofeedback. It was hard to tell what effect it had on Augie, because he was taking swimming lessons that summer, and the pool chemicals were hard on his system. He did have a couple of big creative episodes during that time, a pretty good thing for a boy with an obsessive/compulsive streak. One day after a treatment, he asked to paint inside a plastic bag, and when that didn't work well, he tried painting on wax paper. He also went from cutting out the same animals over and over to cutting out all kinds of other things. At this writing, he is quite flexible and really likes novel experiences.



In the fall of 2003, I went to the DAN! conference in Portland, and all the speakers were excited about Dr. Jill James' research on TMG (trimethylglycine) and folinic acid (a form of folic acid), which together complete a chemical reaction in the body that our kids are missing. We started Augie on these, and he is on them to this day.

About the same time, we consulted with a naturopath in the Portland area. Dr. Jennifer Reid is known for her work with Ambrotose, a nutritional supplement made from the aloe vera plant. We knew a boy with autism who Dr. Reid had treated with Ambrotose, and who had fully recovered. We put Augie on a full teaspoon of Ambrotose powder, a nutritional supplement, twice a day. Recently we switched to another aloe vera product, Aloe Immune. These products are apparently very strong antioxidants.

We also started giving Augie vitamin B12 (methylcobalamin) shots, which we still give him, at home. We could really tell a big difference on the days we gave him the shot. Suddenly he could list for us the things he had done that day.

We decreased the dosage on his Trental because it made him vomit frequently, chew on his clothes, and eat constantly. Eventually we took him off of it altogether. I think it did him a lot of good, but we decided he'd had enough.

We tried changing him from Tenex to Clonidine, because the Tenex had lactose in it, and then took him off the Clonidine, too. In retrospect, I think the Tenex and Clonidine were a big mistake. When he started on the Tenex, his therapists thought he was much calmer. Then when he went off of it, his therapists thought he was much more alert. Maybe we just had the dose too high, but I think it really "zoned him out."

In early 2004, we did about five weeks of the Tomatis method with Dr. Judith Belk. The auditory integration we did with her seemed to give Augie's language a big boost, and it was a joy to work with her.

That winter, Augie had daily episodes of crying and screaming, for no apparent reason. This was quite unlike him. We tried taking him off of all his supplements, and off various foods. None of that worked. The episodes seemed to respond very quickly to Ibuprofen. Finally, it occurred to me that these episodes might be allergy-related, as allergies were running high in our community, though he had no apparent allergic symptoms. I put him back on Claritin, which he had been on for several years, but which we had discontinued. The very day we put him back on Claritin, the episodes completely stopped. Now he takes both Claritin and Singulair every day. (He takes the chewable form of Singulair; I believe the other form has casein in it.)



At one point, our Secretin source dried up, and we decided to stop the Secretin/glutathione infusions, which had really done him a lot of good. Glutathione is a natural substance that is found in every cell of our bodies. Kids with autism tend to have very little glutathione, and Augie has tested very low for it. We switched to a glutathione cream, and when that gave him a big headache one day, we gave that up, too. Dr. Kartzinel said the glutathione itself couldn't have given him a headache, and that it must have been the cream base. For most of 2004, he had no glutathione at all. That was another big mistake.

In June of 2004, we moved from Oregon back to Austin, Texas. In the shuffle, we effectively decreased Augie's B12 dose. Augie started going to a private school where he had virtually no contact with typically developing kids, which I thought greatly upset him. In the fall we adopted a little girl from Russia, who has been a wonderful addition to our family, but who caused Augie no end of jealousy. Augie was not doing well, but we were busy, and I chalked it up to the move, the school, and the adoption.

I looked for some special treats for Augie, and ordered some gluten-free pretzels and sandwich cookies, which he ate in large amounts. About that time, he had a lot of crying episodes, but again I chalked these up to the move, the school, and the adoption. After some testing, we found out that he had become highly allergic to soy, and that the pretzels and cookies contained a lot of soy. When we removed soy from his diet, the crying subsided.

At the end of 2004, Dr. Kartzinel put Augie on Ibuprofen, three times a day. Recent research has shown that kids with autism have inflammation in their brains. One day I was with Augie while he was being evaluated by a school psychologist. I had forgotten to give him his Ibuprofen, and he was not able to point to the numbers the psychologist asked him to point to. During a break I gave him the Ibuprofen, and when we resumed testing, he was able to point to the correct numbers. The sudden change in his ability seemed dramatic to me.

Augie was having a big problem with chewing on non-food items, and Dr. Kartzinel suggested that he was looking for some nutrient missing from his diet. We put him on Child Essence, a strong multi-mineral multi-vitamin formulated especially for kids on the autism spectrum. It really seemed to do the trick, and gradually Augie stopped this behavior.



Dr. Kartzinel added N-acetyl-cysteine and folinic acid to Augie's B12 shots, which we were giving to him every other day. He did so much better on the days we gave him the shots that soon we started administering them every day.

Dr. Kartzinel also put Augie on a low dose of Naltrexone at bedtime. [*Editors' note: Please see related article on page 427.*] This drug is supposed to help with all kinds of autoimmune disorders. I think it is also supposed to help reduce the effect of any casein or gluten that might make its way into his body. It is inexpensive and has virtually no side effects.

In February 2005, we moved Augie from private school to our local public elementary school. Augie moved into a regular kindergarten class for most of the day, with an aide. He really seemed to like the new school, but he was tense. About two weeks after the move to the new school, we resumed glutathione infusions, 300 mg, every other week. His teacher immediately reported that he was significantly calmer. The infusions really seemed to help him think more clearly, and people at the school repeatedly told me how happy he seemed.

Then, in June, he started breathing in glutathione using a nebulizer (we call it the "breathing machine"), 200 mg twice each day. He quickly took a big, big leap forward. About the same time, we resumed chelating with DMSA, but personally I think it was the glutathione that really affected him so quickly and so positively. Recently, we increased the glutathione to 250 mg, twice each day, and he's doing even better. I think the glutathione is perhaps the most important thing we are giving him.

Augie is now in a regular first grade class with an aide most of the day, and gets pulled out two hours each day for one-on-one instruction in language arts. His first grade teacher says he is a joy to have in the class. He can read, write, and do math about as well as the rest of the class. Language is still a big problem, but he is making progress. We supplement what the school gives him with private speech therapy, ABA, and RDI (Relationship Development Intervention). He attends Sunday school and is a Cub Scout. He can roller skate, swim, and rock climb.

We are very proud of Augie. We don't know what the future will bring, but we are doing our best to help him be the happiest person he can be.

# — Chapter 12 —
# But What's Medically Wrong with My Children?

By Julie Duffield

*Julie Duffield and her husband, Joe, are "pros" at battling autism, which affects both their son, Michael (born in 1998) and their daughter, Jessica (born in 2000). The Duffield family recently moved from Utah to Carpentersville, Illinois. This story was written in February 2002.*



Before beginning, I wish to state that I do not believe vaccines to be the only cause of autism, but rather an important contributor. It is often overlooked that vaccines given to the mother can contribute to problems in her child. I have a rubella titer that is off the charts, as a result of my MMR immunization. One known cause of autism is rubella in a pregnant mother. I was required to receive an MMR in order to go overseas, and our family continues to suffer the consequences to this day.

* * * * *

My name is Julie Duffield. I hold a degree in Math and Chemistry from Brigham Young University, and I have two children with autism. We have had incredible successes with our children using biomedical treatment, and we hope for a full recovery. At this point, many educators and psychiatric evaluators comment on our children's improvement socially, but we don't feel that our children are out of the fog yet. This is a short version of our story.

Let me start with my oldest boy, Michael. He was the happiest child we'd ever seen. He was plump and all smiles. He was learning how to sing, talk and dance. He loved to lead music as it played, and I was convinced that he would be a drummer or have something to do with music.

When I became pregnant with my second child, we were so excited, since Michael was such a joy. Relatives and friends warned us that the next one could not possibly be as easy to deal with as our wonder child Michael. We often had people offer—even beg—to babysit little Michael. If it weren't for his frequent ear infections and antibiotics, he would have been the perfect child.

Then we took Michael to his 18-month well-baby appointment. We gave him Tylenol before going to the doctor's office, since he'd had high fevers following his previous vaccines. He received four vaccines on that day. He started screaming, and stiffened his whole body, and jerked in my arms as they administered the rest of the shots. They were prepared to give a fifth shot for chickenpox, but I declined.

I had never seen my boy react like this to pain. The doctors excused the convulsive-type motion as my son's anger at my allowing him to have the injections. I thought that could be a possibility, so I shrugged my shoulders as I took my screaming child out of the office.

Michael had a fever within four hours of the shots. It got up to 104°, but we knew this was normal, so we kept giving Tylenol as the doctor had recommended. On the third day of the fever, I called the doctor's office. The nurse said that if Michael was still feverish on the fourth day, we should come in. We came in on the fourth day, and we were told that it was most likely a viral infection; there was nothing they could do. If it got worse, we should come back. "Worse than 104°?" was to be my question over the next three solid months of fevers. Urgent care centers, nighttime pediatrics, and even emergency rooms were no help, either. The high was 105.7° under the arm; Tylenol would bring it down to 101° or 102° temporarily. The average remained around 104°. We were told that the vaccines could have nothing to do with the sickness, since the pharmaceutical pamphlet said that the fever would last only one to three days. It had to be something else.



During this three-month period, Michael lost all of his social skills. His speech was replaced by angry grunting. He didn't understand what we were saying. He was scared of most sounds, and no longer liked music. He was inconsolable during the Fourth of July fireworks. He would cry all the time. It was absolute hell to watch his regression, which we associated with his being ill. An ear infection developed at the end of the three months, and we treated it with a round of antibiotics, which finally stopped the fever.

The misery we experienced while Michael was ill was nothing compared to the horrors that began when the fever finally stopped. He began to deteriorate into a stick-figure child. He lost weight and wore the same clothes size for over a year and a half. Growing babies are not supposed to stay the same size, and we became quite concerned. Michael wouldn't sleep. He would nap at about 6:00 a.m. and wake up two hours later. Sleep meds only seemed to make him wilder. I was sick from being pregnant and needed to wake at 6:00 a.m. for my science teaching position. My husband often had to work late at his job, so I would be up with Michael until one or two in the morning, while Joe would stay up the rest of the night with him. Our house was a constant nightmare. My husband and I were at our wits' end. We never saw each other, since he needed to sleep whenever we were both home at the same time, to make up for the sleep he lost while taking care of Michael.

The most disturbing behavior Michael exhibited was his willingness to slam his head against walls. He would "zone out" and laugh as though he were drunk. He would often get on all fours and slam his head on the hardwood. Another thing that bothered me was that he'd slowly push his eyeballs backward into his sockets. We would have to restrain him often to avoid serious damage.

When we went back to the office that had administered the shots, the family practitioner treated me as though I were an over-concerned mother. He thought Michael was going through a phase, injuring himself to get attention. He did offer to give me antidepressants. I didn't think that drugging mom would solve the problem, so we never returned to that doctor. It took us five months to find a new doctor who would work with my public education insurance. We were on multiple waiting lists to obtain a developmental assessment.



During that time, we dealt with all of the glaring eyes, with neighbors and relatives thinking we were the worst parents in the world. Everyone had advice: "If you would sing to him more"… "If you would only read books to him!" … "If you just would forbid TV" … "If you would stay home instead of working" … "If you would just get his sleep on schedule" … "Maybe you should get his hearing tested" (even though we knew he could hear an ambulance approaching before the rest of us). No one really understood, and we couldn't explain it, either. It wasn't much fun to visit others, and fewer people came to visit us.

Michael was diagnosed with autism two weeks before Jessica was born. We were told such things as: "You will have to institutionalize him when he gets strong enough to hurt you" … "Therapy is the only option" … "He might learn to use the bathroom by himself by the time he's 18" … "Ritalin and other psychotic drugs are the only way to improve your life at home" … "Autism can't be treated, it is lifelong."

We were essentially written over to the mental health department, with no recommendation for any medical testing. We were told we would have to wait six months before Michael would be able to go to the autism school. This was his only hope of improving.

Ear infections and other illnesses continued, and Michael was often in need of stronger antibiotics. We worried that our options for antibiotic treatment might run out. He seemed to develop resistance to them quickly.

Friends began to bring us literature on biomedical treatment for autism. We put Michael on the GFCF diet. After three days he started to make eye contact, and he began sleeping through the night. We were quite encouraged and began to search for information about biomedical factors involved in autism. We also were worried about Michael's weak immune system and possible IgA deficiency, so we looked for ways to help his immune system.

It was at this point that we ran into the Mother's Milk Club of Utah. They had organized a supply of mother's milk to give to children with weak immune systems. The university hospital provided the bulk of the donations. You must understand that the breast milk was intended to treat impaired immune function, not autism. As we gave Michael breast milk from myself, friends, and the hospital supply, not only did the ear infections stop for good, but his autism also started to go away.



Michael began hugging me. He became quite social and sought attention from others. He started babbling more. He seemed to snap out of his little world. We were so pleased. We found that we weren't the only ones with an autistic child who was benefiting from the breast milk; a growing group of parents in the Mother's Milk Club were reporting similar success stories. I found it fascinating that children with autism often have altered immunity.

Since then, Michael has been diagnosed with a low IgA level, heavy metal toxicity (from mercury, aluminum, lead, cadmium, arsenic and antimony—a profile similar to that of an Alzheimer's patient), autoantibodies that attack his own brain protein (myelin basic protein and neural axon filament protein), abnormal EEG, irritable bowel syndrome, seizure disorder, elevated measles titer, nutritional deficiencies, inability to properly digest food, and magnesium and zinc deficiency, among other diagnoses.

The breast milk seemed to keep most of Michael's symptoms at bay. People raved that he didn't behave as though he were autistic anymore. You could tell he had symptoms if you worked with him directly, but his play and happiness appeared quite normal.

Then we lost the breast milk donations through the university hospital. The head nurse didn't want to use up their freezer shelf space for the program, and she didn't want to be hassled with the inconvenience. The other nurses would still try to collect milk for us for a time, but pretty soon the pressure from superiors and the inconvenience stopped the donations completely.

We kept up with the breast milk for a while through my pumping milk and through donations from friends, but some weeks we'd have plenty, and other weeks we'd go without. The worst part was watching Michael regress into old behaviors when we didn't have enough breast milk.

This is when we discovered transfer factor (TF). A woman who was using this to keep her diabetes at bay called me about it. We started using the TF whenever we didn't have breast milk. We'd use up to nine capsules a day. As far as we could tell, the TF had the same effect as the breast milk. We just made sure we supplemented with vitamin A, taurine, and fish oils in order to ensure that Michael was getting the nutrients he used to receive from the breast milk.

We have since used secretin, chelation for heavy metals, liquid magnesium, zinc, calcium, molybdenum, selenium, and other supplements. We try our best to keep up-to-date on nutritional deficiencies found in autism, so that we may find other helpful treatments for our son. We are also paying more than what we can afford on ABA therapy, which goes well when we get the right supplements into him. Our son is improving quickly. He is now 3½ and is well on the road to recovery. His language is coming the slowest, but he is now imitating sounds and is starting to understand basic commands. He improves each time we chelate the heavy metals. We really feel that the TF sustains him through the chelation process.



As for my daughter, Jessica, her story is completely different. She reacted to her first hepatitis B shot as a newborn. She developed lesions in her mouth and rectum; it was suggested that the lesions may have run all the way through the digestive tract. After that shot, we decided that we'd never give her another one. Supposedly, serious reactions happen in only one in a million cases, but we have seen two of our own children react. Interestingly enough, ***no doctor reported our children's adverse vaccine reactions*** *[emphasis by editor]*. If adverse reactions are not reported, how can we know the true statistics on reactions to vaccines?

This is when we started studying the immunizations and learned that they contain mercury, aluminum, formaldehyde, foreign DNA, and other toxins, including the mutated viruses or bacteria that constitute the vaccine. All of these components are capable of changing humans genetically. Mercury and aluminum have devastating effects. Mercury builds up in the organs—the liver, kidney and brain—and interferes with all of the bodily systems. One major sign of mercury poisoning (since it cannot be detected by urine, blood, or hair analysis unless the exposure is recent) is that the individual seems to lose the ability to detoxify heavy metals and viruses; the toxins accumulate after a lower exposure than others receive, interfering with the body's ability to process necessary minerals properly.

Research reported at recent Congressional hearings compared the symptoms of mercury poisoning to the symptoms of autism, and they matched perfectly. Even though major government groups maintain that there is no proof that mercury is a problem for babies, they are requiring pharmaceutical companies to remove it from vaccines. The government stopped short of recalling vaccines, however, so that no financial burden would be placed on the manufacturers.

The research we read raised many questions: Why do some kids react badly to the mercury, while others do not? Are some vaccines higher in mercury than others? When a nurse preps the vaccine, and uses it on three children, is the child who receives the last dose (where all of the settled vaccine product accumulates) getting a higher concentration of virotoxin with the mercury? Is it purely an allergy issue? Does it depend on how many shots the child receives in a day? Does it depend on the child's previous exposure to toxins?



We were glad to obtain information about the effects of mercury and other toxins so we could do better by Jessica. We decided to avoid heavy metal exposure. We started drinking reverse osmosis-filtered water. We avoided fluoride, which is known to carry lead across the blood-brain barrier. In addition, we avoided milk, in case she had a sensitivity to it as Michael did.

Then we stood and watched Jessica develop, a bit behind schedule. We were highly concerned for her welfare. She was slightly behind on milestones but not enough to greatly worry us. She smiled and made eye contact, and she would imitate us. At her one-year doctor's appointment, she clapped her hands, did the Indian yell and performed actions to children's songs. Her speech was simple babble, but multiple consonants were included in the babble. She knew her own name, and she loved to cuddle.

Then, at some point between 13 and 14 months of age, she started to regress. She could no longer imitate song actions. She stopped babbling completely. She didn't seem to know her name, and she stopped making eye contact. She exhibited some seizure activity, in the form of altered eye dilation and "zoning." Sometimes—without a change in light intensity—her eyes would dilate, and then the pupils would snap back to a small size. She moved strangely in her sleep, as though she were having nightmares. Her arms would spread out and she would have strange tics.

We took Jessica to her pediatrician at 16 months, and the doctor couldn't believe what she saw. Jessica had truly regressed. Her muscle tone had deteriorated, and her walking was now a bit unsteady. Her eye contact was rare, and she avoided looking at me. She refused to go to anyone but me, since I was the one who breast-fed her.

Jessica received a diagnosis of autism at the age of 17 months. We started her on TF and chelation, and she improved dramatically. At the time of this writing, she is 18 months old. We took her back to the psychiatrist who initially evaluated her, and she said that Jessica was a different child than she had been just two weeks before. She is not "cured" or "recovered," but she makes eye contact, smiles, and is regaining her imitation skills. She is playing with toys again. The great thing is that she is so young. At 18 months, she has gained what she lost before the regression, and we know she responds to biomedical treatment and ABA. She should come back even faster than Michael.



As a result of Jessica's regression and dramatic improvement, we tested our home, soil, and even my breast milk. Our home was high in lead. Our soil had elevated lead in certain areas. My breast milk had arsenic and trace amounts of lead. When we tested our family's immune systems we found that Jessica also had autoantibodies to her own brain, and a high human herpes virus 6 titer. This would explain why TF is helping. As for me, I have an incredibly high rubella titer, which suggests an atypical rubella infection.

* * * * *

We have to wonder, did the lead in our home set up our kids for the vaccine reaction, or did the mercury in the vaccines make our children more susceptible to the lead? Are our children hypersensitive to mercury, or did my case of rubella from my adult MMR shots set me up to weaken any children while they were *in utero*?

One piece of good news is that the removal of mercury may reverse the presence of autoantibodies to the brain. In the meantime, TF can regulate the immune system, preventing additional damage.

The seizures took a lot longer for us to figure out. We didn't know that Michael had seizures until we had an EEG done. (Some children with autism have a normal EEG, but seizure activity shows up on a magnetoencephalography, or MEG, scan.) Michael's EEG showed that he has more seizures when he's asleep than when he is awake. We have come to recognize the staring spells and strange eye movements linked to his seizures. Sometimes we notice a seizure when we see his pupils dilate completely, then snap down to size again—with no change of light. On occasion, we have seen more serious seizures, during which he clenches his fists and shakes. We previously thought these were tantrums, since they would usually accompany stressful situations. In fact, we didn't know that stress could trigger seizures. We didn't know much about seizure activity at all. We began to notice seven to 10 seizures a day, once we knew what to look for. I often wonder if seizures are more prominent in autism than previously thought.

We have been able to keep seizures at bay with liquid magnesium, activated vitamin B6, taurine, and pycnogenol (from maritime tree bark). When we can sneak all of these supplements into Michael's sipper cup, he has no more visible seizures. If we leave even one of them out, we see three or four seizures a day. As for pycnogenol, the highest-quality product that we can find is Choice Prime from 4Life. We aren't sure if the pycnogenol from grape seed has the same effect. It might.



We are so pleased that we have found a seizure control method that works without doing damage to the liver or interfering with other body functions. We couldn't use standard seizure meds, since our boy's liver was already in such bad shape.

One lesson we've learned is that treatments benefit different children in different ways, and will benefit some children more quickly than others. For example, children who have a chronic infection with a hidden virus will most likely get sick on TF before they get better. This does not mean that they are reacting to the TF, but rather that the TF is working. If the virus in the child tricked the child's immune system into believing it was not a threat, the TF will suddenly alert the body to the foreign presence. This is why the child might get ill for days, or even weeks, before improving. Remember, illness after starting TF is a good indicator that the TF is working. In some cases, TF may not alleviate autistic symptoms but may still benefit children by helping to maintain their health as they undergo other therapies.

The more cleanup that must be done in the body, the longer it will take to see the positive effects of the supplement. Some people may notice an effect within days, but you shouldn't necessarily give up if it takes months for your particular child. As in all cases, trust your gut feeling to decide if you should raise or lower the amount of supplement given. Parents are the most perceptive in knowing whether or not a supplement is helping their child.

There is so much internal repair to do in autism that it is necessary to keep looking for answers for your child. Even our two children are not alike in treatment and response. Treatments that are perfectly safe, such as essential fatty acids, TF, or standard doses of nutrients, are easy to jump into, whereas chelation therapy or high-dosage vitamins should be studied and used under direction of a physician who is educated about biomedical treatments for autism. Again, you are the only one who will have the insight to see if the treatment is helping your child.

I suspect that most families will not receive all of the diagnoses that my children received, but I hope that the biological aspects of autism will become well known to families and physicians. I must stress that the treatments I've written about are not the only answers for these children. Each child must be looked at as an individual. However, I hope our particular family's case, and the success we have achieved in battling autism not once but twice, will help bring hope to others facing this challenge.

*Update (March 2003):*



It is March 2003. Jessica turns three this month, and Michael is five. We just moved to Carpentersville IL, and we plan to find a DAN! doctor out here soon.

In the meantime, we have been getting help from Dr. Jepson, a DAN! doctor in Utah. He has helped us continue supplements, the diet, chelation, secretin, and IV glutathione. Our kids react well to all of these, and they have side effects to chelation only if we are out of TF. I now refuse to chelate if there is any sign of a runny nose, or if I'm out of TF. We still have mercury coming out, even though we are on stage one of chelation for both children.

Jessica is doing the best. She is singing and performing actions to songs. Her language is mostly imitative, but she does well on labeling and she asks for many things by name. She understands many basic commands, and loves to give kisses and hugs. She doesn't react visibly to gluten or casein anymore, although we are still strictly following the diet. She has a great desire to be potty trained, and we'll start that next month. She loves imaginary play with dolls, cooking, and dress-up.

Michael is doing great, but we are still recovering from a major gluten accident back in November, when he ate Play-Doh at school for a few days in a row. We forgot to put it on the "do not eat" list, even though I didn't consider it a food, and the school was only allowed to give him what we sent from home. He had seizures and didn't sleep for three days. He had 30 vocabulary words (including "I love you, mommy") and 80 sounds/partial words before that day, and we are still re-teaching him those words. He didn't lose any of his sociability following the episode, and he still wants to learn. He loves it when others play with him. He is easy to direct in learning environments. He likes Harry Potter, and sings the theme song very well. We'll also start potty training with him next month.

My kids have taught me a lot about nutrition, and about the importance of being proactive when it comes to my own health. Just knowing that their problems are medical has been a great benefit to me. I know that they are doing the best they know how. They are the bravest kids I know. I can't even imagine the effort it takes for them to initiate eye contact or complete a task. All of the kids today who are putting up with their toxic world, and struggling internally in ways that we don't yet know, are truly heroes. I am in awe of the children and parents who stand strong in the face of such challenges.



We still have every hope for our children. Some days it feels as though we have light-years to go, but that doesn't matter. Our kids are going to be fine, no matter what the final outcome. I still plan on a full recovery for both of them.

*Update for Second Edition (October 2005):*

Jessica is doing great, going to cross-categorical kindergarten in the morning and regular ed kindergarten in the afternoon. Jessica potty-trained herself three weeks into the SCD diet. She is a little behind in her verbal expression for her age, but it's mostly undetectable by others. She makes friends everywhere we go. She is a great singer (she's learning how to sing parts and has perfect pitch), and can sing basic duets with me. She does get upset when the boys tease her at school. She is able to do valuable things like tell me that a babysitter yelled at her and Michael (with tear-filled eyes). She's five, and living well.

Michael is on the slow uphill, and is responding to B12 injections and chelation (Buttars protocol + glutathione cream + allithiamine cream)—WHEN WE CAN AFFORD IT. It is expensive to live in Illinois, and difficult to get a DAN! doctor. We love Dr. Usman, but she has a year-long waiting list and we can't often afford care that our insurance won't reimburse for 18 months or so. At least diets aren't too expensive. Michael potty-trained himself after two months on the SCD diet. He is a great singer, even if he can't pronounce the words. He muffles sounds together, but is imitating words and using about 10-word approximations appropriately. We're struggling with the school district, which believes PECS (Picture Exchange

Communication System) to be the end-all, but Michael has spoken less on PECS than with any other approach. We are frustrated, but I can't easily sue the school district as an untenured teacher, so we just deal with it.

We are waiting for the government to make a verdict on the vaccine compensation cases for kids with mercury toxicity. We have decent documentation, and we filed within the time limit. We hope they will do the right thing, even if Congress is trying to pass laws so no one is held responsible for vaccine damage.

## — Chapter 13 —
# There Is Hope
By Lynn M. Hamilton

*Lynn Hamilton is the author of* Facing Autism: Giving Parents Reasons for Hope and Guidance for Help. *She, her husband, Roger, and their three children live in Colorado. This story was written in January 2003 about their oldest child, Ryan (who was born in May 1992).*

"What treatment brought your son back?"



This is the question we are asked continually. Each inquirer seems to be looking for the magic cure: the one treatment that would reverse the pain, take away all the symptoms and return life to "normal."

Our son began life quite typically in the spring of 1992. When Ryan was born he was instantly a popular little guy. Friends and family poured in from all over to see our new arrival. He was a big baby, weighing eight pounds twelve ounces, and very healthy. Since I had a C-section, Roger was the first to hold Ryan. He stood proudly by my bed, tears flowing from his eyes. He laid our son next to me and said, "Ryan, I want you to meet your Mommy. She is a very special lady and she loves you very much." And I did.

One thing Ryan would never be without was love. We loved to stand by his crib and watch him as he slept, his angelic face so peaceful. We loved to hold him, rock him, and sing him songs. Just being near him brought such joy, and each day that we spent with him brought us closer as a family.

Ryan's first year went by so quickly, full of laughing, loving, and learning. Each day Ryan grew and developed as any other child, hitting each milestone on time or early. However, shortly after his first birthday, things began to change.

The first thing we noticed was that Ryan lost the few words that he previously used. We had just returned from a summer in Siberia, so we attributed the loss to Ryan hearing Russian all summer. But it didn't stop there. Ryan also lost the ability to understand language spoken to him. His happy temperament disappeared and he began screaming often and loudly. Ryan's wide array of foods was no more. He insisted on just a few, specific foods, like Fisher Boy square fish patties. Square Van de Kamp's wouldn't work. Ryan knew the difference by sight and wouldn't touch them.

Besides food, Ryan developed "rules" for many things around him. His *Pinocchio* video cover had to remain to the left of his rocking horse on the floor. If I picked it up and put it on the video shelf, Ryan would scream and tantrum until it was put back where he believed it had to be.

Ryan also lost the ability to play and interact with us. His quick smile disappeared as he began to look through us. For a while we thought he was deaf. He no longer wanted to hear stories read to him and he didn't respond to his name, but he would sit and watch Disney videos all day. If we muted the sound, he would explode in a tantrum. It was as if he had selective hearing. If he wasn't watching a movie, he was content to sit and line up his toys in perfect lines or semicircles, or else he would put toys in a row and turn them upside-down and then turn them right-side up—over and over and over.



During the next few months, numerous specialists evaluated Ryan. After all the meetings, all the tests, and all the questions, we had our answer. Ryan had autism. Up to that point, autism had just been a word in a dictionary. Now it had become personal. Though Roger and I were devastated, we were ready to fight. We didn't know how to begin or who to turn to for answers, but we were motivated. Our son's future was at stake.

Before we knew an official diagnosis, Ryan was offered therapy from a "Birth to Three" program in our area. Through this he was given one hour a week of combined speech and physical therapy.

Once we received the diagnosis, we expanded our search for therapy, which brought us to applied behavior analysis (ABA). Simply speaking, ABA is a system of teaching complex tasks by breaking them down into bite-sized pieces that can be learned more effectively, with each piece building upon the previous one. Rewards, termed reinforcers, are given for correct responses or behaviors while those that are inappropriate are corrected, ignored, or redirected. Precise data are kept for each learning trial and adjustments are made in each educational program based upon the data.[1]

Though Ryan didn't learn any words in five months of conventional speech therapy, he learned his first word on the *first* day of ABA. Within two months, he had over thirty words and was learning more daily! He had also learned to imitate actions and sounds, answer some simple questions, respond to simple commands, and play with blocks and cars. He learned all the letters of the alphabet and the numbers one through seven. To say the change was amazing would be an understatement. Over the next five years we used ABA with Ryan as his educational therapy. This was the beginning of setting our son free from the confines of autism.

Since we were seeing such good results using ABA, I wasn't really interested in other forms of treatment. That is, until other parents wouldn't leave me alone about trying the gluten- and casein-free (GFCF) diet. To be honest, I thought that these parents were a bit fanatical—taking away all wheat and some other grains along with all dairy products. Didn't they realize how impossible a diet like that would be? And even if we did want to try it, Ryan wouldn't eat new foods, so why bother? However, due to the pressure I was feeling from these parents, I began learning more about why this diet could be helpful.

I learned that in a healthy body, the digestive tract takes complex foods and breaks them down into substances that the body can absorb and utilize. To put it simply, food can be compared to a long chain of paper clips hooked together. Through digestion, the links of this chain are unhooked and left as single paper clips, which is the form needed for the intestine to absorb and deliver to the body for use. For children with autism, it is the digestion of certain proteins called gluten and casein that causes the most trouble. Gluten is found in wheat, barley, oats, rye, and spelt, to name a few. Casein is a protein found in all dairy products.



The problem is that our kids are often not breaking down the protein into the simple amino acid form; instead they are remaining as peptides. If proteins are comparable to long chains of paper clips, then peptides are shorter chains. Some of the digestion process has taken place, but the chain was not completely broken down into the desired amino acids. Secondly, our kids tend to have what is called "leaky gut," which means that the intestinal wall is unable to keep the intestinal contents separate from the bloodstream. This allows the peptides to get into the bloodstream where they are not supposed to be. If these peptides are not broken down into amino acids *and* they are getting out of the intestine, when they reach the brain and pass through the blood-brain barrier, they act as drugs like heroin and morphine! Predictably these peptides, termed "opioids," may radically affect behaviors.[2]

After learning all of this, and doing some medical testing related to it, we decided to try the diet. We didn't see any benefits at first, but we kept on with it since the medical tests showed us the diet would probably benefit Ryan. It wasn't until we had been on the diet for several months, when Ryan got a small amount of casein, that we learned about its benefits. Following a small exposure to casein or gluten, Ryan would first have a meltdown, which included aggression, anger, and irrational thoughts. After awhile, this stage would end and he would weep uncontrollably and say how sorry he was for what he did. Watching him go through these stages was like watching a drug addict become "high" and then "come down" off the drug. We were convinced, and we have been on the GFCF diet ever since.

Besides ABA and the GFCF diet, there were many other areas of treatment that brought benefits to our son, including several biomedical interventions. In my book, *Facing Autism: Giving Parents Reasons to Hope and Guidance for Help*, I explain the treatments we tried, how to do them, and how they worked (or didn't work) for us.

In the beginning, I knew almost nothing about treating autism biomedically. As I began to learn more about these interventions, I turned to Dr. Bernard Rimland and the Autism Research Institute. Not only has Dr. Rimland personally made invaluable contributions to all of us in the autism world, he has changed the thinking of many through the *Autism Research Review International* newsletter, Defeat Autism Now! (DAN!) conferences, and the DAN! Protocol. Although there are many biomedical treatments that have helped Ryan, let me focus on how one aspect of Dr. Rimland's work brought benefit to our little guy.



Over the years the Autism Research Institute has gathered data from parental reports on the effectiveness of certain drugs and supplements, and found that certain nutrients have been beneficial to children with autism. One supplement that stands out is vitamin B6 when combined with magnesium. Vitamin B6 has long been promoted as a treatment for autism, with the evidence for its effectiveness growing. The first studies were done in the 1960s, with 18 published studies to date. Each study has shown beneficial effects of vitamin B6, often combined with magnesium, while none has shown harm. The benefits that have been seen range from improved language, eye contact, and behaviors, to decreasing the "excretion of abnormal metabolites in the urine, improved brain electrical activity, improved conditionability, and improved immune system function."[3] Across the 18 studies, an average of 46% of subjects showed improvements from high doses of B6.

Magnesium is recommended with high doses of B6 in order to minimize any side effects, such as irritability, bed-wetting, or sensitivity to sound. Most Americans are deficient in magnesium, which is needed to utilize calcium in our bodies, and also helps to maintain nerve function. Kirkman Laboratories have developed a multivitamin called Super Nu-Thera, which is specifically designed for people with autism. It contains high doses of B6, magnesium, and many other nutrients. Dr. Rimland points out that high doses of B6 should not be taken alone, since this might induce a deficiency in magnesium and other B vitamins which may then cause tingling or numbness in the hands or feet. Super Nu-Thera takes these things into account in its formula, which comes in pill, powder, or liquid form.

After learning about the possible benefits of B6, we decided to try it with Ryan. At first we used the powder, but the taste was so strong that it was hard to hide and Ryan refused it. The liquid taste was very subtle, like weak Kool-Aid, but again Ryan refused it since he only likes to drink water. When he began to swallow pills, we tried again, this time with success.

When Ryan began taking the Super Nu-Thera, I didn't see any noticeable results, but since his diet was so limited, I was thrilled that he was getting some vitamins into his system. After several months, we decided to have Ryan's body chemistry tested so we could develop a nutritional supplement for him based on his needs. While we were waiting for the pills to be designed and made, we were running out of the Super Nu-Thera. About three weeks before they were completely gone, we began to wean him from them and eventually stopped. For the next two or three weeks Ryan was not on any vitamins. In that time his behaviors began to deteriorate. He became aggressive and more hyperactive. When our therapists asked if I knew why Ryan was behaving this way, I took a look at the chart where we log all the supplements that he takes. The therapists mentioned that Ryan's behaviors began to change about two weeks prior, which correlated with the time we withdrew the Super Nu-Thera. That really caught me by surprise, because I didn't think the vitamins were making an impact on him, but I ordered some more Super Nu-Thera. Within two days of resuming, Ryan's behaviors were back to normal.[4]



Since that time, Ryan has usually been on some form of B6 therapy. When we began giving him cod liver oil, as a form of vitamin A, we changed to a different product by Kirkman called Nu-Thera. Nu-Thera doesn't contain vitamins A or D, since they are found in the cod liver oil. Nu-Thera also contains the activated form of B6, called pyridoxal-5-phosphate (P-5-P), which is often more easily utilized by autistic children.

Recently I learned about another reason to use B6 for Ryan, this time in conjunction with zinc. A few months ago I had the privilege of sitting down with Dr. Woody McGinnis. During our conversation, I brought up some of the behavioral issues that still challenge Ryan. Though Ryan has overcome most of his autistic symptoms, he still struggles with his emotions—especially outbursts of anger or frustration. Ryan is a really sweet boy and is often polite and well mannered, but other times he can become very angry, very quickly, with minimal provocation.

When I mentioned this to Dr. McGinnis, he told me that I should check

Ryan's pyrrole levels. I had never heard of pyrroles before, so he explained that they are toxins that can build up in our bodies. At this point, researchers are not sure about the origin or origins of these pyrroles. Typically these toxins are dealt with by our bodies and excreted through the urine. However, if a person is deficient in vitamin B6 or zinc, these pyrroles can build up and cause problems.

Taking this to heart, we had Ryan's urinary pyrroles tested. With a reference range of 0-20, Ryan tested at 481! No wonder Ryan was having outbursts—his toxins were sky high! (Any number above the reference range is considered high and worth treating; Ryan's was unusually high.)

That day we began to treat Ryan with even higher levels of B6. Before the testing, we were giving him B6 once a day. Now we decided to increase it to twice a day. As for zinc, he was getting a little bit of it in his Nu-Thera pills, but we were unable to give it to him separately, so he wasn't getting very much. When we tried to give it to him separately from other supplements, before bed, he would develop a severe headache and vomit. Even though we tried several zinc products, he had the same reaction. Then we learned about zinc picolinate, which was said to have fewer side effects than the other forms of zinc. This time we had no negative side effects, so we added some zinc to our daily regimen of supplements. We also added manganese to our morning routine to help balance the zinc.



To our amazement, these supplements seemed to help right away. The day after we began, Ryan started to get some wonderful reports from school. Ryan seemed to be more in control of himself and his emotions. This happened day after day. At home, we definitely saw a difference. One day, we gave Ryan his B6 early in the morning. For a while, he was OK. Later that day, he went out to play with his sister and some neighborhood kids. Ryan had a remote control car that he got for Christmas and he was anxious to show it to everyone. Once he was outside though, he became agitated. He wouldn't share his car with the others, and he began to cry and scream. He was convinced that the other kids were going to steal his car and break it. Aware that these were good kids, I knew that Ryan was thinking and acting irrationally, so I had him come in. At that point I remembered that it had been a while since Ryan had some B6, so I gave him a dose. Within a short time, to my absolute astonishment, Ryan's whole demeanor changed. He calmed down emotionally and his body became more relaxed. He said he wanted to play with the kids again, so out he went. This time, he offered to share his car and he interacted wonderfully! It was a night-and-day difference.

Due to this incident, and others like it, we decided that Ryan probably needed more than two doses a day of the B6. We started giving him three doses: one in the morning, one at lunch and one right after school. This way he was more consistent and was not demonstrating the ups and downs of being "on" and "off" B6. We also found that if we raised his zinc levels as well, he responded favorably.

Although B6 and zinc are very safe vitamins, we have tested Ryan to make sure we are giving him appropriate doses and we plan on continuing the testing every few months. We're still in the process of figuring out what Ryan's optimal dosages are for both zinc and B6. Since pyrroles can be volatile, his needs for these vitamins may change on a daily basis. When he is more stressed out, physically or emotionally, he may need more. Other days, he may need less. I'm hoping that over time, with much trial and error, we will be able to "read" Ryan and know how to help him appropriately with these supplements.



Vitamin B6, magnesium, and zinc are only a few of the things we have learned about from Dr. Rimland and the Autism Research Institute. Many of the biomedical interventions that we have used with Ryan I have learned about from the DAN! Protocol, from attending DAN! conferences, or from the *Autism Research Review International* newsletter.

Over the past seven years we have used various and often diverse therapies. These have included intensive ABA, the GFCF diet, numerous supplements (including B6 and magnesium, DMG, TMG, cod liver oil, multivitamins, essential fatty acids, amino acids, and others), mercury chelation, sensory integration, occupational therapy, speech therapy, auditory integration, treating a yeast overgrowth in the gut, antigen-specific transfer factors, secretin, and more.

I believe that each of these treatments played a role in our son's recovery. True, some were more significant than others, but each had its place and its time. I have learned that autism truly is a multifaceted disorder and each facet must be addressed in its own way. What treatment brought our son back? I don't know for sure.

What I do know is this: We once had a child who was locked in his own world; now we enjoy life together. We once had a child whose IQ was 53 and who wasn't learning. Now we have a son who has an IQ of 109 and is learning at grade level. We once had a little boy who couldn't speak. Now we have a young man who hugs us and says, "I love you, Mom. I love you, Dad." We once had a son with a very dim prognosis, who we thought would need constant supervision all his life. Now we have a son with a bright future who wants to save endangered animals as a zookeeper.

There *is* hope!

## References

[1] Hamilton, Lynn M., adapted from *Facing Autism: Giving Parents Reasons for Hope and Guidance for Help* (Colorado: WaterBrook Press, 2000), 81.

[2] Hamilton, Adapted from *Facing Autism*, 116-118.

[3] Rimland, Bernard, Ph.D., Baker, Sidney M, M.D. "Brief Report: Alternative Approaches to the Development of Effective Treatments for Autism," *Journal of Autism and Developmental Disorders* 26, no. 2 (1996): 238.

[4] Hamilton, Adapted from *Facing Autism*, 163-164.



*Update for Second Edition (November 2005):*

Two years have passed since I shared our story in this book, and the biggest change is that our boy is becoming a man. Yes, our "baby" is growing up. He is only 13 years old, but his body has now changed and we've hit puberty. Ryan is now as tall as his Dad, with a deep voice to match. Where, oh where, did my little boy go?

Ryan constantly amazes us. We've had our rough spots, as anyone with a teenager will tell you, but Ryan is still developing daily and doing really well. He still has a love for animals, and hopes to work in a zoo. By the grace of God, the future becomes brighter for Ryan with each passing year. For that, we are very thankful.

## — Chapter 14 —

# Becoming Aware of Our Son's Autism and Finding Hope for His Future

By Marian Helmick

*Marian Helmick and her husband Dave live in Cleveland, Ohio with Davey, who was born in 1998. This story was written in the spring of 2002.*



At the Cleveland Clinic in Cleveland, Ohio, on April 25, 2002, my son, Davey, was diagnosed with ASD/PDD (autism spectrum disorder/ pervasive developmental disorder) by pediatric neurologist Dr. Gerald Erenberg. Davey was 3½ years old.

As a first-time parent it was hard for me to tell that Davey had autism. It was equally hard for my husband, Dave, even though he had three children of his own from a previous marriage years before. I didn't believe Davey had autism until I attended a 15-hour autism spectrum disorder seminar held in August 2001 by Barry A. Prizant, Ph.D. It was two months before Davey's third birthday.

It took a long time to understand what was going on with Davey during his first 2½ years. Before we began interventions and nutritional alternatives, his means of playing and communicating were unusual. We would find him playing with shoestrings, throwing our socks, and sliding anything that would fit under our china cabinet. When playing with a puzzle, he preferred to slide the puzzle pieces under the tray instead of putting the puzzle together in the tray. He was not interested in playing with toys, other than throwing them. He had no speech, only babbled, and did not imitate any words.

Through early intervention and nutritional alternatives (GFCF and Feingold diets), Davey has achieved much in the last nine months. He can now imitate over 125 words, and is beginning to use a few words such as "bye-bye," "see ya," "coat off," "vest off," and "sit down." He sings phrases of songs such as "Row, Row, Row Your Boat." He is able to count to 12, say parts of the alphabet, and name farm animals and their sounds when pointing to pictures of them. Just recently I pointed to a picture of a rabbit and said "bunny," and he said "rabbit." I was very pleased! He plays appropriately with toys, is interested in trying new ones, and likes to put puzzles together.

It was through the seminar, and other information I found on the Internet and in magazine articles, that I came to believe that Davey had autism. Here is the story of how our awareness of autism came about, and what we did to help him.

I was a first-time mother at the age of 37, and had not been around newborns for a long time. I had been working for about 17 years, and in 1995 my career took a new direction when I became involved in graphic art and design. I had been longing to have a child of my own since I was in my twenties, but it was 10 years before Davey came into our lives (because of our financial standing and infertility issues, and also because my husband wasn't ready).

When Davey was born he was very healthy, weighed seven pounds, fourteen ounces, and was 21½ inches long. Davey accomplished the major milestones, such as lifting his head, rolling over, sitting up, crawling, and walking. He was slightly behind on some of the milestones but always caught up within a month or so.



Throughout his infancy it was difficult to connect with him because he seemed to prefer being in his baby swing or vibrating infant seat rather than being held. I thought it was because he enjoyed movement rather than being still. By the time he was six weeks old I learned that I could play soft music and dance with him in my arms. This was my way of being able to hold him. I had tried rocking him in a rocking chair or glider before, but it wasn't enough movement for him.

Although I found ways of appeasing him, Davey was irritable quite often. Before feeding it was as if he were facing starvation; his crying sounded loud and demanding, and nearly pierced my eardrums. I made his bottles ahead of time, and it only took a few minutes to warm them, but I wasn't fast enough for him. By the time he was four months old my nerves were shot, and I decided to use industrial-strength earplugs.

Often when we changed his diapers Davey would scream as if he were in intense pain. This was bewildering to us. He did not have skin conditions that we could see, and dressing and bathing rarely bothered him. We tried using a diaper wipe warmer, and we handled him as gently as possible each time we changed him. This helped some.

I noticed that his most irritable times were close to his naptime. He couldn't fall asleep in a still position. To get him to nap I created a "sled" using an infant carrier. The carrier had two ridges on the bottom that were about an inch wide and curved along the back of the infant seat. I put a small amount of furniture wax on the bottom part of the ridges to aid in a smooth ride. I then attached a nylon rope to the carrier handle to pull it. When Davey was placed in the carrier, he was in a comfortable, reclined position. Every time I used the sled I put soft music on and pulled Davey around our first-floor living room, kitchen, hallway, and bedroom. He enjoyed the ride and would fall asleep within 15 minutes. Sometimes he fell asleep within a minute. On occasion the sled wasn't enough movement for him, so I would take him for a ride in our van and he would fall asleep then. This way I had him on a good naptime schedule most days.

There were times when Davey was not consolable even after I tried the sled, the van, or the baby swing. Since this put my nerves on edge, I had to put him in his crib and allow him to cry. I remember occasions when there was extra stress in my life, and I would end up crying out my frustration and pain. This is when I felt like a failure at motherhood. At times I wondered if I was meant to be only an aunt or babysitter.



One time, when my brother-in-law and his wife came to visit us, Davey became irritable. My brother-in-law suggested that we have him examined for colic because his youngest son, who often had been irritable as an infant, had been diagnosed with colic.

When I took Davey for his routine checkup, I asked our pediatrician to examine Davey for colic. After she examined him and asked questions, she said that he did not have indications of colic. She mentioned that he might have excessive gas, which could cause a lot of discomfort. She explained how to look for signs of gas and recommended an over-the-counter treatment called "Little Tummies." On occasion when I thought Davey had gas I looked for signs as directed by my physician, and used the medicine, and it did help. This eased some of his irritability. During all of his infant checkups the doctor made a general assessment of his development, but there was never an indication that anything was wrong.

During Davey's early infancy, I didn't feel close to him. Even though I loved him, I couldn't feel those wonderful nurturing feelings I had when I held other babies. I felt numb and disappointed and didn't know what I could do about it. I knew I needed some support, so I decided to get counseling. While in counseling, I was referred to "Early Start," a program for children from birth to three years old. This sounded like a good idea for both Davey and me. That week I signed up for the home-based visits. I decided to continue with counseling until I felt better.

The Early Start coordinator came and assessed Davey's development using a developmental checklist. She also observed and interacted with him. A few weeks after the assessment, a home visitor came and began seeing us on a weekly basis. Every three months we reviewed Davey's developmental progress until he was 12 months old. This is how we found out that he was behind on some minor developments, but would catch up within a month or so.

By the time he was between seven and eight months old he was becoming mellow, pleasant, and happier. (Our pediatrician had predicted that this would happen.) It was a pleasant time and I was thankful for this period!

Davey began talking at around 13 months, saying "da da," but did not progress much. By the time he was 16 months old, we were growing concerned with his language delay and his lack of play skills. He wasn't responding to us when we called him.

When some family members were visiting, my sister-in-law mentioned that she was concerned about Davey's hearing because she thought he didn't respond to sounds around him. I had never noticed a problem with Davey's hearing. I knew he wouldn't respond to us calling him, but I thought it was because he was always so preoccupied doing other things.



At Davey's next checkup, I mentioned that our family members were concerned about his hearing. Our pediatrician wrote an order for a hearing test, but during the test Davey would not cooperate. He wanted to do his own thing, and he had tantrums when we tried to get him to sit and listen for the sounds. After trying several times and using different methods, the technician said that the test was inconclusive; there wasn't enough information to accurately indicate Davey's hearing ability. Our pediatrician said the next step would be to get an auditory brain response (ABR) test. This is a hearing test that can accurately record brain response to sounds while the patient is sedated. My husband and I took Davey in for his ABR test, which was simple and took less than 20 minutes. A few weeks later we received a report that indicated normal hearing in both ears.

For a while, I had been trying to figure out what I could do to help Davey with his play skills. I decided to join a weekly playgroup that a friend of mine had organized. I thought it would help him to be around other children. The moms took turns hosting the playgroup at their homes. Getting started in the playgroup was a struggle. I had to stay with Davey the whole time for the first month because he was quite fussy and irritable, and it was frustrating for both of us. The second month he was less irritable. As time went on, he gradually became comfortable, and I felt better allowing him to be on his own. He mostly played by himself.

I talked with my friend about Davey, and she said she didn't see a problem, only that he was fussy and it seemed that he just had a different personality than the other children.

Between 16 and 18 months of age, Davey became more irritable again and began to throw tantrums. I went to our library and looked up books and articles on infant and child temperaments and I found a description of Davey's temperament listed in one book. The book stated reassuringly that some children have difficult temperaments. It also suggested that a child with a difficult temperament would benefit from being kept on a strict routine throughout the day, and being informed ahead of time about transitions. Back then it was difficult for me to keep Davey on a strict schedule other than his waking, napping, and feeding times, and planned trips.

When Davey was about 18 months old, my sister-in-law suggested that we have him checked for autism. She had been talking to a neighbor of hers who had a teenage son with autism, and thought this was a possibility. It was a struggle for me to talk with her about it. The idea of autism frightened me—I wanted to believe it was only a temperament issue and developmental delays. Also, in a sense, I felt that I was protecting my son from autism by avoiding the issue.



I decided to call around to find anything I could to help Davey overcome his developmental delays. I started in the yellow pages and went from one agency to another. I can't remember the details but I remember making a lot of phone calls, and feeling like I was going in circles. Somehow I found an organization that recommended early intervention to help children with developmental delays catch up. This was in August 2000.

I decided to try early intervention. At the time we knew that Davey had a speech delay. A coordinator was sent to our home to assess Davey. After her assessments were done, she said that he was behind on many play skills. For example, he was behind on stacking blocks and stringing beads, but those activities never interested him. I didn't know how important those things would be. He mostly enjoyed running, jumping, romping, throwing, and basically acting like a toddler boy.

A few weeks after the assessment, our first early intervention specialist came. She was very kind and helpful to us and had worked with autistic children before. After a few visits I asked her if she thought Davey had autism. She couldn't tell, but recommended that we see a pediatric neurologist. Davey was about 21 months old at the time.

Before going to the pediatric neurologist, I started to consider the possibility of Davey having autism. I wanted to know everything I could about it.

I began by searching the Internet for information. One site was for the

Autism Society of America. At the time, there were some descriptions of autism that I thought didn't really fit Davey—for example, toe-walking, arm flapping, rocking, head banging, lack of eye contact, and repetitive play. Davey wasn't exhibiting these behaviors. I thought Davey's repetitive play was appropriate for his age of 22 months.

When we took Davey to the pediatric neurologist, I explained everything Davey was able to do and what I knew about autism. By this time Davey was stacking up to 11 blocks at a time and attending to the stack. He had good motor skills, and he seemed to me like a typical toddler boy. Also, by this time he didn't mind being held for short periods, and he had some eye contact. The neurologist examined and observed Davey. He said his behavior and the way he was playing were appropriate for his age. He said he didn't see autism in Davey at this time, but he acknowledged his speech delay.



In February of 2001, our early intervention specialist told me about a parent/toddler playgroup that was organized for children with autism. She said this would be helpful for Davey even without a diagnosis. I signed us up for the playgroup, and we met once a week. As part of the playgroup therapy we were introduced to what is called the "Miller method." This is a therapeutic way of helping children with socialization, motor planning, and following directions. We also attended the preschool on Mondays for a parent/tot "Movement and Music" class and swimming. In addition, we had a speech and occupational therapist from the school visit our home for an hour twice a month.

In early spring of 2001, my early intervention specialist recommended a "Floor Time" seminar to help me interact with Davey and expand his play skills. It had been very difficult for me to sit and play with him. He would never really play with one thing, and he would often prefer to simply run around the room. I could not get him interested in playing with any toys, and it was very frustrating for me.

The day I went to the Floor Time class I was sitting in the waiting room and noticed an article called "We Cured our Son's Autism," by Karyn Seroussi *[Editors' note: A chapter by Karyn Seroussi is included in this book].* This article explained that a gluten- and casein-free diet helped her autistic son dramatically.

I decided to try the diet that Karyn Seroussi had written about, just to see if it would help Davey. I reread the article and began my research into the diet to make sure this was the right direction for us. I also read her book, *Unraveling the Mysteries of Autism*, and *Special Diets for Special Kids* by Lisa Lewis.

In addition, I checked on the Internet for more information on the GFCF diet. I went to the ANDI (Autism Network for Dietary Intervention) website that had been mentioned at the end of Karyn Seroussi's article, and found a section for parent support. These parents volunteer their time to help other parents who are trying to learn more about the diet. I found two mothers that I kept in touch with by email for a short time. They were very helpful in sharing information with me about the diet and how they were doing with it. They also mentioned Kirkman Laboratories.

After all my research I consulted with our pediatrician about the diet. Although she was hesitant about it, she suggested that I consult a registered dietitian, which I did. The dietician requested a three-day list of Davey's meals to make sure that he would be getting enough nutrition.



I started Davey on the diet in the middle of July 2001. I decided to go into it carefully, replacing one item at a time. He liked flake cereals and breads, so I started with a GFCF flake cereal; he liked it right away. One week at a time I replaced bread, macaroni, and other gluten products. Now he eats a variety of organic foods such as scrambled eggs with no yolk, chicken nuggets that I make with only rice flour, lean ground beef in rice spaghetti, vegetables (such as peas, green beans, carrots, and soybeans), and fruits (such as pears, pineapples, and bananas). He even eats a very small salad with the dark green leaves. I continue to add more variety and to try other foods carefully. At times I have found foods that cause problems with Davey's digestion so I have discontinued those foods for the time being. I am glad I replaced the items slowly over a month and a half because Davey adapted to the diet very well, and it was not a tremendous struggle. This diet has been worth the effort for many reasons, especially because he is eating a much healthier selection of foods than before.

Sometime after starting the GFCF diet, I was shopping at Wild Oats where I had been finding appropriate foods. I found a computer with dietary information on it (Healthnotes Online). I printed out a lot of information on gluten-free foods, and also information on fruits and vegetables. While I was looking at the information on fruits, I found a section on the Feingold diet. From what I understood about this diet, avoiding foods containing salicylates and certain preservatives could reduce ADHD in autistic children. I used this method along with the GFCF diet, and I really believe it has helped Davey to pay attention to tasks such as finishing puzzles, and to be able to interact with adults.

In August 2001 I attended a two-day seminar on understanding and supporting children with ASD. This seminar, presented by Barry A. Prizant,

Ph.D., gave me a much clearer view of Davey's disposition. There were several video clips of children with ASD whose characters were like Davey's. After the seminar I was 99 percent convinced that Davey had autism.

After having Davey on the GFCF diet for 1½ months, I decided to try Super Nu-Thera, the vitamin and mineral supplement for autism mentioned by the two mothers from the ANDI parent support website. I went to the Kirkman Labs website to read about the product and its benefits (www.KirkmanLabs.com). The information was very interesting, and it looked as if the supplement would be helpful to Davey. I ordered the trial size of Nu-Thera. Beginning in September, I started Davey on it.

On September 19, we witnessed the beginning of results from the diet and Super Nu-Thera. Davey started repeating alphabet letters that he was seeing on "Sesame Street." He had never imitated language before. I ran and got the video camera and was able to videotape him saying the alphabet letters! My husband and I were so proud.



In September 2001, we started Davey in a 4½-day toddler program that is similar to preschool. Davey's teacher had known him from the previous year when we attended her parent/toddler group. After the first week of school I asked her if she noticed any difference in Davey, and she said, "Yes, I see a big change in him." She mentioned that he was far less irritable and easier to work with, and was starting to imitate words. She asked if this was a result of the diet, and I said I believed it was.

In October, I started Davey on a trial of EnZym-Complete with DPP-IV from Kirkman Labs. (This is an all-natural dietary enzyme to aid in digesting and breaking down proteins, sugars, and carbohydrates.) The enzymes have been helpful in improving his digestion and firming his stools.

In March of 2002, I was at our public library looking for children's videos when I found vocabulary-building videos for infants and toddlers by "Baby Bumblebee." I was excited about this find and couldn't wait to view the videos with Davey. He enjoyed them, and he would view them three to four times a day. The first week he began repeating many of the 25 words on the first video. A week later I went back to the library and found four more videos. Week by week I played them for him, and eventually he was able to imitate approximately 125 of the words on the videos. Now he's labeling things such as ball, cup, bowl, hat, dog, cat, and bicycle, and says the names of farm animals and the sounds they make.

Over the last nine months while in preschool, Davey learned to use eating utensils and a regular cup, and he started potty training. He also learned to paint, and to use writing utensils, paste, and scissors. I have many pictures that he's made hanging on our living room wall. In school they also had circle-time for socialization, and there he learned "Ring Around the Rosy." I remember the first time he pulled my husband and me into our living room, taking my hand and putting it into my husband's hand. Then he started jumping for joy, and we said, "What do you want to do?" He grabbed our hands and made a circle, then he said, "Ring Around the Rosy" (only not so clearly and not so directly, but we got the idea). I'm thankful to his teacher and her assistants for helping him to achieve these things.

Davey has more to achieve in order to catch up to the level of typical children, but we are so thankful for all of his achievements in the last nine months. For me, the most rewarding part of his development is the relationship and connection I now have with him. I feel close to him, and it's easy to tell that he enjoys being with his dad and me. It also pleases me that Davey is connecting with his grandmother and some of my friends. He makes eye contact with them and also participates in some play with them. One special moment I'll always remember is the time when his dad did something funny, and Davey's and my eyes met and we laughed together.



*Update (March 2003):*

Davey is four years old now. He is very aware of his environment and is into EVERYTHING, including other people's homes. I used to wonder why other mothers would complain about their children exploring. Well, now I know why they complained.

At times I really have fun with Davey and a few times I've felt as if we're best friends—he is my little buddy. But he has been driving us nuts with his constant screaming about everything lately—I think something is up with his diet.

Davey is doing better at potty training. He has gone two times so far by himself with no cues at all, and he brings a diaper to me to put on him. We will be going to pull-ups soon, although I prefer disposable cotton diapers with no gel or chemicals.

Davey says his entire alphabet and can identify letters and numbers randomly. He also says colors and shapes. His vocabulary is about 300 words, but he only uses 20, to request things he wants. He is using some verbs such as jump, shake, walk, and drink. He can label many items, but doesn't make conversation yet. He has on occasion used up to three-word sentences, but this is rare, and he uses language when he is pretend playing, although I don't know what he is saying. He likes to play with pull toys now, when he'd never had much interest in them before.

Recently Davey's Sunday school teacher commented to me about how much he has changed for the better over the last year and a half. She said he is so much calmer, more cooperative, and more easygoing.

I continue to keep abreast of new interventions and research. As of August 5, 2002, I started an Internet parent support group that meets on Wednesday evenings. Please write to me if you or someone you know would like to join our group, "Parent to Parent – Parents Chat." You can write to me at ParentsChat@aol.com, or visit "Parent to Parent 4SN" at http://hometown.aol.com/parentschat/homepage.html.

A Copy of this story is also available on my website and will be revised as Davey grows older. Please see the website for future updates: http://hometown.aol.com/GFCF4Davey/Davey.html.



*Update for Second Edition (October 2005):*

Life brings many ups and downs; there have been so many times I've been in the valley wanting to quit. I cried and prayed my heart out over my son's autism in the spring of 2004 when it seemed that his progress diminished as he was becoming quite irritable, whiney, and hyper.

This year I've been on mountain tops rejoicing and thanking God with all my heart.

This is our current update:

A few years ago, though I had hope, it was difficult to imagine my son sitting in my lap and reading a book with me page-by-page, taking turns reading sentences. I also didn't know then that my son would be able to write his first and last name, or spell words if I asked, "Davey, how do you spell dog? Cat? Pig? Dig?..." The biggest blessing of all is that when I come home he runs to greet me with a big, "Hi, Mommy!" and a beautiful smile and love sparkling in his eyes.

One more thing I believe that all parents of autistic children wish for is to have a calm child. Davey is calm most of the time now, and it's great that he can sit for periods of time and listen to a story being read. Just yesterday we took a friend to the store and we waited for her in our van for 20 minutes. Davey was quiet and calm! No fussing or whining! Can you even imagine that? How about imagining your child actually doing his school homework with your help? This is what is happening for our six-year-old and us. Believe me, I am so thankful!

Socially, Davey now has friends at school whom he mentions by name at home, and he often asks to see Grandma. Davey has a friend we see almost every day and he is now interacting with his friend when they have playtime together. It's mostly boy stuff, like chasing each other and climbing things. Davey will also mimic his friend at times.

Our current therapies for Davey include continuing the GFCF diet and the specific carbohydrate dietary intervention (SCD) we implemented in the spring of 2004. The SCD diet eliminates all grains and starches to greatly reduce yeast growth in the body. This has been a very helpful intervention for Davey, resulting in better cognition and comprehension. Along with the SCD diet, I am continuing the vitamin, enzyme, and probiotic supplement therapy from Kirkman Labs that was mentioned in the main story. I added CoEnzyme Q10 and Yeast Control a month after implementing the SCD diet, and recently added evening primrose oil, one dose three times a week; these have resulted in improved cognitive/comprehensive function. We're also continuing occupational therapy and speech therapy.



The greatest improvements have occurred over the last four months (from mid-May to the present, October 2005) when I implemented chiropractic care. Davey started out by seeing a chiropractor three times a week. He's done well with it and is now down to twice a week, soon to be once a week. I researched chiropractic care and learned that vertebral subluxations can cause reduced energy to vital organs in the body. The chiropractor has been correcting the subluxations for the immune and thyroid systems, along with the C1 vertebra in the upper neck, which provides energy to the sinuses and other parts of the head. So far (knock on wood), my son has not been sick since last spring (that itself is a great blessing).

I can't thank God enough for my son's recovery, and my prayer is to continue his healing as much as possible. Along with my website and international parent support group P2ParentsChat (http://groups.yahoo.com/group/P2ParentsChat), I started a local group for my Northeast Ohio area (http://groups.yahoo.com/group/AutismNE).

A very important thing to remember is that any treatment has to be done carefully and over time so as not to cause trauma to the body. Also, hang in there, keep researching, pray hard, and get as much support as you can. I have followed my gut instincts on most of the treatments. It is very difficult to determine which treatments are the right ones for each individual person. That is why it's so important to keep researching, weigh your options, and carefully think of all alternatives before making a decision on anything.

Main Website, Parent to Parent for Autism: http://hometown.aol.com/

parentschat/homepage.html. For fellow authors of this book: http://health.groups.yahoo.com/group/TreatingAutismAuthors. Please write to me if you would like to correspond at: DMHelmick1@wmconnect.com.

## — Chapter 15 —

# Steven: Hopes, Prayers, and Progress

By Dan Hoffiz, with Jennifer Hoffiz

*Jennifer and Dan Hoffiz live in the California Bay Area with their two children, Steven, who was born in August 1999, and Sabrina. This story was written in February 2002.*



When I look at my son, Steven, I think of my own condition in 1994. After a diving accident that year, I was left paralyzed and was to undergo an operation. The doctor said that I had no choice, as my neck was so badly broken that if I did not have the operation I would not recover and would be paralyzed for life. I underwent the operation while, at my parents' request, over one thousand people prayed for a successful recovery. I recovered completely in four months. I thank God, Dr. Hoff, Dr. Papadapoulus, my parents, and all the people who prayed for me.

Eight years later, we are asking everyone to pray for our 2½-year-old son, Steven. He's been in an accident too, only his accident was not his fault. Someone injected into his body what they thought was a prescription for health: regularly prescribed vaccines. Instead, it was a sentence of lifelong illness, as the vaccines were laden with mercury, one of the deadliest poisons known to man.

When Steven was born, he scored high on the Apgar. His respiration was fine. He had no problems. However, as he grew, he did not react the same way as our daughter, Sabrina, who is three years older. So, we kept watching him. As time progressed, it became more apparent that something was wrong. Steven had almost no solid stools. The stools he did have emitted an extremely strong odor. As has happened in so many other cases, our pediatrician said he was fine, that boys were slower than girls, and not to worry.

However, by the time Steven was 16 months old he was in occupational therapy at the Contra Costa County, California, Regional Center. After six months of this conventional therapy, Steven had made little progress. The Regional Center itself became more concerned. So we prodded our pediatrician, who referred us to a medical doctor who specialized in behavioral pediatrics.

The behavioral specialist said that Steven had a neurological problem, but that he was not 100% convinced it was autism. However, he said, the diagnosis that fit Steven best was autism. The doctor's opinion did not surprise us because it was consistent with our own independent research. The doctor also said that the gluten- and casein-free (GFCF) diet might help make Steven more lucid. At the same time, the Regional Center said he might benefit from ABA therapy.

On Steven's second birthday, we went back to our hometown, Bloomfield Hills, Michigan, where Steven visited his uncle, a pediatric ophthalmologist. The examination revealed that Steven had the worst astigmatism in one eye that the doctor had ever seen, with a severe astigmatism in the other eye. This also did not surprise us as we had suspected that his eyesight was poor, though neither side of the family had any such history.

Amazingly, when Steven got his glasses, the first thing he did was to hug his sister. It then hit us. Steven's eyesight was so poor that he never had seen his sister clearly before. I knew there must be a connection to his autistic behavior. In fact, further research showed that the rods in the eyes need zinc to develop properly and that mercury blocks zinc absorption.



So, thinking that our child was autistic, we attended the DAN! conference in San Diego. After one day, I was convinced that Steven had nothing more than mercury poisoning. After all, the symptoms of mercury poisoning include rocking back and forth, poor speech development, poor balance, toe walking, hand flapping, and a general inability to concentrate except on repetitively moving objects. This describes our son perfectly. If he was not mercury poisoned, then who was? If it walks like a duck, talks like a duck, and looks like a duck, then it must be a duck.

To make sure we were not going down a dead-end street, we took several steps. First, we had an MRI done to see if Steven's brain showed any signs of abnormality. It showed none.

Next, we had his blood examined under a high-power microscope by a naturopath, without telling the doctor that we were looking for anything in particular. In our son's blood the doctor found heavy metals, which appear as black rings around dry blood cells. He also found that our son had a very high level of parasites. These look like pulsating and glowing wet red blood cells. Once the cells are smashed, wormlike parasites can be seen swimming across the slide.

The doctor told us that a number of people had successfully eliminated parasites from their systems by taking olive leaf extract. In fact, one of the doctor's other patients, who had difficulty with reading and concentration, proved to have an extremely high number of red blood parasites. The patient's reading and concentration improved markedly once she took olive leaf extract and the parasites were eliminated. So we put Steven on the extract.

After a month of giving him the olive leaf extract, we had Steven's blood tested again: the parasites were gone. His energy level picked up as well. This was a great result, but the heavy metals remained.

At the DAN! conference, a paper on chelation had been distributed describing the process of removing heavy metals from children. We knew that our son needed to have this done, but we did not have any test results showing his mercury levels. Moreover, we heard that without provocation with a chelation agent, such as DMSA, the mercury levels would not appear to be high. Just to see, though, we had his urinalysis done and, guess what—he was at the 98th percentile for mercury, with high tin, aluminum, and arsenic.



So we selected one of the contributors of the chelation paper for Steven to see. When we got there, the doctor was blown away. He had never seen such high levels of mercury without provocation. The doctor administered secretin and a chelation agent on the visit, and we left.

Within a week, Steven seemed more alert and was producing three-word sentences. After a month, the results of his urinalysis came back; his mercury was off the chart. We visited the doctor again and had Steven tested for food sensitivities. Steven received another dose of secretin and a chelation agent.

Steven is now producing five-word sentences. He is speaking without prodding, and he is asking meaningful questions. The difference is amazing. As a result, Steven is currently on a cycle of DMSA for three days, then no DMSA for 11 days. We expect this to continue until the mercury is gone.

Although most physicians do not believe it, we are certain that Steven's toxic mercury levels are a result of his vaccines. He lives in a newly constructed home. He has had no contact with broken meters, thermometers, or other mercury sources. And the vaccines he received contained mercury levels far in excess of the EPA safe levels.

There is a precedent for this: pink disease, which is the name given to poisoning from a teething powder containing mercury. A misnomer, like autism, pink disease was nothing more than an injury inflicted by a product. Pink disease disappeared after the product was removed from the shelves 50 years ago.

In the year 2000, drug manufacturers stopped manufacturing vaccines with mercury, but vaccines containing mercury remain on the shelf, and some injections, for example flu shots, still contain mercury. Once these mercury-containing supplies are gone, rates of autism should drop as sharply as they have risen (in California, for example, one in 150 boys born today is diagnosed with autism). However, there are other concerns, including the other potentially poisonous substances in vaccines, the impact of multiple live viruses (such as in the MMR vaccine), and the more aggressive vaccination schedule used today. In fact, in Japan when they went to a less aggressive vaccination schedule, sudden infant death syndrome (SIDS) dropped to a statistically insignificant level.

Our hope is that our son and every other injured child will recover. We would like to thank everyone who has prayed for our son. As of this writing, he is two years and seven months old; he continues to progress. He is in ABA therapy 40 hours a week and is on the GFCF diet. Additionally, he takes a large number of vitamins, minerals, and herbal supplements. We believe his progress is due to God's healing and that God is using the therapy, diet, and supplements to help him achieve higher levels of intellectual and physical development.



*Update (March 2003):*

As of today, our son Steven is 3½ years old. The progress he has made is wonderful. Steven's spontaneous language has finally become natural and interactive. In fact, he interacts normally with other children his age, on occasion, and loves his sister's friends. This is brand new for Steven and his teachers are very excited about it. He has a few friends at school and is beginning to call them by name. Steven is able to ask Who, What, Where, and Can questions, and he consistently produces five-word sentences. This is a triumph for someone who could utter only the word "wa" for water when he turned two. Steven is in ABA therapy 20 hours a week and attends preschool five days a week, two days without an aide.

Of course, we continue to chelate him. We started chelating Steven in January 2002 when his urine showed a mercury level of 74 micrograms per gram of creatinine. This level dropped to five micrograms by November 2002, which was a miracle. Up until November 2002, he received two chelation agents, DMPS and DMSA. After that period, he received an additional chelation agent, alpha lipoic acid, to start drawing the remaining mercury out of his brain.

Unfortunately, Steven still has difficulty digesting foods. He remains on the GFCF diet with no expansion of his diet. Diarrhea is a big problem at the moment and what is causing it remains a mystery. We are using a natural antibiotic, colloidal silver, to treat this condition and it appears to be working.

Steven's next phase of chelation entails a new process designed to reverse the effects of the vaccines that have so damaged his intestines and immune system. We are extremely excited about this and are praying that the process will have the desired effect. We thank Jesus Christ our savior for guiding us through this maze and healing our son Steven.

*Update for Second Edition (November 2005):*

Since the last writing, we found that Stevie (as he likes to be called now) was improperly processing sensory input, particularly in the areas of auditory, visual, and vestibular (movement and balance) information. His sound sensitivities were obvious, though his ABA therapists could not see his light processing imbalances. However, we thought he needed help in all these areas so we enrolled him in a sensory integration program. His results from the program were great, but we wanted him to progress even further.



For this reason, we enlisted the advice of the top doctors and professionals in the country and created sensorycenter.com with a new program to correct sensory processing imbalances. The Sensory Center Individualized Sensory Program (ISP) allowed Stevie to graduate from ABA therapy in December 2004. He simply did not need it any more. Amazingly, he also became very social and no longer needed to be enrolled in his social interaction group called Friends Club. In fact, Stevie was subsequently invited back to Friends Club as a special guest and now he assists other children on the spectrum in interacting.

As for diet, we found that Stevie was improperly processing foods with a high natural dye content (phenols), like berries. These foods increased his rocking and hand flapping so we have restricted them within his specific carbohydrate diet (SCD). Stevie was put on the SCD because it was the only approach we found that resulted in normal bowel movements.

On the biomedical front, provoked chelation lab results show that Steven is excreting 2.4 micrograms of mercury. While not down to zero, this is great as he started at 74 micrograms. What is interesting is that the results showed that lead started to pour out at the level of 12 micrograms. Often, this pattern of mercury first, followed by lead, occurs in these children, according to Dr. John Green, Steven's God-given specialist. To target the lead, Dr. Green changed Steven's chelation agent from transdermal DMPS to EDTA.

Stevie is now six years old and he is in a mainstream kindergarten class. He has a one-on-one aide to redirect him, but that is it. By next year, he should be in first grade with no aide. The average person cannot tell he is autistic and he has been invited to a number of birthday parties recently. As most parents will tell you, this is the biggest indicator of his recovery, which is at least 75% complete.

For years we have prayed for a complete recovery for Stevie and now it is in sight. God directed us to tools to enable the recovery and we would like to encourage all parents that it is possible. Do not stop hoping, praying, and most of all acting to put in place the pieces of the puzzle on the road to recovery.

## — Chapter 16 —
# My Son, the King of Metals
By Amy S. Holmes, M.D.

*Physician Amy Holmes and her husband, Charlie, are the parents of Mike, born in 1994, whose autism led Amy to become a DAN! doctor and to focus her efforts on investigating the role of mercury in causing autistic symptoms. The family lives in Louisiana. This story was written in October 2002.*

I was once a "very mainstream" physician. I did everything by the book. I was taught, "if it is not a drug, it doesn't work," and "parents know absolutely nothing." And I truly believed this.



After 15 years of fertility treatment, I had my first and only child, Mike. He was normal and quite healthy at birth. At six months he was a very happy baby. He also had very good, if not exceptional, social skills for an infant. By the age of one year, he had 20 to 25 words, and his development was normal in every sense.

But around 15 to 16 months of age, he started to "go away." This was most noticeable in the disappearance of his eye contact. Looking back, I see that his photos clearly show his regression. He changed from a loving, social child to an unloving, unresponsive mess. He started treating my husband Charlie and me like furniture, and he would spend hours holding and staring at two leaves. Charlie and I knew that something had happened to him within a relatively short period of time, but we had no clue what it could be. We started our journey to find an answer; and when we eventually discovered that answer, we were shocked.

We took Mike to his pediatrician who simply told us, "Boys talk later." We knew better. He had no explanation as to why Mike had started talking, and then stopped. We finally saw a pediatric neurologist in our area, and Mike was diagnosed as having "severe" autism—not just autism, but an extreme case of autism. The pediatric neurologist then suggested that we try a number of different treatments, such as speech therapy, ABA, and "mind-altering" drugs; but she also said that these treatments would not be very helpful to him. As you can imagine, this was incredibly hard for Charlie and me to deal with: first, being told that our son had a severe case of autism and second, being told that very little could be done to help him.

(Unfortunately, I now realize that our situation was not unique—many families are in this same situation right now.)

We followed the neurologist's discouraging advice and even tried additional treatments, such as play therapy, Floor time, auditory integration training, occupational therapy, and some nutritional/biomedical interventions such as IVIg, GFCF diet, vitamin B6 with magnesium, and dimethylglycine (DMG). We did notice some improvements from these interventions, but Mike still was severely autistic. We were desperate—Mike was 3½ years old (March, 1999), and he no longer talked.

I heard about a terrific physician in Baton Rouge, Louisiana, Dr. Stephanie Cave. I brought Mike to see her, and she performed several DAN!-type tests, including a test for toxic metals in his hair. Surprisingly, Mike had very high levels of lead in his hair. My husband and I were starting to suspect that Mike was suffering from lead poisoning. It is important to note that his mercury was at an undetectable level; I will discuss this in more detail later.



We then began the standard course of treatment to remove the lead from Mike's body. This involved giving him DMSA (Chemet) for 2½ weeks. Within a short time, we noticed better receptive language and better attention. He also was less "zoned out." We felt we were on the right track, but we were not sure where the track would eventually take us.

Over the next four months, we did not see any additional improvements in Mike; and obviously, we wanted much more. We repeated the 2½-week course of DMSA, then let his hair grow out. His lead level was much lower this time, but it was still at an unacceptable level. Interestingly, his mercury level was extremely high; but at this time in our lives, we were focusing on the lead.

Although Mike was getting better, slowly, he was still quite autistic. I knew I was missing something, but I did not know what it was. I then reviewed all of Mike's test results, and the high mercury level from his last hair test made me start to think. I knew that mercury was highly neurotoxic, and I knew that many vaccines contained the preservative thimerosal. I decided to add up all of the mercury to which Mike was exposed through his vaccinations, not considering other possible sources of mercury, such as fish. When I did, I discovered that he had received 212.5 mcg of mercury, which far exceeds any government standard for mercury exposure in adults.

At this time, I did not, nor did others, understand what had happened to Mike. Since he was exposed to extremely high amounts of mercury, why didn't his first hair test indicate a high mercury level? Why did later hair analyses, performed after DMSA treatment, indicate a high mercury level? I wouldn't know these answers for a few more years.

However, I did know our next course of action—get the mercury out of him! Before we started another course of DMSA, I had a developmental psychologist evaluate him. Mike was now 4½ years old, had no expressive language, was constantly stimming, and rarely interacted socially. His language level was less than two years, and he was also behind in cognitive and fine motor skills. His only age-level skill was gross motor. Additionally, his developmental quotient (DQ) was 58, which indicated moderate mental retardation.

With help and support from Dr. Cave, I followed the DAN! Protocol. We cleaned up Mike's gut because he was loaded with yeast and *Clostridium* (bacteria). We also gave him numerous nutritional supplements. We then did a provoked urine DMSA challenge, and the mercury poured out of him. A stool test also indicated that he was excreting huge amounts of mercury, as well as other heavy metals. Our little boy, we discovered, was the "king of metals." We decided to place him on an aggressive chelation program.



Within a short period of time, Mike's social and cognitive skills began to improve by leaps and bounds, and his stimming behavior decreased to almost nothing—but it was still there.

When Mike was five years and seven months old, I had him re-evaluated by the same developmental psychologist. In only 13 months, he had gained 20 months in language and 21 months in cognition. His DQ was now 80, a gain of 22 points. Mike was not just beginning to develop, he was slowly catching up with his age level. As you can imagine, my husband and I were thrilled beyond belief.

In July, 2001, at age six years and eight months, Mike no longer met the full criteria for autism spectrum disorder (ASD). His receptive language, cognition, and fine and gross motor skills were at age level. Hooray! Hooray! Hooray! However, he is still two years behind in expressive language, and on rare occasions he still likes to "stim."

Mike now has *severe* attention deficit disorder. He has no problem attending when he is interested in something, but non-interesting things cannot hold his attention. He reads at grade level, and believe it or not, is a math whiz. He participates in limited conversations, plays with other children sometimes, and likes to ride bikes and scooters. He has a great deal of trouble paying attention in a classroom setting, and a resource teacher offers him extra assistance with reading and language. It is very difficult for him to focus and stay on task.

Initially, Dr. Cave and I thought Mike was the only one with such a high mercury level. But at around the same time, Sallie Bernard, Lyn Redwood, and others started to argue, quite convincingly, that mercury is likely to be a major contributing factor to autism. At that point, Dr. Cave and I realized that Mike was only one of many, many, many children.

Since February 2000, I have been working with Dr. Cave. Our main focus is to treat those with ASD who have laboratory evidence of mercury toxicity. Basically, we follow the DAN! Protocol. We first work on cleaning up the gut and figuring out what nutritional supplements these patients need. After this is done, they receive DMSA alone until the mercury is flushed out of their bodies; then they receive DMSA with lipoic acid to remove the mercury from their brains.

We are also collecting data in order to learn as much as we can about the effectiveness of the DAN! Protocol. We are finding that younger children respond much faster than older children, and younger children do much better in the long run than older children and adults. In other words, the earlier the mercury is removed from their bodies and brains, the better their prognosis. Furthermore, those who were normal at birth and later regressed into autism do much better than those who were different from birth.



In 2002, I conducted a study that provides insight into the mercury problem in autism. With help from Drs. Bernard Rimland and Steve Edelson from the Autism Research Institute, I was able to obtain first-cut baby hair from normal children from around the country. I compared the mercury levels in these samples to the mercury levels in children with ASD. The findings were very consistent, and almost unbelievable. The baby hair from normal children contained a low-level amount of mercury, whereas the baby hair from autistic children contained almost no mercury at all. According to Dr. Boyd Haley of the University of Kentucky, this provides clear evidence that many autistic children cannot excrete mercury from their bodies. An excellent example would be my son, Mike, whose first hair analysis indicated no mercury. Once he began receiving DMSA, the mercury poured out of him.

I also found that mothers of autistic children were more likely than other mothers to have numerous mercury amalgams, and that they were more likely to have received RhoGAM, which once contained mercury, during their pregnancies. (RhoGAM is given to Rh-negative pregnant women.) Fortunately, according to the 2002 edition of the *Physician's Desk Reference*, RhoGAM and all other Rho D immunoglobulins no longer contain mercury.

Mike is not unique among autistic children. In fact, I have often achieved better results with my other patients than I have with my own son. The younger the child when treatment begins, the better the chance of improvement or even complete recovery.

*Update for Second Edition (December 2005):*

Mike and his family are well, but have asked to be excused from providing an update as their lives have been in upheaval as a result of Hurricane Katrina.

## — Chapter 17 —
# When Lightning Strikes Twice
By Nancy Jelen

*Nancy Jelen and her husband live near Philadelphia, Pennsylvania, with their three children, Michael, Betsy, and Jerry. Betsy, born in 1987, and Jerry, born in 1994, are autistic. This story was written in October 2002.*

This is the story of our family's journey as we face the challenge of autism, which has stricken two of our three children.



As my husband, my 17-month old son, and I excitedly awaited the arrival of our second child, we were unaware of the road that lay ahead of us. We had it all: a beautiful family, a happy marriage, and a successful business. Life couldn't have been better.

It's a girl! Elizabeth Lauren, born March 28, 1987, six pounds, two ounces, a beautiful baby girl, with big bright eyes and perfect little features. The nurses whisked her away, returning shortly to inform us that she was having some difficulty breathing, but not to worry, she would be OK.

The doctors told us that because she arrived three weeks early, her lungs were not fully developed (this was quite common, we were told). After she spent eleven days in pediatric intensive care, we finally got to bring our baby girl home. Her big brother was thrilled, calling his sister by name, "Alittlebit" (Elizabeth). We decided to call her Betsy. We quickly forgot the rough start our daughter had as we enjoyed each milestone she made, and life continued to be picture perfect.

Her first birthday. I still relive it in my mind. She was dressed in her party dress, talking, walking, and thoroughly enjoying all the attention and presents. Her favorite gift was an old-fashioned wicker baby stroller given to her by her doting grandparents; she would push it and her baby all over the house.

When she was 15 months old we moved into a larger house. At that time, we started having some concerns. At first we thought Betsy had difficulty hearing. She no longer came when we called her by name, and her vocabulary of 20 words or more began to fade into silence. She developed severe diaper rash after receiving her series of immunizations, but it was the change in her behavior that worried us. We watched helplessly as our daughter slipped into her own world.

What was happening? Where did this babbling, happy little girl go? These questions were answered with even more questions.

So our quest for answers began. First we went to the pediatrician, and then to the audiologist to see if Betsy could hear. Her hearing was found to be grossly intact, so the doctor sent her for a brainstem test to see if all levels of her hearing were functioning. Her hearing was fine. So off we went to see more specialists: a neurologist, a psychologist, and a pediatric developmental specialist who made up a team at Children's Seashore House. After two days of evaluations, this team of specialists came up with a diagnosis: pervasive developmental disorder, or PDD/autism.

I sat there in disbelief. The words didn't seem to fit—they couldn't possibly be talking about my little girl.



Although the team of professionals was able to diagnose our daughter, they had no answers to our many questions as to what the future would hold for her. The team looked at us with pity in their eyes, and their only suggestion was to enroll her in early intervention. We left with no written information on autism and no other suggestions, only a piece of paper with the phone number of our county's early intervention program.

The drive home was morbidly silent. I felt like my little girl had died, and all the hopes and dreams a parent holds for a child had just been wiped out. I wasn't sure what I was dealing with, but from the look in the specialists' eyes I knew it wasn't good.

The next year was rough, an emotional roller coaster, and a blur of emotions as we tried to come to grips with this diagnosis. It was beginning to take its toll. At gatherings, family and friends stared blankly, carefully choosing words when talking to us. I felt people pulling away from us. They didn't understand what autism was, and their only reference point was a movie called "Rain Man" starring Dustin Hoffman and Tom Cruise. They didn't know what to do for us, so they faded out of our lives. We felt so alone.

I made a concerted effort to shield Betsy's older brother, Michael, as much as I could. He spent hours on outings with his grandparents. He loved all the individual attention.

Betsy's behavior problems began to escalate. She would wake up in the middle of the night and not go back to bed until the next night. Her diaper rash seemed incurable, and even though we had taken her to the pediatrician and two dermatologists, none of them diagnosed the yeast infection that was causing it. It was cleared up later with nystatin. She began to bite, pull hair, hit, scratch, and bang her head. I would figure out later that this was out of frustration at not being able to talk.

An intensive program of daily speech therapy, developmental therapy, behavior therapy, and early intervention school was beginning to prove helpful. In addition, we continued our quest for answers to our many questions. We went all over the country seeing other so-called specialists. Their answers always were the same: "Your daughter has autism and there is no cure."

In the meantime, my research was beginning to pay off. A name kept resurfacing: Dr. Bernard Rimland from San Diego, California. He was the founder of the Autism Society of America, father of an autistic son, a Ph.D. in experimental psychology, a published author on the subject of autism, founder and director of the Autism Research Institution (ARI), founded in 1967, and editor and publisher of the *Autism Research Review International* newsletter.



We were fortunate that my husband had a business conference in La Jolla, only a 30-minute drive from the address I had for Dr. Rimland. So we packed up the family and made the trip across the country, still trying to find answers to our many questions.

When we arrived, I put Betsy in the rental car and drove to Dr. Rimland's address, not knowing what I would find, but determined to make a connection with Dr. Rimland and gain some direction.

The address proved to be a modest storefront. We walked in and found one secretary and boxes of papers everywhere. I asked if Dr. Rimland was around and could I possibly talk to him. I was surprised and thrilled to find him there and willing to speak with me. An older gentleman with a slightly gray beard emerged from a back room. My daughter recognized him as "Santa Claus," and in a way he was.

A humble man full of compassion and years of knowledge, he spoke with me for 30 minutes, and for the first time I felt hope and optimism.

I learned more in those 30 minutes than I had in the previous six months. I pored over the countless research articles he gave me to read about the effectiveness of vitamins, DMG, and other therapies that parents and researchers had found helpful for autistic children. He told me about Dr. Stephen Edelson from Oregon who was looking for autistic children to participate in a study to see if auditory integration training (AIT) was helpful for these children.

We returned home with a new sense of determination and a wealth of knowledge. The next four years were spent trying vitamins B6 and magnesium, DMG, AIT, music therapy, and dance. Each year, Betsy made steady progress; her behaviors were under control, and she was sleeping through the night. We were a family again, enjoying things that families do: going to restaurants and movies, being invited to new friends' houses. As Betsy got better, people seemed to be more accepting of her. She had good language skills but was still lacking in conversation skills and socialization.

We always had wanted three children, and thought that having another sibling would be beneficial for both Michael and Betsy.

October 17, 1994: it's a boy! Jerald Anthony. We were thrilled. He looked perfect. Everyone was excited. Michael loved having a little brother. And Betsy loved playing mother to her little brother. I carefully watched for each milestone, and I felt relief when each one was met.

In Jerry's second year, life would take another dark turn. My father, who had been so supportive of our family, was diagnosed with terminal cancer. We spent that year visiting with Poppy as much as possible. After my father's death, I took Jerry to the pediatrician to catch up on his shots. That day they gave him five immunizations. There is heated debate over immunizations and the possibility that they could be related to autism. My personal opinion is that there is a connection involving the immune system. I will leave it in the hands of the research scientists. What I do know is that within two months Jerry had slipped away, too. All of his eye contact and speech vanished. I didn't need a specialist to tell me what it was. I knew.



We couldn't believe that this could happen to us again. After all, the first time had been a fluke, or so we thought. Everything we read told us that autism usually strikes the first male and Michael was fine. And it affects boys more often than girls. Betsy was a girl. So how could this be? We didn't waste any time getting the diagnosis. I can't say that the medical specialists had advanced much since the last time we had seen them eight years earlier. But they did have more information the second time. And now they seemed interested in us because we had two autistic children. They wanted us to participate in a genetics study. They did the workup but didn't find anything.

The year was 1996, and autism was making headline news. It seemed to be reaching epidemic proportions. There were so many books, new treatments, new research, breakthroughs, and stories of recovery.

After the initial shock of a second diagnosis, we had no choice but to move forward. We had done this once before so it didn't seem so hard the second time around. I had made good contacts and had stayed up-to-date on the latest autism developments. We engulfed ourselves once again in an intensive program for Jerry. A strict 40-hour-a-week ABA program brought his language and eye contact back quickly. Enrollment in an early intervention program was also helpful for social skills. AIT helped with language development and focus. My experience with AIT has been positive; however, I feel that the effects wear off somewhere at the year-and-a-half mark. And so my children have undergone it several times with good results. Vitamins and a modified diet were also helpful. Jerry had a lot of sensory issues, and a good daily sensory integration program was a must.

We had many treatment options, and we tried many of them—some that caused only slight improvement, others that caused more significant improvement. We tried the secretin injections with good results. However, I felt the results were short-lived and the treatment was very expensive. When secretin became unavailable in the United States, we looked to Japan where they were manufacturing a similar product (Secrepan) at one-third of the cost. I give my children daily doses of Secrepan in their morning water. I found this to be the most beneficial approach because secretin is a hormone found in small amounts, and small daily doses seemed to keep just the right level in their system. Their sleep patterns and eating habits improved with the secretin. I am anxiously awaiting FDA approval of secretin for autism here in the U.S.



I would be remiss if I did not mention the school system. Some programs are good and some are bad. Know your rights and be (or get) an advocate. You are the only voice for your child. You know your child the best. Fight for a program and education that is right for your child.

As I write this story, Betsy and Jerry continue their journey to recovery. It has taken a village and then some to accomplish this much. It is an emotionally, financially, and physically exhausting journey. But the rewards are immeasurable. There is so much I didn't say. There are still no answers to some of my questions. We still don't know what causes autism or the true treatment for it. But so many organizations have now joined our fight to find the answers, including Defeat Autism Now! (DAN!), Cure Autism Now (CAN), and others. Millions of dollars are being spent on research. With the prompting of parents, doctors and specialists are educating themselves about new and nontraditional ways to treat autism. The Internet has hundreds of sites with information about autism. We have come a long way from the "refrigerator mother" theory.

If you are just embarking on your journey through the world of autism, this is what I have learned from this experience: it has taught me that you must have patience and perseverance, never give up, fight for what you believe, try to get as much help as you can, believe only half of what you read, stay as active in the community as you can (or at least make a good connection with an autism support group—a lot of these parents have fought the fight and won the battle), and try to nourish yourself whenever possible. You are the best advocate for your child.

So take care of yourself.

To the parents who went before and blazed a trail, I cannot thank you enough. Your courage and determination were an inspiration to me. The same is true of my husband, my mother, and my father, who didn't always know what to do but just by being there made all the difference. To my son Michael, who has endured more than a child should have to, we are proud of your many accomplishments and your compassion and help with your siblings; they are blessed to have such a loving brother. To our family and friends, your understanding is greatly appreciated. To the therapeutic support staff who helped our children, we couldn't have done it without you. To the countless scientists and researchers who are looking for a better tomorrow for our children, thank you for your tireless efforts. To Dr. Stephen Edelson, thank you for being more than a resource; your friendship has made a world of difference for our children and our family. And last, but certainly not least, our thanks to Dr. Bernard Rimland, for over 40 years of dedication to the field of autism and for giving mothers and families the courage and the knowledge to move forward.



I feel blessed to have had so many wonderful people touch our lives. I may not feel like I have it all, and I may not have the same dreams I had when I was first married, but Jerry and Betsy continue to improve, and we have new dreams, and life is good.

*Update (February 2003):*

My kids are doing well. We haven't experienced any miracles or cures, but Betsy and Jerry both continue to progress in positive steps.

*Update for Second Edition (October 2005):*

Betsy is doing great. She graduated from high school in June 2005 and is currently working part-time as a secretary in an accounting department. She has her own office equipped with her own computer, telephone line, and desk. She also continues her studies and job training on a part-time basis. Her social life is full of family functions, singing and dancing in youth theater, and continuing dance and art classes.

Jerry is now in fifth grade and is mainstreamed 30% of the time. His behaviors and focus have improved dramatically with a dairy- and wheat-free diet as well as B12 shots. He enjoys bowling, soccer, basketball, baseball, swimming, and watching and playing with his trains.

Each and every year has brought positive changes and improvements beyond my wildest dreams from the original diagnosis of autism. Keep the faith. Recovery IS possible.

## — Chapter 18 —
# Coming to Terms with Autism
By Bryan Jepson, M.D.

*Dr. Jepson is the Medical Director of the nonprofit Children's Biomedical Center of Utah in the town of Sandy, where he lives with his wife, Laurie, and their son, Aaron (born in March 1998). This story was written in May 2002.*



I have always considered myself a traditional allopathic physician. And like most traditional allopathic physicians, I have also been very skeptical about the "other side," meaning alternative medicine practitioners. I am much more knowledgeable about treating illness than preventing it, much better at masking symptoms than correcting the cause. Couple that with the fact that my area of specialty is in emergency medicine, where my job is to treat acute disease and leave the chronic conditions for others to worry about.

There is definite comfort in specialization. The human body is so complex and medical research so vast that it would be impossible for one person to be an expert in every aspect of it. Allopathic physicians in particular tend to separate out organ systems and focus on them individually, referring to other "specialists" when their patients' symptoms don't entirely fit within their fairly narrow realm of understanding.

Nutrition is one of those areas in which very few of us are adequately trained. I recall spending less than two weeks of medical school focused on nutrition. We spend more time memorizing biochemical pathways than on learning how they apply to normal and impaired body functioning, and what we do learn is soon relegated to the hidden corridors of our brains as soon as the exams are completed. And yet, we find it easy to discount the importance of nutrition in the treatment of illness.

Doctors, in general, are not very good at admitting ignorance, and tend to discount theories without spending much time looking into them. And yet, we are influenced much more than we like to admit by the aggressive marketing tactics of pharmaceutical companies.

I have developed through my years of medical training a healthy skepticism of the medical literature. I spent a lot of time in residency learning evidence-based medicine, i.e., practicing according to the best available evidence rather than relying on established medical dogma. Very often, the treatment methods that have been passed down through the medical community and accepted as truth or standard of care are later disproved or modified as further research is done. Often, these dogmas are based on nothing more than the opinions of a few individuals. Unfortunately, much of the time the evidence doesn't exist or is incomplete, leaving practitioners to rely on their best judgment based on sound biological principles. Through the critical study of the literature, I also learned that much if not most of it is biased on several fronts, and that often the conclusions do not match the data. Unfortunately, most physicians do not regularly take the time to read the methodology of the studies, and thus they often change their practice based on biased conclusions or incomplete evidence. Many physicians simply rely on the standard practice of those around them and then follow the crowd as new medications or interventions are introduced, without even looking at the literature.



So, it is with this background that I entered this journey into the field of autism. My second son, Aaron, was diagnosed with autism shortly before his third birthday. He had an uncomplicated gestation and birth and seemed to be developing normally for the first year and a half of life. He was an engaged, happy, interactive baby, and we had no reason to suspect that anything was wrong.

Sometime in Aaron's second year, however, we noticed that he didn't seem to be hearing us when we walked into the room. He would never acknowledge me when I came home from work. He would not want us to play with him or read him a book. Our first thought was that maybe he had a hearing problem. But we knew that he wasn't deaf. He could recite the ABC's; in fact, he did this repeatedly. We were thrilled that he was so smart. He would also frequently repeat lines from his favorite movie, "Toy Story." My wife, Laurie, felt at this stage that there was something wrong. I discounted this as just his "independent personality."

When Laurie talked to our pediatrician about her concern that Aaron wasn't developing language at the same rate as his peers or our older son, she was told that some boys don't start talking until much later and not to worry about it. At that stage, the word "autism" had never crossed my mind. What I knew about autism was probably not much more than anyone else who had watched the movie "Rain Man." I had treated some teenagers with severe autism in the ER before, and they were severely disabled, minimally verbal individuals who shrieked whenever they were touched. My son, certainly, was not like that. He loved to be held and was a happy child who was usually very content and seemed to do okay with breaks in his routine.

I agreed with his doctor that we should just watch him, and I fully expected him to just "grow out of it."

By the time Aaron was 2½, though, it was clear that he was not just going to get better. In fact, he was getting worse. He would now play only with "Toy Story" toys or ABC letters; he would spin in circles in the middle of the floor; he would giggle and shriek. He wouldn't call us by name and would never look us in the eye. Although he knew some words, he never used language to communicate. Shortly before this, our nephew was diagnosed with Asperger syndrome. So, we began looking on the Internet where we read stories of other children with autism, and realized that they were describing our little boy.

We went to the school system, tested Aaron's hearing, saw a speech pathologist and were sent to a child psychologist. Before we walked into the psychologist's office, we knew that our child was autistic. We were not prepared, however, for what he was about to tell us. We were told that our son met 10 of the 12 DSM-IV criteria for autism and that he carried a poor prognosis for any functional recovery. The psychologist told us that through their educational program, Aaron might improve to the point of minimal social functionality but that we should mentally prepare ourselves for the time when he might need to be institutionalized. He also told us that we would hear about a lot of "experimental" interventions that many people were trying, but not to waste our time and money because none of them had been proven. Needless to say, we left his office in a state of shock and hopelessness. How could this possibly be the future for our cute, happy little boy?



Laurie and I dealt with this news in very different ways. I was more inclined to just accept this as one of life's challenges and learn how to cope with it. After all, I was a doctor and had never heard anything different about effective methods of treating autism than what that psychologist had suggested. I knew that as long as we were physically able to care for him Aaron would live with us, in our home. We would love him and cherish the opportunity to learn from him, and we hoped that he would be able to reciprocate some of that love.

Laurie, on the other hand, was not willing to accept this bleak prognosis. She immersed herself in the Internet, searching for anything related to autism. She learned about the gluten-free, casein-free diet, and started Aaron on it in remarkable time. She learned about vitamin supplementation, DMG, antifungals, and probiotics. This all sounded to me like a good way for vitamin makers to capitalize on another "untreatable" illness. I basically stayed uninvolved and uninterested in these initial interventions because I didn't believe they could treat my son's developmental disorder. In spite of my skepticism, however, I felt that the only thing these interventions were harming was my pocketbook, and that was a small price to pay for Laurie's need to "do something."

But when she brought to my attention the possible link to immunizations, I could no longer be impartial. After all, this was striking at one of the few areas of preventive medicine about which allopathic physicians are passionate. Immunizations are good! They eliminate life-threatening disease! I have seen firsthand the success that immunizations have had at turning fairly common illnesses into rare cases. Autism, I argued, is just one more of those coincidental childhood illnesses that the crazy anti-government people are using opportunistically as an excuse to push their agenda. But I looked at the research, largely to prove to my wife that it was unfounded. The further I looked, the more interested I became. And before long, I realized that in fact, concerns about vaccines weren't based on whims of angry activists or the wallets of vitamin manufacturers, but on real science with a foundation of strong biological plausibility, and that these concerns were being raised by knowledgeable and motivated physicians, scientists, and parents of autistic children who weren't afraid to question dogma. I was further convinced after attending a DAN! Conference and hearing the presentations and stories of many other people like ourselves who are looking for answers.



It was shortly thereafter that I decided that I could not be a silent participant but had to educate people about biological interventions for autism and offer them to people in my area. Prior to that, the parents we had met whose children were undergoing biomedical intervention were flying halfway across the country to be treated by a physician knowledgeable in these protocols. We established a nonprofit clinic named the Children's Biomedical Center of Utah, which opened officially in March 2002. Our mission is threefold: to provide up-to-date medical intervention to people on the autism spectrum, to educate the public and medical community about the issues surrounding this disorder, and to prevent future cases by offering vaccines on an alternative schedule that incorporates the philosophies of the DAN! movement. In the short time that I have been treating people with autism, I have been rewarded—rewarded with stories of children getting better and with looks on the faces of parents who have a renewal of hope for their children.

*Update (February 2003):*

When I first wrote this story, I had just recently opened my clinic. Over the last year, I have treated over 150 autistic children. I have witnessed remarkable improvements in many of these children using biomedical interventions. Unfortunately, there remains a wide range of responses between individuals. The more I learn about autism, the more I realize how complex a disorder it is and how far we have to go before we understand it all. It is like a thousand-piece puzzle and, although we are adding pieces more rapidly now than ever before, we still don't have the whole picture. It has been great to see the growing momentum for environmental research in spite of forces from the "other side." I am confident that with heightened awareness and sufficient funding, the progress in understanding this disorder will continue rapidly.



My son Aaron is doing well. He is certainly not cured and the battle is a daily one, but his progress is steady and we have every reason to believe that it will continue.

*Update for Second Edition (October 2005):*

It has now been over four years since I began treating autistic children. I have had many success stories of children improving dramatically and some dropping their diagnosis. There have been others who haven't made much progress. My son Aaron is somewhere in between. His progress has been much slower than we would have hoped for, but he is making gains.

We continue to try new things and hope that someday soon we will be able to find the key to unlock Aaron's potential and that of the other kids who are struggling. This quest has led me to join Thoughtful House Center for Children in Austin, Texas, a new treatment and clinical research center that opened in the fall of 2005. Our mission is to simultaneously research and treat children with autism spectrum disorders and related conditions, integrating biomedical, gastrointestinal, and behavioral treatment modalities. Through publication of our research in high-quality medical journals, we intend to bring the treatment of autism to mainstream medicine. Our goal is that autism will soon be accepted as a true medical condition and its treatment widely available and covered by medical insurance. For more information, visit www.ThoughtfulHouse.org.

## — Chapter 19 —
# Michael... "That's Mike, Ed"
By Edgar Kitt

*Most of the stories in this book are written by parents of autistic children or by doctors who treat autistic patients, but Edgar Kitt's story offers a different view of the strides that autistic children can make: the view as seen through the eyes of a teacher. Edgar and his wife, Mila, received the 1999 Wendy F. Miller ASA Recognition Award for "Professional of the Year." The subject of his story, Mike, was born in December 1977. Mr. Kitt began writing this story in 2000 after he retired from work.*



When I would call Michael by his name, Michael, he would immediately respond by saying, "That's Mike, Ed."

During 37 years in education, as a teacher and principal, I have met many children. One who stands out from the others is Michael. I was privileged to witness a complete reversal of Michael's inappropriate, abusive behavior, a transformation that I feel was accomplished by the implementation of megadoses of vitamins as suggested by Dr. Bernard Rimland.

When I first met Michael, he was aggressive toward others and self-injurious. He would hit anyone who entered his personal space, and sometimes he would hit someone outside his personal space. He hit himself, other people, and objects.

Megadoses of vitamins helped bring Michael's aggressive, non-compliant behavior under control. He is now very pleasant, compliant, and able to perform tasks. He also realizes that the vitamins help him. If his father forgets to put the vitamins out for him to take at mealtime, Michael will search for the vitamin containers and then take them himself.

The following information is provided as a guide to show how, over the years, Michael had a problem with inappropriate behavior and how, after being introduced to a vitamin regimen, he was able to change his behavior. This information includes statements by teachers and psychologists that were in Michael's confidential folder. I received permission from his father to share and publish this information.

One reason for sharing Michael's story is that I feel that the use of megadoses of vitamins would be beneficial not only to the autistic population but also to other children who have difficulty with behavior. Toward the end of the article is a section entitled "Megadoses of Vitamins" that describes the dosage of vitamins Michael has been taking. In addition, I have provided vitamin and dosage information for another autistic child who was also a student in my class.

The first knowledge I had of Michael was when I heard that he struck a teacher at school in 1987. My wife was that teacher. She related incidents of Michael striking out at her and other individuals when he didn't want to perform a task, when someone invaded his personal space, or when he became frustrated. She learned from discussions with his other teachers that he appeared to always be in a "bad" mood. There was little or no smiling or pleasant attitude at school.



Michael's parents separated in early 1992, and Michael lived with his mother. One day, during that summer, Michael became angry and aggressive and began striking his mother. (When he was upset and lost control, he would aggress against anyone nearby.) The police came to the apartment and removed Michael in handcuffs and transported him to a state residential facility for the handicapped. He was placed in a special ward because of his behavior.

During one period of inattentive supervision, at approximately 11:00 p.m., Michael left the grounds of the state facility. He proceeded in the general direction of his father's condominium. Michael had no comprehension of safety when crossing streets. He was able to cross one heavily traveled street safely; but when starting to cross another street, he stepped into the path of an oncoming vehicle. He was struck on the left side, and the impact shattered his left femur. He was transported to a local hospital, and he was unable to communicate who he was or who his parents were. It took an extended period of time for the hospital to determine his identity in order to treat him. During his hospitalization his behavior was so bizarre that he was given heavy medication to reduce his aggression. He would strike the nursing staff with his fists so severely that restraints had to be placed on his arms. He required 24-hour monitoring at bedside due to his severe aggressive behavior.

Michael entered my classroom in October of 1992. He was heavily sedated and wheelchair-bound with his broken leg. He appeared in an almost catatonic state with very limited interaction. The state technician who brought Michael to the classroom felt that he was a nice boy and was very happy. While she was talking to me, Michael swung his arm at her but missed because she was out of his reach. This was my introduction to Michael.

The first couple of weeks Michael attended school on a half-day schedule because of his broken leg. When first placed at a desk, Michael started making loud "uh-uhing" sounds and pushed himself away from the desk. When we attempted to have him remain at his desk he would strike out—hitting me a couple of times. He made no intelligible comments. Communication was nil.

Michael had been receiving Haldol at differing levels. He was receiving 16 mg when he first entered the classroom. His father started to reduce the amount of Haldol, and in December of 1995, his father stopped giving Michael any drugs.

In January 1996, Michael had a severe altercation with his father in which his father actually lost a front tooth. He brought Michael to school the next day and told me what had occurred. He said that after the altercation was over Michael cried and hugged him. His father asked me what he should do. He had stopped giving Michael Haldol, and he felt he saw vast improvements, as did I. He didn't want to put him back on Haldol again, but when he contacted the psychiatrist at the state agency, the first reply was that Michael most certainly needed to be given psychotropic medication to bring him under control. I responded that there was a treatment regimen recommended by Dr. Bernard Rimland using megadoses of vitamins. I told him that it would not hurt to call Dr. Rimland and explore this possibility since vitamins are not harmful to the body and are definitely beneficial to health.



Michael's father started him on megadoses of vitamins early in 1996. Improvement in Michael's behavior was not immediately apparent because the changes occurred slowly. His behaviors improved so much over the next couple of months that we had forgotten how aggressive he had been during the past years. When he returned to school in the fall, he had become a pleasant individual in the classroom. Michael became very easy to work with and had a positive nature.

As noted in a report from January 1997, Michael's aggressiveness had not completely disappeared. However, he had quit hitting with the exception of a few isolated incidents in which another individual "pushed his buttons."

According to the report, "Michael's behavior has improved so dramatically it is difficult to describe. He has demonstrated positive and appropriate interactions. The negative responses, which had previously been 90% of his attitude and interaction, have improved; and he is well-liked by almost all staff and students. In the past he would say, 'No hello' to certain students; he now stops, shakes hands, and usually makes a very appropriate comment."

Michael's behavior improved so much that he was offered an opportunity to participate in a structured vocationally oriented program. Two years previously, my feeling had been that Michael would have *extreme* difficulty finding success outside a sheltered environment that would be able to accept and deal with his aggressive behavior. Now we were looking at, talking about, and developing a vocational program outside the school environment.

About a year later, in February 1998, a school report stated that Michael's behavior had not changed over the past year. He continued making positive interactions and accepting assigned tasks. However, there were still isolated incidents of "banging" into others. Usually the precursor to the behavior involved someone touching or saying something to Michael. Michael was able to change his behavior immediately if he was given a sharp stare or an appropriate admonishment for his act. He no longer became 'unglued' when verbally corrected.



During the summer of 1998 Michael had a vocational placement at a Goodwill store. I monitored his behavior on a weekly basis by meeting with his supervisor. His behavior was outstanding. One day Michael was at the window of the store watching a thunder and lightning storm. The supervisor told his father that Michael said, "Isn't the rain beautiful? That's God watering the grass." The father and I were amazed with the response because, just a couple of years before, he would have been extremely upset and aggressive during such weather. He would have gone somewhere to avoid seeing the rain and lightning, made bizarre noises, and hit himself. This pattern of behavior has disappeared. And now, on occasion, he will go out and stand in the rain.

Michael was well accepted at the Goodwill store and was liked by everyone. He was also very social. He would greet everyone who entered the store. His attitude and behavior were very positive but his evaluation showed he did not make sufficient progress by increasing his production. He was therefore released from the training position and returned to school in the fall of 1998.

In a 1999 report, I wrote: "Mike has developed a very good behavior. He is pleasant and eager to work. He makes a super impression on others with his social abilities. Mike continues the positive interaction that has been present the past couple of years. He accepts direction and does his tasks in a positive manner. He has had only two or three instances that would be considered aggressive during the past year. These have been very isolated and minor. Michael is able to accept redirection and admonishment without becoming upset."

With respect to his social communication skills, I wrote: "Mike responds appropriately to questions the majority of time. He continues greeting anyone and will make every attempt to learn the names of those he doesn't know. Mike has the social profile of an autistic person. He continues to improve his pleasant and positive manner. Mike is on vocational placement at a nursing home and is well accepted there. He spent the past summer at a Goodwill store and worked very well."

Michael finished his vocational placement at a nursing home and was transitioned to a placement at a Red Lobster restaurant. His job was wrapping silverware in napkins. The placement at the Red Lobster was positive and continued for over a year. His work was satisfactory but he lacked the skills to become more proficient in other duties. Consequently, his placement was discontinued because he was unable to expand his skill level areas.



I retired from teaching in June of 1999. Michael quit attending school around the same time. He was 22 years old, and he was no longer eligible for public school services. I have remained in contact with Michael and his father, checking on his condition about every four months. Michael stays home by himself, spending much of his time watching TV. His behavior remains appropriate. His father hopes to find a facility that will take him during the day rather than have him remain relatively inactive at home. His weight has also increased, most likely due to his inactivity.

*Update (February 2003):*

I recently visited Michael and his father. Michael's behavior has leveled off and has remained the same for the past couple of years. He is pleasant and remains in "his own world." There are instances that can upset him, the same as in everyone's life. His routine can be changed and he is able to handle the change. For example, if Michael is looking forward to something on the weekend and the event is canceled or changed, he accepts it without becoming upset. When he becomes upset, he does not react in an aggressive manner as he did prior to the megadoses of vitamins. There have been instances when the supply of vitamins was low at the end of a month, and the dosage was altered. In these instances, his father noticed a definite change in Michael's behavior; that is, Michael became more agitated and engaged in chest hitting, leg slapping, and vocal noises.

His father also told me that Michael does not sleep very much at night.

The most he will sleep is five to six hours. Michael is by himself for eight hours a day while his father works. He drinks one to two gallons of water a day. He loves sweets and soda but his father does not give him any except on special occasions. Michael is allowed to have one diet soda in the evening.

Michael's father spoke at one of our local Autism Society of America (ASA) meetings. He described the changes in Michael's behavior and attitude. He was asked many questions and the answer that lost the interest of almost all of the audience pertained to the *amount and cost* of the vitamin regimen, which ranges from $300 to $400 a month. There was one exception to those who lost interest: the family of another student became interested because their son also engaged in self-injury. They started with DMG, and they definitely felt that it was beneficial in controlling his behavior. They have been giving him DMG for over 3½ years. I contacted the parents recently. Their son still engages in some bizarre behavior but not to the extent that he did three years ago. They have expanded his regimen to include the following:



| | | |
|---|---|---|
| Vitamin C, 500 mg each | 1 tablet, 2x day | Morning and night |
| Fish oil, 1000 mg each | 1 tablet, 2x day | Morning and night |
| Multivitamin | 1 tablet, 1x day | Morning |
| DMG, 100 mg each | 3 tablets, 3x day | Morning, noon, night |
| Other multivitamin | 1 tablet, 1x day | Morning |
| Regular aspirin | 1 tablet, 2x day | Morning and night |

Other parents said that they had tried the megadose procedure but that they had not observed any improvement in behavior. When asked what dosage was given they said that they gave one or two vitamins, DMG, etc., but after a week or two there was no difference in the child's behavior. I indicated that "mega" means many, the same as Michael was taking.

**Megadoses of Vitamins**

Michael has taken several different vitamins and nutrients over the years. I have listed the vitamins and nutrients, along with their amounts, below.

Super Nu-Thera: Casein- and Gluten-Free (Kirkman) - tablets
DMG: 125 mg - tablets
Folic Acid: 800 mcg - tablets

Fatty Acid: (DHA Ultimate Omega) - tablets
Kavatrol: tablets

Michael's initial dosage was given for four weeks. This was to see if there would be a change in behavior. If there was no change, his father increased the dosage for another four-week period. (Michael's weight was approximately 192 pounds.)

*March/April 1996*

| | |
|---|---|
| Super Nu-Thera | 4 each meal – 3 times per day |
| DMG | 2 each meal – 3 times per day |
| Folic Acid | 2 each meal – 3 times per day |

*June 1996*

| | |
|---|---|
| Super Nu-Thera | 4 each meal – 3 times per day |
| DMG | 4 each meal – 3 times per day |
| Folic Acid | 4 each meal – 3 times per day |

*July 1996*

| | |
|---|---|
| Super Nu-Thera | 6 each meal – 3 times per day |
| DMG | 6 each meal – 3 times per day |
| Folic Acid | 6 each meal – 3 times per day |

*August 1996*

| | |
|---|---|
| Super Nu-Thera | 8 each meal – 3 times per day |
| DMG | 8 each meal – 3 times per day |
| Folic Acid | 8 each meal – 3 times per day |

Michael remained on the dosage started in August 1996 until September 2002. About two years ago, fatty acid (DHA Ultimate Omega) was added at the suggestion of Dr. Rimland, along with Kavatrol to calm Michael for sleep.

Michael is now taking the following dosage with excellent results.

*September 2002*

| | |
|---|---|
| Super Nu-Thera | 9 each meal – 2 times per day (mealtime) |
| DMG, 250 mg each | 3 each meal – 2 times per day (mealtime) |
| Folic Acid | 15 ea. meal – 2 times per day (mealtime) |
| Fatty Acid | 3 each meal – 2 times per day (mealtime) |
| Kavatrol | 1 in evening and 1 before bed |

*Update for Second Edition (November 2005):*

This November 2005 update on Michael is very similar to the February 2003 update in the first printing of *Treating Autism.*

Mike is Mike. The most prominent observation of Mike's life is that a positive atmosphere persists, rather than a negative one.

Negative occurrences are noted when Mike's father runs low on certain vitamins and needs to cut the dosage for a couple of days. Mike's father said, "It's just like Bernie (Dr. Bernard Rimland) said, 'mega means large.'"

The vitamin regimen was started in March of 1996 and increased through September 1996 to the amount of vitamins Michael now takes, which is listed in the original chapter as the dosage taken in September 2002. The cost remains at $300 to $400 per month.



Mike's mother feels that his comprehension has increased and his social attitude is much more appropriate.

Mike lives with his father and remains at home, by himself, all day while his father works. On days his father is off, Mike is very considerate and does not bother him. Mike answers the telephone appropriately, although his responses to many questions are inappropriate. Mike continues to be very orderly in the house by keeping "everything in its place." He continues to sleep about five to six hours per night. He won't leave home by himself and is very careful and cautious. Mike also performs his work duties at home, which include taking out the garbage, washing the dishes, and vacuuming. He enjoys attending the local minor-league baseball games. Mike's father will be visiting the sheltered workshop to seek assistance for employment or placement during the day.

Mike's father recalls the terrible episodes that occurred during the days when Mike was on psychotropic drugs. It has been 14 years since Mike started megadoses of vitamins. For those 14 years Mike has been a pleasant, though still autistic, person. His father is very grateful to Dr. Bernard Rimland for his help in proposing megadoses of vitamins for—MICHAEL "That's Mike, Ed."

# — Chapter 20 —
# Max's Story: A Homeopathic Cure of Autism

By Amy Lansky, Ph.D.

*Amy Lansky, her husband, Steve, and their children, Izaak and Max (born in July 1991), live south of San Francisco, California. Amy's book,* Impossible Cure: The Promise of Homeopathy, *details Max's recovery from autism.*

Excerpted by permission of the author from
*Impossible Cure: The Promise of Homeopathy,* R.L.Ranch Press, 2003
For more information, visit: www.ImpossibleCure.com



Homeopathy is a system of medicine developed by German physician Samuel Hahnemann, M.D. in the early 1800s. Because of its successes, it quickly spread to become one of the four most widespread forms of medical treatment in the world. The homeopathic system is based on a simple law of therapeutics that determines which remedy will be curative for an individual: the Law of Similars. This law states that if a particular substance can cause a set of mental, emotional, and physical symptoms in a healthy person, then it can also cure a sick person who is experiencing those same symptoms; in other words, "likes cure likes." That is precisely what the word homeopathy means—similar (homeo) suffering (pathy).

* * * * *

One of my first teachers of homeopathy told me that a person's views about homeopathy's curative powers tend to be colored by their first experience with it. For some, it is a cure of intransigent warts that suddenly dry up and drop off. For others, a case of shingles, allergies, migraine, or chronic fatigue yields and fades away, when years of other kinds of treatment had no effect. Then there are the cases that truly defy explanation: expulsion of a tumor; a man awakening from a coma minutes after taking a remedy; the discharge of mercury in the menstrual blood of a dental hygienist, after years of accumulation in her system. All of these have occurred with the correct homeopathic prescription.

The power of the homeopathic remedy has repeatedly had its impact on every member of my family and on many of my friends. I have seen tics stop overnight, a bout of cramping and diarrhea that had persisted for several days disappear in minutes, a welt from a wasp sting suddenly fade away, and my own summer allergies disappear, after years of growing increasingly more severe. But all of these pale in comparison with my first and greatest homeopathic miracle. My younger son, Max, was cured of an "incurable" condition—autism. Today, years later, I sometimes have a hard time believing it myself. We were very lucky, you see. Our homeopath found Max's *simillimum*—the perfectly matching remedy to his state—on the first try. Within a week, his therapist, my husband, and I were witnessing subtle yet noticeable changes in him.



## The Warning Signs

It all began in the spring of 1994, when Max was 2½ years old. Something wasn't right. He wasn't talking. Although he had about 10, maybe 20, words in his vocabulary, most of the time he didn't seem to understand language at all. And it was getting worse. On some level, Max seemed to be slowly drifting away.

On the bright side, Max did know all the letters of the alphabet and his numbers one to 10. He could stack blocks with amazing dexterity and could build highly intricate and perfectly symmetric structures. He even knew his way around the computer—pointing and clicking, dragging the mouse, and opening games. Max also displayed some amazingly advanced analytical skills. For instance, he could play a "Concentration"-style game, matching pairs of overturned tiles in a four-by-five grid, better than we could. And he could definitely hear. He enjoyed television and danced rhythmically to music. Indeed, for the most part, Max was a happy, though distant, toddler at home. He usually had a smile on his face and liked to play with his older brother Izaak—a precocious and mature 5½ year old.

But when we all sat around talking and laughing in the evening and on weekends, Max would prefer to be off on his own. He'd go off and watch TV, play a computer game, stack his blocks, and retreat into himself. He also wasn't as affectionate as Izaak. Although, he didn't push us away, he never reached out for affection. For a long time I thought, "Oh, he's just late to speak. He's a more self-contained, more private person than Izaak." But it was more than that.

At school, problems began to emerge. I began to sense that the teachers at his preschool were concerned. They greeted Max each morning with a kind of hesitancy. Although he had started off the school year exuberantly at age two, he had never fully settled in. Instead, he would rely on his beloved "baba"—a bottle of milk—for comfort. And though he enjoyed many of the toys in the classroom, Max never interacted with any of the other children. He was also unable to sit through story-time unless he was in a teacher's lap. He was antsy, as if there was a motor running inside him. It wasn't like classic hyperactivity—he didn't run about. He just wasn't paying attention. It was as if the story the teacher was reading was in a foreign language. Left to his own devices, Max would just wander off and play quietly with toys in the classroom that interested him. He wasn't disruptive; he just wasn't really "there." When the children were outside playing, he would wander off to some other classroom. The teachers would find him raptly staring at some animal in a cage or a toy.



I knew that one of the teachers suspected autism. She told me that Max manifested self-stimulation activities—for example, spinning in a circle—and that he didn't have good eye contact when spoken to. But I didn't want to believe it. He did have some eye contact with us at home. He didn't really spin around at home either; he was generally happy and content.

But increasingly, there were noticeable oddities. One morning while driving to school, I asked him, "Do you know where we're going now?" No response. Max just stared into space. At night, when I'd try to read a story to him, he could not sit quietly. He would fidget and squirm all over the bed. He'd stand on his head, with his feet against the wall, or run his fingers up and down things—the table, the wall. I also noticed that he had the habit of poking his finger against people's chests or butting his head against them—not to hurt them, but as a kind of contact. Over a year later, I learned that these behaviors are all characteristic of autistic children.

What to do? I began to grasp at straws. Perhaps it was attention deficit disorder (ADD)? I read all the books. Perhaps it was the teachers? That they didn't "understand" him? But deep down, I knew Max had a serious problem. And it seemed to be getting worse. He was growing more distant, more disconnected. By the end of the school year, just before Max turned three, the preschool called us in for a conference and advised us to seek medical help. One teacher confided to us, "Max will never be able to attend the private school that Izaak goes to. He will always need special education."

And so our family embarked upon a quest. I knew that we would never rest easy as long as Max had a problem like this; I knew that all of our lives would be severely affected. I felt instinctively that Max's entire future hung in the balance and that I had to do everything in my power, leaving no stone unturned, until I found the key.

My resolve was also deepened by another factor. This was one of my worst nightmares coming true. For years my mother and I had been deeply affected by my brother's struggle with severe mental illness. This past propelled me even harder to find a solution to Max's problem. I felt a call to arms, and in retrospect, it served me and my family well. I knew that there was no running away or avoiding the issue—no room for resignation. I knew that problems like this don't just go away; they cannot be ignored. I'd explore every nuance of our family dynamic, every food we ate, and examine every aspect of Max's life with a fine-toothed comb, looking for clues. This outcome for my son just didn't seem right to me. I was a mother on a mission.



## The Search—Without and Within

In the summer of 1994, when Max had just turned three, we began to take action. On the advice of a speech-therapist friend, my husband and I decided not to take him to the local child-development clinic affiliated with Stanford University that had been recommended to us. Our friend told us that they'd just label Max and create a sense of hopelessness in us. Instead, we took him to a highly respected speech and language therapist who runs a clinic in Palo Alto, Donna Dagenais. Donna was (and still is) considered to be the best language therapist in our area, with vast experience in working with children with communication and language disorders. She didn't label Max—she merely assessed him and set to work. In addition to his private therapy sessions, she also placed him in group sessions with two other children, including one who had already been formally diagnosed with PDD (mild autism). Of the three, Max was the best behaved but the least verbal, and certainly the most "spaced-out."

Next it was food. In my reading about ADD, I had run across the recommendations of the Feingold diet for improving children's behavioral problems [Feingold]. One of the most suspect problem-foods was cow's milk. That sure rang a bell! Max was addicted to it. He had formed a "lovie" attachment to his bottle. When he'd watch TV, when we were in a car or plane, at all times of the day, he'd request his "baba." Some days he'd drink nearly eight bottles—half a gallon of milk! Perhaps this attachment was subconsciously related to the fact that, as an infant, Max had surgery for pyloric stenosis, a condition that closes the valve that controls the flow of stomach contents into the intestine. The most common symptom is persistent violent vomiting. Because of this condition, Max increasingly threw up all the breast milk he drank during the first month of his life. Perhaps, after a month of not getting enough milk, Max enjoyed his milk all the more now.

In any case, Max's craving for and large intake of milk was certainly suspect. We took him off cow's milk and cut his consumption to one cup of goat's milk per day. This step alone had a dramatic effect. Before it seemed like Max was behind a curtain, living in a different world. Now, the first veil lifted. He finally began to talk and build two-to-three word sentences. And he was clearly more present, more aware of his world. His behavior and language were still by no means normal, but it was a start. By the end of the summer, we also began to limit his intake of artificial food colorings, another recommendation of the Feingold diet.



Interestingly, a recent study has linked some cases of autism to a kind of brain-reaction to milk protein. This study will be discussed later, as well as the possibility that this reaction might be triggered by childhood vaccinations. Certainly, cutting down on Max's intake of milk did create a dramatic change in him. But it did not cure him.

In the fall of 1994, Max continued his speech and language therapy with Donna and, after testing, qualified for special education benefits. He made slow progress. Despite the fact that he could now talk, Max still had a decidedly autistic interaction style. For example, he could only answer questions of the most literal kind, and only about objects directly in front of him. Thus, he could answer the question, "What color is this block?" but he could not answer an abstract question like "What is your favorite color?" He also had another autistic symptom, echolalia, or speech echoing. Rather than answer a question, he would sometimes merely repeat the last few words the other person had said. For instance, if you said to him, "Say goodbye," he would reply, "Say goodbye." Sometimes this was a remarkably effective strategy for him: "Do you want to go outside or stay inside?" "Stay inside." But soon we realized that he was merely parroting our words. If we asked the same question in a different way, his answer would change: "Do you want to stay inside or go outside?" "Go outside."

During the fall of 1994, we intensified our examination of our family dynamic and other social factors in Max's life. On Donna's advice, we took him out of his play-oriented nursery school and enrolled him in a Montessori school. The Montessori framework is extremely structured and focused on reading, mathematical, and manipulatory skills—things that Max was interested in. It also encourages children to do their work completely on their own. This was perfect for Max, who could not interact well with other children but could work fine alone. The school did not see him as disabled but simply as quiet.

Next, we looked deeper at our family dynamic. At the time we were using a nanny for childcare three days a week. Steve and I each worked four-day workweeks so that one of us could stay home with the children the other two days of the week. Our nanny was a somewhat distant young woman with health problems of her own. Fortuitously, she left the area at just around this time, and we were able to find a new nanny who was extremely sweet and loving. We encouraged her to focus a bit more on Max than on his highly verbal and engaging brother. Indeed, this was one of the challenges confronting Steve and me as well. We realized that we had to make a concerted effort to spend more concentrated and focused time with Max. It was often easy to "forget" him—he was always wandering off to be by himself. So we decided to take turns, each spending intensive time with one child or the other.



Finally, and perhaps most importantly, we examined ourselves—our own feelings and attitudes toward Max. Deep down, I realized that I had feelings of rejection toward him in his current state. It can be truly difficult to be genuinely accepting and loving toward children with challenging problems. Yet they are the ones who need the most from us. They are also the ones who are most psychically sensitive to parental feelings and attitudes. I instinctively knew that I had to cultivate a state of unconditional acceptance and love toward Max, and that this acceptance was critical for his recovery. Coupled with this attitude, I also knew that I had to truly believe, to have true confidence, that he would recover. Steve went a long way toward helping me in this regard. Somehow, he always knew that things would turn out all right.

### Homeopathy

It was now January of 1995. Curled up in bed, I was reading the latest issue of *Mothering*, a progressive parenting magazine. It included an article by Judyth Reichenberg-Ullman about homeopathy for childhood behavioral problems [Reichenberg-Ullman, 1995]. She claimed that she was able to create substantial improvement in ADD cases 70% of the time. Back then I knew nothing about homeopathy. Like most people, I thought that it was some kind of herbal medicine. Occasionally I had taken over-the-counter homeopathic remedies for colds, but I didn't really know anything about homeopathy itself.

As I read Reichenberg-Ullman's article that evening, I was filled with an increasing fascination and excitement. I'll never forget the moment I finished reading it. A bell went off in my head. I knew that something important had happened. Little did I know that our lives were about to change forever. "Read this!" I said to Steve. The next morning I called an acupuncturist friend of mine and asked her where I could find a homeopath. She referred me to John Melnychuk, a professional homeopath new to the Palo Alto area. We quickly got an appointment and went with high hopes and expectations.

John is now a close family friend. Many years later, he told me that he was a bit stumped the day Steve, Max, and I walked out of his office in January 1995. Max was surely in an autistic state, but what other symptoms did he have to work with, besides those that were simply common symptoms of autism?



You see, although the nature of a patient's chief complaint or disease can be helpful in selecting a remedy, the symptoms that are merely typical signs of the disease aren't always that useful. Instead, the most fruitful symptoms are those that are peculiar to the individual. For example, nearly anyone with asthma will have difficulty breathing coupled with some anxiety about their condition. What will be most useful to a homeopath in choosing a remedy, however, will be that which is unusual about the patient and their asthma. The more peculiar or characteristic of the individual person, the more useful a symptom will be in guiding a homeopath toward a precisely individualized remedy. Symptoms as peculiar as "asthma, during the full moon" or "asthma, worse when listening to music" can be found in the homeopathic literature. Such symptoms are usually associated with only one or two very specific remedies that could be truly curative to a patient who experiences them. In contrast, a shallow or "routine" prescription for asthma, based only on common asthma symptoms, will most likely only palliate asthmatic symptoms, much as allopathic medicines do. Only a remedy that truly matches the person as an individual will actually cure them.

Given Max's youth and withdrawn state, it was a bit difficult to find symptoms that were particularly unique to him. However, some of the things that stood out included: his strong craving for milk, coupled with the fact that it aggravated his condition; his love of dancing and music; the tendency for his head to become very sweaty when sleeping; his preferred sleep position (on his back with his hands over the top of his head); his restlessness and intensity; a family medical history of both cancer and diabetes on Steve's side of the family and schizophrenia on my side; and a stubborn, perfectionistic, yet sweet personality. For example, during that first interview, Max became very upset when he didn't successfully write "Mom" on a piece of paper just the way he wanted to.

All of the above characteristics are associated with the remedy that Max ultimately was given—Carcinosin. It is a relatively unusual remedy, but it is not uncommonly used in such cases. Of course, other remedies have been used successfully in autism cases as well. The key is to find the remedy that best matches a child's unique symptom profile.



Ultimately, what clinched John's recommendation for Max was a particular symptom that he found in a homeopathic repertory—a reference book that provides a reverse index to the materia medica. This symptom was associated with only one remedy, and it read: *"Talented, very: Carcinosin."* Apparently, I had mentioned ten times during the initial interview that Max was talented! Perhaps I was an overly proud mother, defensive of her "special needs" child. But I was quite certain of his innate talents. His observational skills and memory for visual detail were (and still are) quite extraordinary. He could watch television and perfectly imitate nuances in various characters' behavior and mannerisms. He could memorize dance routines and perform them for us. Even today, Max has an extraordinary memory for visual detail. He can watch a fast-paced cartoon and remember, days later, every bit of action that occurred. At age eight, he saw an interesting geometric figure within a painting on the wall of a restaurant, and remembered this same figure as the logo of another restaurant we had eaten at only once before—a month earlier. In recent years, he has emerged as a talented artist, with a flair for comic drawings.

As it turns out, Max had many other symptoms that are characteristic of Carcinosin as well. Because this remedy turned out to be his simillimum, I went on to study it further and write journal papers about his case for the professional homeopathic community [Lansky]. Introduced as a remedy in the early twentieth century, Carcinosin was relatively unknown until D.M. Foubister, M.D., a British physician, began utilizing and writing about it in 1958 [Foubister]. Its many symptoms include ones that Max also exhibited: bluish scleratics (i.e., the whites of the eyes have a bluish cast); a tendency to have numerous dark brown macules (large freckles); a hairy back and legs; a craving for salt, butter, and spicy foods; perfectionism and tidiness; oversensitivity to reprimand or criticism; and a love of animals. Even Max's "poking" behavior, so common among autistic children, is described in one article about Carcinosin that appeared in the July 1963 issue of the British

Homoeopathic Journal:

*"I have noticed that Carcinosin often has bizarre tics; one of my patients constantly tapped his brothers' skulls with his fingertips; another used to gently bite the tips of children's fingers, one after the other..."* [Hoa]

Of course, my goal here is not to go over all of Max's and Carcinosin's symptoms. It is merely to illustrate the kinds of symptoms that play a role in homeopathic prescribing. It is not a formulaic "take this for that" medical system. That's what makes it so hard to practice well.

## Initial Changes

Max began taking his remedy on a Thursday morning. John had recommended a liquid dosing regimen—a kind of slow and steady approach—where a small amount of remedy, diluted in water, is given on a regular basis. In Max's case, we gave him a teaspoon each morning. Each time we gave him a dose, we also tried to imbue it with our love and good intentions.



Two days later, Steve and I began to notice some changes. Max was using some phrases he had never used before and was somehow a bit more socially aware. It was subtle, but something had definitely shifted. We also noticed that his speech was slightly more fluid. Usually, he spoke in a kind of "cogwheel" fashion—as if he had to think about each word he said. Over time, we found that noticeable and sudden improvements in speech and social-awareness became Max's earmark for the effects of the remedy upon him.

The following Tuesday, five days after starting the remedy, Max had a session with his therapist, Donna. We did not tell her about the remedy, but she quickly noticed that something had changed. "What did you do?" she asked. One of Max's exercises was to try to follow a list of instructions, such as "Put the ball on the red chair and bring the green block to me." Usually he was able to follow only a single command, rarely two. Suddenly he was able to perform two commands consistently.

And the trend continued. Each day we saw just a bit more improvement. As time went by and we went through successively increased potencies of the remedy, we began to see a definite pattern of response. A bottle of the remedy usually took a month to finish. When we began a new bottle, containing a slightly higher potency of the remedy, Max would show some increased signs of hyperactivity. These aggravations were not extreme, but were noticeable to myself and Donna. This period would usually last three to five days. It was followed by a sudden jump in verbal, cognitive, and social ability—a discrete and noticeable step upward. At this point, the hyperactivity would also tone down. Max would become more contained and relaxed. This was followed by a period of gradual improvement for about two weeks. At the end of the month, as we neared the end of the bottle, we would begin to see a gradual slipping backwards. Donna and I used to call this Max's "end-of-the-bottle behavior." This heralded the need to move on to the next dosage level.

## Skepticism



After a few months, the changes in Max had become quite noticeable. However, being scientists, Steve and I were naturally a bit skeptical about the whole affair. Was it the remedy that was changing Max? Was it our own expectations and attitudes? We decided to conduct a simple and, admittedly, not totally rigorous test. For two weeks, I would make daily observations about Max and write them down. Steve would give Max his morning dose, changing from one dosage level (bottle) to the next, at a time unknown to me. The bottle would be hidden. Truthfully, I expected Steve to change the dosage level fairly early on in the two-week period. Each day I made my observations and jotted them down, straining to see that sudden shift, but seeing none. However, on the second to last day of the experiment, it happened—I noticed a sudden improvement in Max's speech. And, indeed, Steve had changed the dose three days earlier.

As it turns out, our skepticism about the miracle happening before our eyes was not that unusual. Over the past few years, I have seen several striking homeopathic cures. In those cases where the true simillimum has been found, the curative process is usually so natural and graceful that it seems that the person is just "getting better" by themselves. Of course, this is what happens; a remedy enables the body to heal itself. It does not "do" something to the body in the way that allopathic medicines do. It does not force a chemical change, so the body will not feel forced. For this reason, a person who is accustomed to the action of allopathic medicines will often think that a remedy did nothing; they will feel that they just "got better." Or they might attribute their cure to something else. But in truth, an appropriately selected remedy in the appropriate dose should be so gentle and effective that the person feels they just got better.

Of course, there are also situations where an inappropriate remedy or an inappropriate dose is given. In these cases, a person will either feel that nothing has happened at all, or, if they are sensitive to the remedy, that something unpleasant has come over them. For example, my mother once experienced a week of recurring mild fevers that began an hour after ingesting a remedy given in too high a dose. On another occasion, I found myself sitting and crying over some cooked onions that had been thrown away by mistake. Puzzled by the way I was overreacting, I suddenly realized, "Of course! I took a high dose of Ignatia (a grief remedy) yesterday." There I was, conducting my own personal proving of Ignatia, grieving over lost onions.

Interestingly, people often do not attribute these negative effects to a remedy either—they just don't feel like allopathic-drug side effects. Luckily, such reactions usually disappear soon after a remedy is discontinued or after its potency is adjusted. However, such phenomena do underscore the importance of treatment under the guidance of a trained homeopath.



Because Max's cure seemed so natural and proceeded fairly gradually, it seemed to many of our friends and family that he just grew out of his autistic state. But those of us who saw him almost daily—Steve, Izaak, our nanny, our housekeeper, Donna, and I—saw the direct correspondence between changes in dose and improvements in behavior. Donna, who is extremely experienced with children like Max, repeatedly assured me that what happened to Max was atypical. When he was clearly better, after a year of daily dosing (at which point we discontinued the remedy altogether), she confided to me that Max had been autistic. She said that she had seen autistic kids improve before, but not lose their autism like Max did. In fact, our pediatrician made the same confession. Once he was better, she admitted that he had been autistic. She was quite surprised by the change in him. Many years later, when I brought the boys in for a checkup, she commented that she was still amazed at what had happened to Max.

## Osteopathy, Reiki, and Prayer

Six months after starting on Carcinosin, Max continued to improve in his ability to speak and understand language. His social awareness improved as well. However, much of his inner restlessness and social distance remained. When he was four, about six months after starting homeopathic treatment, I took Max to see a traditional osteopath on John's recommendation. While most osteopaths in the United States (with the D.O. credential) function as allopaths, a traditional osteopath heals only through hands-on manipulatory techniques. One of the goals of treatment is to balance and free the flow of cerebrospinal fluid, through very gentle, sometimes almost imperceptible, manipulations of the cranium, spine, and sacrum.

Max had a course of three osteopathic treatments in a month, followed by an occasional treatment once every few months. After his first examination, the osteopath felt that Max had signs of cranial compression, which he was able to correct. And indeed, Max's initial response to treatment was striking. While the homeopathic remedy had its primary effect on his language production, comprehension, and social awareness, osteopathy created the first major shift in Max's desire for physical affection. It also seemed to create a calming effect in him, quelling that sense of internal restlessness.

The night after his first osteopathic treatment, Max crawled into my lap and said, "Mommy, sing me 'Rock-A-Bye Baby'!" Although he did not usually push me away, this was the first time he directly asked me for this kind of physical loving attention. From that point on, Max did. Soon he began crawling into bed with me in the morning and snuggling at bedtime. He also began to run after my husband or me when we left the house to make sure he got that extra kiss goodbye. What a change from the distant "self-contained" Max!



Throughout the healing process, I also prayed for Max on a regular basis. When times were particularly rough, I would go into his room while he was sleeping and use a form of therapeutic touch called Reiki [Stein]. I truly believe that the effects of prayer and hands-on healing are not to be underestimated. In fact, an increasing number of studies have proven the beneficial effects of both on cases ranging from open-heart surgery to AIDS [Targ]. Many nurses are training in the use of such techniques and are beginning to use them in hospital settings. In my own experience, osteopathy, hands-on energy work, and prayer all work marvelously with homeopathic treatment. They seem to be complementary, boosting each other's beneficial effects.

## Joining the Crowd

In the fall of 1995, after nine months of homeopathic treatment, Max began his second year at the Montessori preschool. At this point, his speech had definitely become more complex, spontaneous, and fluid. Donna tested him again and found that he was approaching age level. She decided to discontinue therapy, but kept him "on the books" as far as eligibility for special education.

Now that Max was talking, he was also trying to join in with the other children socially. But he was behind. Having started so late, he was awkward in his initial attempts at social interaction. He was stubborn and cried too easily when he didn't get his way. To get attention and acceptance, he often resorted to excessive silly "toilet talk." Of course, as a parent, I was thrilled that he was beginning to reach out to other children. But the school was not as supportive. They had pegged Max as a quiet child and did not like the new changes they saw in him. They gave him no support in his awkward transition from social withdrawal to social acceptance and savvy. One of his teachers said to me, "Max was such a nice boy before. Can you put him back the way he was?"

Although it was awkward to change schools in the middle of the school year and cope with this teacher's attitude, I had learned by this point that not changing to meet Max's needs would stall his progress. It was clearly time for some changes on the school front. So, when Max was 4½, we found a new school for him—a more socially oriented school that followed the Montessori style, but not as strictly. His new teachers had no preconceptions or biases toward him, and they easily helped Max adjust. Within a few months he knew everyone at school, was interested in what was going on around him, had a couple of friends, and was having playdates.



During that school year we also made some more changes on the home front. When our nanny decided to leave her position to follow her dream to become a beautician, Steve and I decided to stop using nannies altogether, opting instead for after-school childcare three days per week. This change had many beneficial side effects for our family. For one thing, we finally began to eat dinner together every night as a family. Given the hectic schedule of families with two working parents, the institution of the family meal has gone by the wayside in many American homes. Returning to it created a feeling of greater coherence and stability in our lives. It also assured a better diet for our kids.

### Remedy Adjustments, and a Hint of Vaccination Damage

By the end of 1995, it became increasingly clear that Max was being aggravated more than helped by his remedy. He was consistently more hyper and revved up. We began to decrease the frequency of his dose, but the aggravation remained. Finally, in January 1996, a year after Max began homeopathic treatment, we stopped it completely.

Sure enough, just like Max's marked improvement with each monthly change of dose, going off the remedy now led to a huge leap in language and social ability. This leap continued for about four months until it evened out.

Max calmed down and his true personality began to emerge full force. He is an entertainer. He is sociable and sensitive. Although he was still immature at this point, he was ahead of his peers academically. He was respected and liked by both his teachers and classmates. In May 1996, Donna tested Max once more. He was testing above age level! On the day that Steve and I joyfully signed papers releasing Max from eligibility for special education, Donna told the county social services representative that it was not her therapy that had done the trick for him; it was homeopathy. She also invited John and me to present Max's case to her clinic, which we did that summer.

Max was now almost five years old, and it was tempting for Steve and me to believe that he was fully cured. However, John was less sure, and he turned out to be right. There were still vestigial signs of his former autism, though they were not readily apparent. For example, his language production continued to be awkward at times. In times of stress (for instance, if he was sick), he would retreat into himself and use echolalia as a speech strategy.



But overall, Max was functioning extremely well. He engaged in real discussions with family and friends. He asked for explanations about his body and his environment. He related stories about his day at school and about TV shows. He was also fascinated with fantasy play and dress up. Max was even becoming popular at school, with children running up to him and greeting him. He was able to adjust easily to new social situations the summer of 1996, readily adapting to two new summer camps. Max had also become an avid reader—another Carcinosin quality. Before he began kindergarten he could already read simple Dr. Seuss books.

However, by the end of the summer of 1996, I began to notice a slight decline in Max's speech and social awareness. It also happened to be time for his five-year-old checkup at the pediatrician. And for the first time, I declined the routine vaccinations. At age five, it is customary to give the full battery—measles, mumps, and rubella (MMR), diphtheria, pertussis, and tetanus (DPT), and polio. Having read about a possible link between autism and vaccination damage, I didn't want to rock the boat. Our pediatrician did not argue with my decision either. But she did convince me to give Max the tuberculosis (TB) test that is required for kindergarten entry in California—now administered as an injection rather than the old tine test.

Unfortunately, this injection led to a marked aggravation and deterioration in Max's state. For the next week, he became increasingly sensitive, crying for no reason. The teachers at his camp and at school remarked about the change in him. He had become more withdrawn and fearful. He was not his usual self. This reaction made us wonder if, indeed, vaccination was the root cause of Max's problems in the first place. Years later, I discovered another hint of this. After going through his medical records, I realized that at age 18 months, Max had been given a dose of the MMR vaccine only one week after recovering from roseola—an ailment related to measles. Perhaps he had been in a compromised state. Indeed, the MMR vaccine has been highly implicated in triggering autism [Wakefield].

Luckily, after a couple of tries with other remedies, our homeopath suggested that we simply return to Carcinosin. After a single dose, Max was back to his normal self within hours. We breathed a sigh of relief. Max started back on the remedy and remained on it for another eight months, once again changing dosage level about once a month. Again we saw the same characteristic monthly pattern of response. After eight months, in March of 1997, I readily recognized the consistent aggravation and stopped the remedy. And once again, this was followed by a long period of noticeable improvement.



## An Ongoing Process

Since that time, Max has no longer needed daily doses of Carcinosin. Just like the rest of our family, he visits our homeopath and osteopath about two times a year, or when the need arises. Sometimes he receives a remedy to deal with minor behavioral or emotional problems that crop up. Sometimes he receives a remedy when he gets an infection or virus and needs a bit of extra help getting over it. The same is true for me, Steve, and our other son Izaak. We are all part of an ongoing process of healing and growth.

In the fall of 1997 I felt that Max was ready to leave his Montessori school. At age 6, he entered first grade at the private school that Izaak attended. Since then he has done well both academically and socially. He is an openhearted, sensitive, and somewhat comedic fellow who loves drawing and art (he is especially fond of the quirky and enigmatic paintings of M.C. Escher), playing computer games, reading fantasy and science fiction books, and writing and illustrating his own works of science-fantasy.

But like all children, Max is growing and changing and occasionally needs homeopathic and social supports. When he was in second grade, input from his teachers alerted us to the fact that he was still having some difficulty processing auditory input. For example, he sometimes missed parts of oral instructions or key points in stories, especially when they were read out loud to the class. Being quite sensitive to disapproval, Max tended to cover up for these deficits and did not ask for help or clarification from the teacher. The result was sometimes an excellently executed assignment or essay, but written about the wrong topic. The teachers were puzzled. Max's behavioral affect was quite normal and his execution of assignments was always excellent if he understood what was expected from him. There seemed to be something askew to them.

You see, up to that point, I had not told Max's teachers about his former autism. I didn't want to bias them in any way. And perhaps I wanted to forget about these problems myself. When these new issues arose, I told the teachers about Max's history. As a result, they tried to provide visual or written instructions for him when necessary, and occasionally would check up on him to make sure he had understood class assignments. The net effect was excellent.



Max is now doing quite well in life. After third grade, his auditory processing problems seemed to disappear, thanks to ongoing homeopathic treatment. His teachers no longer report any problems at all. Today his behavior, demeanor, and day-to-day interactions with friends and family are not in any way autistic. He's a sociable fellow with many friends, and an excellent student working at his age and grade level. He takes piano and tennis lessons. He attends summer camps, including a month-long sleepaway camp. He is resilient within his peer group, always able to defend himself with a kind of entertaining humor and charm. He is also a gentle soul, loved by his teachers. Of course, he still has his issues, like any other child. But we continue to work on them and Max continues to improve. Invariably, his spirit and talents outshine any limitations. Max is no longer autistic, but he is still a "*talented, very*" child.

**Why Autism?**

According to the Autism Society of America, between 500,000 and 1,500,000 Americans now have some form of autism. And the number is rising. Check around your community—autism cases are popping up everywhere. Every day I hear about more cases of this once incredibly rare and heartbreaking condition. In a statement to Congress in 1999 supported by the Central Missouri District School Nurse Association, Patti White, R.N. estimated that the rate of autism-related disorders had risen in her district from 1 in 10,000 to 1 in 150 [White]. A 1999 California government report also found an alarming increase in the number of autism cases in that state [AutismCalifornia]. In fact, in 2001, the U.S. Department of Health reported that the incidence of autism is rising at a rate of more than 20%

a year [Herald].

Where did this alarming trend come from? As mentioned earlier, one proposed physiological explanation is a wayward reaction to milk protein. Two studies conducted at the University of Florida [Ross, Sun1, Sun2] have found that some autistic and schizophrenic individuals may lack the ability to break down proteins found in milk, possibly due to a malfunctioning enzyme.

Now obviously, the recent dramatic rise in autism cannot simply be attributed to milk —something that children have always been consuming. What has changed is these children's ability to assimilate milk. Indeed, autistic children are known to be sensitive to many other foods as well—for example, wheat, gluten, corn, and food colorings—and their autism sometimes improves when these foods are eliminated from their diet.



But why have these food intolerances developed? One very compelling theory is that the ever-increasing use of vaccinations is to blame. Indeed, several studies and books have directly correlated the rise in autism—indeed, the very phenomenon of autism itself—with the introduction of the American vaccine program. The earliest reported cases of autism in the United States were in 1943, among affluent families—the families who were the first to give their children all the benefits of modern medicine, including vaccinations [Coulter90].

Since then, the situation has only gotten worse. It is now an incontrovertible fact that the incidence of autism, ADD, and other learning and behavioral disorders has risen precipitously over the past twenty years, along with a sharp increase in severe allergies and various other kinds of autoimmune disorders. This rise has occurred at the same time as the increased and mandated use of vaccinations for just about every childhood illness. Indeed, the number of different disease antigens (the vaccine constituents that trigger an immune response) that are recommended for children by the time they are five years old has more than tripled in the last two decades [MercolaVaccine].

Can this correlation between an increase in vaccination and an increase in behavioral and autoimmune disorders be explained scientifically? Some scientists are starting to believe the phenomenon can be explained by the fact that vaccines stimulate a different branch of the immune system (the humoral or Th2 function) than is stimulated by actually experiencing a disease (the cell-mediated or Th1 function). As a result, it may be overstimulation of the body's Th2 function (by an ever-increasing number of vaccines) that may be causing wayward autoimmune responses [Incao].

Another popular theory is that various vaccine ingredients—mercury, in particular—are to blame.

Whatever the explanation, people are beginning to take notice. Missouri nurse Patti White's statement to Congress asserts her suspicions about the now-popular hepatitis B vaccine. Once a staunch advocate of vaccination, White has seen a dramatic rise in childhood behavioral problems in her school district, as well as asthma, diabetes, and other chronic diseases, ever since the hepatitis B vaccination was mandated for infants in 1991 [White]. Autism and other behavioral problems have also been linked to the DPT vaccine, because of convulsions or cerebral inflammation that occurred hours or days after administration of the vaccine [Coulter90]. More recently, the MMR vaccine has been implicated in an English study by Andrew Wakefield, M.D. [Wakefield]. This vaccine is suspected to cause abnormal intestinal problems in autistic children, and is also suspected as a trigger for Crohn's disease. Although Wakefield's work has met with the criticism one would expect for such an unpopular scientific result, his suspicions about the MMR vaccine have been buttressed by other studies. For example, American researcher V.K. Singh has found evidence that autism may be an autoimmune disorder of the brain that is triggered by the MMR vaccine [Singh]. Today, many parents within the American and British autism communities feel that this vaccine, in particular, is the culprit for their children's condition. I have come to believe that this was the case for Max as well.



It will be a shocking and sad day when we as a society admit to ourselves that, in our effort to avoid the childhood illnesses (many of which are usually benign) or to needlessly protect newborn infants from diseases primarily found among intravenous drug users (hepatitis B), we may be inadvertently crippling many of our children, both mentally and physically, for life.

Luckily, homeopathy has a longstanding and successful track record in repairing vaccination damage. It also has been successful in curing (not just palliating) the allergies, asthma, and behavioral problems that may result from this damage. Max's story is a case in point. Homeopathic remedies are also available for treating and preventing the very same childhood diseases that vaccinations are trying to prevent. Thus, homeopathy provides not only a remedial tool, but also an alternative way to deal with the diseases vaccines are designed to prevent.

### The Path of Healing

Max's cure was a miracle. There is still not a day that goes by without my thanking God for delivering Max and the rest of our family from what could have been a tragic outcome. But Max's healing was not without its ups and downs. Invariably, overcoming a serious problem like autism is a process that takes time.

In retrospect, I realize that we were amazingly lucky to find a perfect remedy for Max right away. Because we were able to see at least some form of progress throughout Max's healing, it was easy to stick with the process. More often than not, however, it takes time for a homeopath to find a good remedy for a patient. This is especially true in complex, chronic cases. The net effect can be a sort of zigzag path to cure, a gradual and more circuitous return to health. After all, a homeopath can do nothing more than try to match a patient's current symptoms to the best fitting remedy they can find.

Of course, there are times when a quick miraculous cure does happen. I've seen it myself. But usually, the path to the cure of chronic disease is not so smooth. There may be periods of aggravation to deal with and modifications of dose and remedy to be tried. It takes patience, perseverance, and enough education about homeopathy to cooperate effectively with the treating homeopath and to cope with the bumps along the way.



Don't forget, a homeopath needs to know lots of symptoms—including some very personal ones—to make a good prescription. Without fully understanding a person's physical, mental, and emotional state, a homeopath can work only on the surface and can have only a superficial impact on a patient's health. Even when all of the relevant symptoms are known, it is often difficult to interpret a case correctly and find the simillimum. Because of this, the practice of homeopathy, like that of many other holistic healing therapies, is an art that requires years to master. In difficult cases, even the most experienced homeopath may need some time to understand a patient well enough to find a path to cure.

Since I first published my original paper about Max's cure in 1998 [Lansky], I have been contacted by many parents of autistic children from around the world. Recently, one parent called to tell me that because of this paper, he had sought out homeopathic treatment for his autistic son—and that his boy was now recovering. That one phone call made all of my efforts to spread the word about Max's case worthwhile.

However, in most of my conversations with these beleaguered parents, I have discovered a great deal of resignation and fatalism about their child's condition. Despite my spending hours on the phone or email with them, assuring them that autism had been cured in Max's case and had been treated successfully in other cases as well [Herscu-Aut], most of these parents have not given homeopathy a thorough trial. In one case, a mother sought out a homeopath and got a remedy for her child, but was too afraid to give it to her. In other cases, parents discontinued treatment after only a month, either because they didn't see enough effects from the remedy, or because they were scared by aggravations.

From these experiences I have learned the proverbial lesson—"You can lead a horse to water but you can't make him drink." It is my hope that, in the case of humans at least, further education can lead to an awareness of the need to take that first sip and keep drinking. That is why I kept sharing my story about Max's cure and why I ultimately wrote a book about it and this astounding medical system [LanskyBook].

If someone comes to a homeopath because they are suffering from a longstanding chronic illness, they must give the homeopath time—at least six months—to find a good remedy and dosing regimen. Indeed, if an allopathic doctor has said that a condition is incurable, why are people surprised or discouraged when they are not cured quickly and easily by a homeopath? So often people turn to alternatives like homeopathy when all hope is lost, and they expect a miraculous cure to happen overnight. But cure usually takes time.



It also takes confidence. In the case of autism and other severe childhood diseases, parents often become afraid and despondent, and understandably so. It is hard enough for them to truly accept their child's illness. It is even harder for them to cultivate an attitude of confidence and trust that their child will be cured. In many cases, it is also difficult for them to face the potential disappointment of failed treatment. But what is worse? Disappointment, or a lifetime of handling a child with a crippling disability?

I believe that it is an attitude of loving acceptance coupled with confidence in cure that is the key to recovery for anyone. I have read that it is not the fighters who recover from cancer. Rather, it is those individuals who are able to embrace their illness and its gifts, while still maintaining confidence that they will get to the other side of it. A very difficult state of mind to achieve—no doubt about it! While acceptance of disease may be achieved by some, if it is not coupled with confidence in cure, it can sometimes lead to psychological investment in disease. When this happens, the positive intentionality that fosters the curative process becomes derailed.

For example, I have met parents who have convinced themselves that their children are just fine being autistic. While this attitude may help a parent feel better about their situation, it does nothing to help a child recover. Certainly, their child would be better off if they weren't autistic! If we want our children (or ourselves) to recover, it is imperative that our love and acceptance be coupled with an inner vision of recovery. I believe this coupling of attitudes can be the single most powerful force in achieving a cure—the second most powerful, of course, being an accurately prescribed homeopathic remedy.

Being a homeopathic patient is invariably a journey of growth. It is a transformation, not a bandaid; a fulfillment of potential and a return to proper function, not a cut-and-paste operation. It may take effort, but cure (rather than unending palliation or suppression) is worth that effort. It takes awareness of one's symptoms and a willingness to divulge all aspects of oneself to a homeopath. It takes a "stick with it" attitude.

I hope that Max's story has also illustrated another point—the need to accommodate to improvement and growth as it occurs. Because a person undergoing homeopathic treatment may actually change in fundamental ways, it is important to make lifestyle modifications that accommodate that change. In a child's case, this may require changes in schooling or childcare arrangements. In an adult, the movement toward health may cause changes in work or relationships. After all, in order to really heal, a person must often repair those circumstances that contribute to their illness.



Finally, homeopathy is ideally a family affair. For one thing, the healing of a child may actually depend on a parent's ability to change and become well too. Likewise, the healing of a child may free up family energy so that other family members can fulfill their own potential. In the end, homeopathy can improve the whole dynamic of a family, as a cycle of change and growth is set into motion. In our family, once Max was better, Steve and I were able to work on ourselves and our marriage. Eventually, Izaak was enabled to express his needs and have them addressed too. And the cycle still continues. I hope that my telling you about our experiences will help you, your family, and our society and world at large to find true healing. Because cure *is* possible.

## References

[AutismCalifornia] "Changes in the Population of Persons with Autism and Pervasive Developmental Disorders in California's Developmental Services System: 1987-1998," Report to the Legislature, Department of Developmental Services, California Health and Human Services Agency, 1600 Ninth Street, Room 240, Sacramento, CA 95814 (March 1, 1999).

[Coulter90] Coulter, Harris L. *Vaccination, Social Violence, and Criminality: The Medical Assault on the American Brain*, North Atlantic Books and Homeopathic Educational Services, Berkeley, California (1990).

[Feingold] Feingold, Ben F. *Why Your Child Is Hyperactive*, Random House (1985). Also see the extensive site of the Feingold Program, www.feingold.org.

[Foubister] Foubister, D.M. "The Carcinosin Drug Picture," *British Homeopathic Journal*, 47, 201 (July 1958).

[Herald] Reported in *The Sunday Herald*, "Autism Figures Soar in America," www.SundayHerald.com/21347 (Sunday, January 6, 2002).

[Herscu-Aut] Latchis, Spero. "Homeopathy and Autism: Report on a Presentation by Paul Herscu, N.D., DHANP," in *Homeopathy Today*, Volume 21, Number 10, pp. 20-21 (November 2001).



[Hoa] Hoa, J. Hui Bon. "Carcinosin: A Clinical and Pathogenetic Study," *The British Homoeopathic Journal* (July 1963).

[Incao] Incao, Philip, F. "How Vaccinations Work," www.garynull.com/Documents/niin/how_vaccinations_work.htm (May 1999).

[Lansky] Lansky, Amy. "Max's Story: A Carcinosin Cure," *Homeopathy Online*, Issue 5, http://www.LyghtForce.com/HomeopathyOnline/Issue5 (January1998). A condensed version of this article appeared in *Similia*, Publication of the Australian Homoeopathic Association, Volume 11, Number 2 (July 1998). Also see: www.RenResearch.com/autism.html.

[LanskyBook] Lansky, Amy L. *Impossible Cure: The Promise of Homeopathy*, R.L.Ranch Press, Portola Valley, California (2003). For more information and ordering, visit www.ImpossibleCure.com.

[MercolaVaccine] Mercola, Joseph M., "Vaccine Insanity," The Mercola Newsletter, www.mercola.com/2002/feb/2/vaccine_insanity.htm (February 2, 2000).

[Reichenberg-Ullman-Mothering] Reichenberg-Ullman, Judyth, "A Homeopathic Approach to Behavioral Problems," *Mothering*, Number 74, pp.97-101 (Spring 1995).

[Ross] Ross, Melanie F., "Milk in Diet May Be Linked to Autism and Schizophrenia," University of Florida Press Release, Science Daily, www.ScienceDaily.com/releases/1999/03/990316103010.htm (March 17, 1999).

[Singh] Singh, V.K., Lin, S.X., and V.C. Yang, "Serological Association of Measles Virus and Human Herpes Virus-6 with Brain Autoantibodies in Autism," *Clinical Immunological Immunopathology*, 89:105-8 (1998).

[Stein] Stein, Diane. *Essential Reiki: A Complete Guide to an Ancient Healing Art*, The Crossing Press, Santa Cruz, CA (1995).

[Sun1] Sun, Zhongjie, J. Robert Cade, Melvin J. Fregly, and R. Malcolm Privette, "Beta-casomorphin Induces Fos-like Immunoreactivity in Discrete Brain Regions Relevant to Schizophrenia and Autism," in *Autism: The International Journal of Research and Practice*, Volume 3, Number 1, pp. 67-83 (March 1999).

[Sun2] Sun, Zhongjie and J. Robert Cade, "A Peptide Found in Schizophrenia and Autism Causes Behavioral Changes in Rats," in *Autism: The International Journal of Research and Practice*, Volume 3, Number 1, pp. 85-95 (March 1999).

[Targ] Targ, Elizabeth. "Distant Healing," *IONS Noetic Sciences Review*, Number 49, pp. 24-29 (August-November 1999).

[Wakefield] Wakefield, Andrew, et al. "Ileal-lymphoid-nodular Hyperplasia, Non-specific Colitis, and Pervasive Developmental Disorder in Children," *Lancet*, 351, pp. 637-641 (1998).

[White] White, Patti. "Hepatitis B Vaccine: A school nursing perspective for the congressional hearings on May 18, 1999 regarding the safety of the hepatitis B vaccine that is being mandated for newborns and now older children in America," Statement to the Subcommittee on Criminal Justice, Drug Policy, and Human Resources of the Committee on Government Reform, U.S. House of Representatives,

http://www.AlternativeParenting.com/health/HepB.asp.



*Update for Second Edition (September 2005):*

Max is now 14 years old and a freshman in high school. He remains completely autism-free—no teacher or friend suspects his past. I still try to keep him away from cow's milk, corn, and food colorings. But when he goes to sleep-away camp in the summer, he eats all of these things with no problems. (Given the opportunity, he will eat a whole pile of tortilla chips before I can stop him!)

Max, like the rest of our family, still sees our homeopath about once or twice a year. He gets remedies to help with acute ailments or with the stresses of being a teenager. I would still classify him as a bit more on the spacey or forgetful side—especially in comparison to my older son, who is much more Type-A. Max can tune out conversations easily if he wants to, gets a bit lost in his thoughts, and sometimes does miss social cues. But by and large, he is a more resilient teenager than his brother. He is loving high school, has many new friends there, is doing well with his studies, has grown his hair out long now (he likes the artistic counterculture image), and is most interested these days in girls (he has already had a girlfriend or two), music, and his passion: computer animation. So Max remains the talented fellow—the sensitive artist type!

Readers might be interested in hearing more about homeopathic treatment of autism by tuning into my monthly radio show at: www.AutismOne.org/radio, or checking out the information and referral lists at my book website, www.ImpossibleCure.com.

## — Chapter 21 —

# Entering the World of Autism: A Mother's Story

By Carolyn Lewis

*Carolyn Lewis lives in Montana with her husband Allen, who is a pediatrician, her son Brian (born June 1999), and Brian's older sister, Rachael. She is the founder of a support group for children with special dietary needs due to autism, celiac disease, asthma, or other conditions, and hosts a website that provides parents with information on implementing nutritional interventions (www.DietarySupport.com). This story was written in June 2002.*



We moved from my hometown of Salt Lake City, Utah to Billings, Montana, nearly three years ago with the dream of spending more quality time together in the great outdoors. Although I looked forward to leaving the crowded city for wide-open spaces with cleaner air, I wasn't excited about moving away from my parents, four siblings, and friends. However, even though exhaustion had set in from caring for our son, Brian, who was four months old at the time and already proving to be extremely difficult to care for, I was ready for a change.

Brian was different starting the first week of his life. I remember how he began to imitate my coughs and sneezes to get attention, instead of crying. At first I thought it was funny and cute, but after awhile I realized it wasn't normal. He would scream if I didn't respond immediately. Feeding him was also very difficult. It had to be perfectly quiet and still before he would eat—even if he appeared to be starving! He would become irritated and refuse to eat if the ceiling fan was on, if someone walked past him while he was feeding, or if the temperature of his bottle varied even a little bit. While feeding he had to be constantly pushing his feet against something; I used to joke that he was going to wear a hole in the tapestry chair in the living room because of this habit. Brian's developmental delay became more obvious as he approached 15 months of age, as he didn't crawl, walk, or even babble. He had difficulty sitting up and would only rarely roll over. His temperament was the most difficult thing to deal with on a daily basis. Brian would tantrum for hours at a time and resist most attempts to comfort him. Despite trying everything we could think of, at times we could not figure out what he wanted; he would lie on his back screaming and kicking, sometimes for hours.

Brian didn't consistently sleep through the night for the first two years of his life. He would wake up screaming almost hourly through the night for one of many reasons. He would get himself stuck in the corner of his crib with his head against the bars, and he couldn't get himself out. He would allow me to pull him into the center of the crib and cover him with his blanket, and wouldn't fuss as long as I only touched his feet in the process. He would wake up screaming every time he heard an airplane or a train, and he couldn't seem to calm himself afterward. It was exhausting with no sleep, having little idea what he wanted, and not feeling like he even noticed what I did. Brian also suffered from multiple ear infections, acid reflux, and food intolerances. At 22 months Brian received his second set of ear tubes because of repeated ear infections. He also had his tonsils and adenoids removed because they were chronically infected, and they had contributed to sleep apnea and poor health. It was just two days after this surgery that he slept through the night for the first time.



It's a good thing I am married to a pediatrician! My husband, Allen, had suspected autistic features by the time Brian was 13 months of age; but when he mentioned the possibility of autism to me, I became very defensive. I had seen documentaries on TV about autistic children who rocked for hours while being totally oblivious to the world around them. Brian didn't care to be held, didn't care for interaction with others, and only wanted to be left alone to watch movies; however, it was just too hard to believe that my little boy could be autistic. When I look back at his behavior knowing what I know now, I realize he had some of the classic autistic features. He would stare at movies from his crib for hours a day, happy to be left alone in his own world. If anyone tried to pick him up or even say his name, he would scream.

Brian's sister, Rachael, who is 3½ years older, used to feel bad about his rejecting her; but she has always seemed to have a connection to him and an understanding of him that is quite amazing. By herself she found a way to interact with Brian that finally broke down his resistance. We played "imaginary circus" in our living room, and I would announce all of the acts before Rachael performed them. Rachael began doing a silly clown walk that got Brian's attention and seemed to make him look at her more often when I would announce, "Ladies and Gentlemen!" One day, Rachael placed Brian on the floor and before he knew what was going on, she did her silly clown walk, tripped over him, and fell to the floor. Brian giggled for the first time ever, and he didn't stop for several minutes! He liked this game so much that he began to lie down on the floor to initiate it. This was the beginning of Rachael's unique ability to interact and play with her brother. A day doesn't go by without my husband or me thanking the Lord for her gifts of love and understanding.

Brian started receiving services from Early Childhood Intervention (ECI) around 15 months of age. He had occupational and speech therapy for several months, but he wasn't responding as well as we had hoped. It was then that we took him for an evaluation by a child neurologist and learned he had pervasive developmental disorder (PDD). The formal diagnosis of autism was confirmed just before his second birthday. As one might imagine, the diagnosis rocked our world. The images I had previously spoken of seemed to haunt my dreams and waking moments. Yet the words "mild" and "high-functioning" stuck in my head and offered hope that Brian could grow out of his autism. It was two weeks after his PDD diagnosis, while I was in a state of denial and shock, that I met another mother with an autistic son. As part of a volunteer job, I was scheduled to sell tickets for a fundraiser, and she came on shift with me. We spent most of our two-hour shift discussing autism and the importance of intensive early intervention. The next day she brought three books on autism to our house. That was the beginning of an incredible and unbelievable journey ... into the world of autism.



The research began in earnest with me giving Allen daily briefings when he came home from work. After combining information we'd gleaned from several books, the Internet, and conversations with parents and professionals, we decided applied behavior analysis (ABA) offered the only proven chance to see Brian recover. Our ABA program is based on the methodology developed by Dr. Ivar Lovaas, who showed in a study published in 1987 that nearly 50% of autistic children who had undergone this intervention were able to complete the first grade in a normal classroom and less than 5% did so with less intensive therapy. ABA is no small undertaking, as 40 hours per week of ABA is recommended for the best outcome, with the need to continue therapy for 18 to 36 months. Yet families across the nation are spending up to $50,000 a year for this 50% chance of succeeding in having their children mainstreamed in regular schools. The earlier the age this program is started, the greater the chance for this outcome. As this program is not funded in Montana as it is in New York, New Jersey, and California, we had to hire an out-of-state company to teach us how to train, hire, and maintain a therapy staff and keep us on course to Brian's recovery.

In the middle of hiring therapists, preparing a therapy room, and purchasing all of the required therapy essentials, I came across Karyn Seroussi's book, *Unraveling the Mystery of Autism and Pervasive Developmental Disorder: A Mother's Story of Research and Recovery [Editors' note: A chapter by Karyn Seroussi is included in this book].* Karyn's book was a huge eye-opener for me. Brian began the gluten-free, casein-free (GFCF) diet cold turkey just three weeks before his ABA therapy began. My husband had not yet had a chance to read information about the GFCF diet or the DAN! Protocol at that point, but he agreed that it was worth a try if I was up for it. In one week Brian showed good response to the diet with unquestionably increased eye contact. During car rides, he no longer stared blankly; instead, his eyes began darting around as if he could see for the first time. He also said his first three-word phrase, "I got more," after I handed him a rice cracker. Brian's health improved quite dramatically with the diet. His nose quit running for the first time in his life, and the constant flow of ear drainage stopped. The dark circles under his eyes began to disappear. But the most wonderful change of all was the reduction and virtual elimination of his constant tantrums. Hours of tantrums per day were reduced to minutes per day by the second and third weeks on the GFCF diet.



But GFCF alone was not enough for Brian. Corn and soy triggered his tantrums too, so we eliminated those foods as well. We also realized how essential it was to give Brian nutritional supplements, including essential fatty acids (found in cod liver oil, borage oil, and evening primrose oil) and probiotics. It was extremely difficult to give supplements to Brian in the beginning; even if we could get them down him he would often throw them up several minutes later on the carpet or furniture. Our house and our clothing smelled like a fish market for a few months because of the cod liver oil. Brian has always been a picky eater and has preferred and almost exclusively eaten beige or brown foods. This was another reason giving supplements was such a challenge.

We later learned that Brian is allergic to several other foods including eggs, all citrus fruits, and tomatoes. He could not tolerate nitrates in meat and would become ill shortly after eating a single hot dog. His reaction to nitrates is different from his other reactions to food: nitrates cause Brian to have bloodshot eyes and reduced physical energy overall. He clearly didn't feel well for up to four days after eating meat with nitrates. Brian has not had bloodshot eyes since we removed nitrates from his diet, and his energy level is normal. We challenged the nitrate/bloodshot eye theory several times, and nitrates certainly were the reason for his adverse reaction—no other food or environmental factors had changed.

Now, after many months of experience with dietary intervention and administering nutritional supplements, we have success with nutrition! For Brian, feeling better means performing better in therapy and doing better in all other aspects of his life. Some may question the validity of the GFCF diet; all it takes is a challenge of offending foods to prove its necessity. There was an incident a few months ago when Brian ate a few pieces of gluten-containing berry licorice from the health food store. He began to shout "no!" and "don't!" shortly after eating it. A few hours later he had gone into a full-blown tantrum that lasted for hours during which he grabbed his head and screamed "ouch!" over and over as he was lying on the floor. He recently got into some Cheerios and his behavior deteriorated within three hours. These incidents are confirmation to me that dietary intervention is worth doing!



Brian's ABA program began August 1, 2001. I'll never forget that weekend because he cried and had tantrums for much of the three-day workshop. I was drained by the end of the third day. The only thing that kept me from breaking down was the hope that this program would pull our son out of the world of autism. His first task was to sit quietly on a chair for approximately five seconds. As he didn't want to do this, all of his crying and tantrums were in protest. Actually, this was a lot to ask of him, but it was the key to getting him into a teachable setting. He pointed for the first time during the workshop. He extended his arm and pointed to me for help, but I was instructed not to respond, and this just added to my despair in seeing him so upset.

Now Brian looks forward to each session of therapy, and he even hand-leads the therapist to the therapy room. He builds towers with blocks, can put together 24-piece puzzles, matches words, matches pictures with their names, and is even beginning to say many new words. Fifty percent of his time in therapy is play, and he gets much reward from success and the interaction with his therapists. Some have criticized ABA because they believe it "kills the spirit." I believed in the beginning, and still believe now, that without ABA we may never have known Brian's spirit.

Brian's daily schedule is full, and I am much more homebound than before ABA started. We schedule six hours of therapy a day, seven days a week, in our home. We plan three hours of therapy in the morning and three hours in the evening, allowing time for naps, meals, and playtime between sessions. It is not always perfectly regimented, and I use the times when therapists can't make it to spend time in new adventures with Brian and Rachael. ECI provided several hours of OT and speech therapy per week. In total, Brian has had weekly visits from 10 different people. All of his therapists and his daycare providers are very much contributors to his continued progress, and we are very thankful for their commitment and care of him. We are looking forward to Brian attending preschool this fall, as he just graduated from the ECI program.

Allen and I have become fascinated with our new knowledge of nutritional health and intervention in autism. With attention to our own diet, we are much healthier; with the future ahead, we will need good health. In fact, I have started a support group for parents with children who have special dietary needs. In the beginning, this was a small group of parents with children in the autistic spectrum, but it is now open to parents who have nutritional concerns for their children, whether these children are well or have allergies, ADHD, asthma, celiac disease, or other problems. I now hear from new people every week who are interested in joining the support group. Allen is working closely with a dietician to provide simple guidelines for nutrition needs and safe supplements. I have reviewed over 20 cookbooks created for those with allergies and for those who wish to implement a whole-foods diet. I am very excited about sharing the power of good nutrition and have been reading as much as I can each day from our new home library on nutrition and health. Our family is now eating free-range meat and organic fruits and vegetables, and we are avoiding excitotoxins (flavor enhancers such as MSG, aspartame, and hydrolyzed vegetable protein), as well as artificial flavorings and colorings.



I meant to share some of Brian's successes when I spoke at a fundraising dinner for our parenting agency earlier this year, but I was too emotional to get the words out. Just a few days before the dinner Brian hugged his favorite teddy bear, smiled, and said, "I love you." This is the kind of story parents of autistic kids live for. He has shown so much improvement that it is hard (but not impossible) to believe how difficult he was. Brian plays with his sister every day now and, like any three-year-old, finds ways to tease her. He also seeks out and plays with other kids at his part-time daycare. In fact, Brian recently noticed a little girl who was crying and offered her his own blanket for comfort as he patted her on the back. Clearly, this is something that he wasn't capable of doing or perceiving several months ago. We can even take him places. He used to freak out in stores, but now enjoys shopping and will lead me to places he wants to explore. Travel used to be out of the question. During an overnight trip a year ago, we thought we would never be able to travel again. He screamed when he saw the pattern on the carpet and wouldn't even set foot on it. The braided rug at the restaurant set off a tantrum that ruined our dinner out. Sleep in a new room, in a new bed, and a new place didn't happen. Just last month we actually had a fantastic vacation in Salt Lake City. Brian adjusted more easily to new situations, his sensory integration overloads were gone, and we could relax for the first time on vacation since Brian was born. He even let the hairdresser cut his hair in preparation for the trip! I am amazed at the progress that he has made in a relatively short period of time.

As the mother of Brian, who is autistic, and the wife of a husband who happens to be a pediatrician, I cannot say enough about the DAN! Protocol and all of the good things that come along with it! Brian is clearly improving at a steady pace. He has come so far in less than one year of intervention that many of us who see him and work with him cannot help but comment on how many ways he has improved in all areas of his life. Brian is a loving, affectionate, playful little boy who prefers to interact with others instead of watching TV. Brian has acquired the skill of pretend play. He is learning to speak in sentences and will request what he wants with the appropriate words. He has mastered many programs in his ABA therapy. Brian has a passion for life and enjoys the company of people. He seems to like everyone. He likes animals and can make many animal sounds. Brian especially loves trains, cars, and airplanes. Sometimes I watch Brian as he plays outside and notice for a few moments he will appear to stare into space as he reacts to the sensation of the gentle breeze blowing against his face. I worry for a moment that he is locked into his own world, that place where he used to be all the time. But then I see his eyes connect with mine as he smiles at me, sharing the joy. This is the Brian we had hoped for. Brian is no longer a stranger in our house, and he gives love back to us in so many ways. Brian is a miracle beyond belief to those of us who knew where he used to be. We have many people to thank for his progress, many of whom we have never met. We are grateful to those who have paved the way for us by recognizing the importance of biomedical treatments in autism. We are especially grateful to Dr. Bernard Rimland for starting the movement that has contributed greatly to our son's improvement.

No parents can be ready to have their child be abnormal, or anticipate the many changes it will bring to their lives. However, we have found many chances for growth and love in our family in the short period since Brian's diagnosis of autism.

*Update (February 2003):*

Brian surprised our family upon a return trip home after a weeklong vacation near Glacier National Park this summer (June, 2002). He walked up to the doorstep, pointed at the doormat, and spelled the word "Welcome." The amazing thing about this is that no one had taught him the letters of the alphabet. I then wrote an "A" on a notepad and showed it to Brian, and he instructed me to draw a "B," continuing to name each letter of the alphabet all the way to "Z." Then Brian began spelling words on signs, trucks, books, and everywhere else. His language has developed into appropriate requests and comments, and he is starting to speak in full sentences. Although his language is still delayed for a three-year-old, we are realizing improvements every day, and his receptive language is much better than we had hoped for.



Brian's social skills have blossomed over the past year. He prefers to play with other children! In fact, his sister Rachael complains that Brian won't leave her alone, and when her friends come over to play he won't leave them alone, either. He races toward the front door when the doorbell rings, to eagerly greet our guests with a smile. When Rachael comes home from school, he often leads her to whatever activity he was working on before her arrival.

ABA and speech therapy continue. Recently, ten days of auditory integration therapy resulted in small but notable improvements, such as sleeping through the night. At his last ABA workshop our consultant told us that Brian no longer looks autistic. He also noticed that Brian doesn't "stim" anymore, his cognitive ability has improved dramatically, he is much more social, and his play is appropriate for a three-year-old. In fact, he told us that Brian has made six months worth of progress in three months.

In general, Brian's facial expressions are normal. His eye contact is wonderful. Brian's energy level is a lot better—he used to be sedentary and now he is much more active. His imagination has blossomed and he uses it extensively in play. He has so much personality, a great sense of humor, and the most wonderful smile. It is even easier to take him places and expect more normal three-year-old behavior. Trains are his passion, and he gets to visit the train yard in Laurel, Montana, a few times per week; his face lights up with joy when the trains are in sight. He is a very loving boy with a desire to be connected and share with others, no longer caring to be alone in his own little world. Visits to the pet store reveal his gentle nature toward animals, and he has adopted the neighbor's Boston terrier as his personal therapy dog. Brian even tries to communicate with our pet cockatiels, which for the longest time had more language than he did.

It is wonderful to see Brian looking healthier each day. His health isn't perfect, as we continue to strive to truly heal his gut through proper nutrition, supplements, and a diet of mostly whole foods prepared from scratch, free of additives and dyes. We know that Brian is on his way to becoming the best he can be.

After much research into diet and nutrition, I strongly believe that autistic children need much more than just a gluten-free and casein-free diet. They need a diet rich in fresh fruit and vegetables, fresh meat free of nitrates, cage-free and omega-rich eggs, nuts, and seeds, and limited starches and grains (if they aren't allergic). Preparing whole foods from scratch has been the most important contribution to optimal health for our entire family. Dietary intervention is absolutely critical to break the cycle of poor health in autistic children, despite the difficulty planning meals for such restricted and picky appetites. Although nutritional supplements are also very important, they cannot replace nutritious food. I recommend finding a doctor or a nutritionist who is well versed in nutrition and really knows the healing power of good, wholesome food.



Allen has grown in so many ways as a result of autism becoming a part of our world. He has become a better husband, father, and physician. His better understanding of the role of nutrition and holistic medicine has helped him look for and find underlying causes of illnesses more effectively. Rather than simply treating his patients' diseases, he is more able to teach them about health and wellness.

It gives me great joy to share experiences with the other parents from the dietary support group I started one year ago. In many cases, the health of entire families has improved as a result of dietary intervention. The information I share at my support group meetings is being incorporated into a website: www.DietarySupport.com. It is my hope that parents everywhere can benefit from the valuable information I have found. In addition to meeting Brian's needs, I have been motivated by other parents to learn more about nutrition. I am so grateful to them for their support and for sharing their success stories with me.

It is truly amazing that our wonderful son in his state of autism has brought about so many positive life changes in our household and our community. It is my hope that others will realize similar blessings. I've always believed that miracles are a result of hard work, and now I know it is true. Brian is our miracle, and he will continue to amaze us all.

*Update for Second Edition (September 2005):*

Brian is doing very well in mainstream first grade, and he behaves as a typical six-year-old most of the time. He still has some deficits, but he is catching up quickly. He is very social, has a great imagination, plays well with others, and has a great sense of humor. His interests have expanded to include much more than his previous obsession with trains. He is interested in sports, science, construction, animals, games, and art.

We have scaled back on therapy for Brian over the past two years since moving to Naperville, Illinois. Our school district and Brian's teachers have done a good job preparing him for a mainstream classroom, and he looks forward to school every day.

We continue dietary and biomedical interventions, which have proven to be extremely important for Brian. It took years to find the right supplements in the right amounts for Brian to be his best. The most important supplements have been cod liver oil, probiotics, zinc, B6, and MT Promotor (compounded at Pfeiffer Treatment Center).



Brian's diet continues to be free of gluten, soy, and citrus fruits because he reacts to those foods. We choose to avoid hydrogenated oils, dyes, MSG, nitrates, food additives, preservatives, and pesticides. We continue to prepare most meals and snacks at home from the healthiest ingredients available. Brian eats a varied diet, including plenty of fruits and vegetables. He even drinks fresh veggie juice! He eats many healthy foods in a variety of colors and textures with only an occasional protest. We are able to eat out at restaurants every week as a family, and it is a relief that there is always something for Brian to select from the menu.

Allen is now the medical director for Pfeiffer Treatment Center in Warrenville, Illinois. He dedicates much of his time to treating patients with autism, ADD/ADHD, schizophrenia, bipolar disease, and other neurological disorders. Pfeiffer Treatment Center is a facility specializing in biochemical testing and individualized nutrient therapy for children and adults.

I continue to host the Website DietarySupport.com and hold monthly dietary support group meetings in the Chicago area. It is great getting connected with so many other parents who agree that autism is treatable.

Many interventions have contributed to Brian's success. His big sister, Rachael, is also a huge help, as she has taught him so many things with great understanding, patience, and unconditional love. Thanks to the help and insight we have received from friends and colleagues all over the country, our family is now enjoying a much more normal life!

# — Chapter 22 —
# How Chelsey Changed Our Lives

By Jaquelyn McCandless, M.D.

*Dr. McCandless is the author of* Children with Starving Brains: A Medical Training Guide for Autism Spectrum Disorder *and the grandmother of Chelsey, who was born autistic. She is certified by the American Board of Psychiatry and Neurology, specializing in the treatment of developmentally delayed children. She and her husband, Jack Zimmerman, live in southern California. This story was written in January 2003.*



As a physician and as a grandparent of Chelsey, diagnosed with autism in 1996, I have come to see more and more in the last six years the enormous gift that Bernard Rimland, Ph.D. (affectionately called "Bernie" by all of us in the DAN! movement) has given to the world of autism and especially to those of us who love and work with autistic children.

The Autism Research Institute (ARI) Internet website and Dr. Rimland's studies about the treatment efficacy of vitamin B6 first started me on the path to seeing autism as a biochemical disorder. I consider Dr. Rimland the "grand godfather" of the movement for understanding and implementing the biomedical treatment of autism. The organization Defeat Autism Now! (DAN!), which he cofounded, is made up of the most generous, helpful, hopeful group of physicians, researchers, and parents that one could ever encounter. Many of us in DAN! are parents or grandparents of children with an autism spectrum disorder (ASD). The DAN! group's willingness to share information about the biological nature of autism and ways to help our children affected by this disorder has my utmost respect and appreciation.

I began suspecting something was different about my granddaughter Chelsey (my 13th grandchild) very early on. She had two older sisters, aged two and four, when she was born in 1994, so needless to say my daughter Liz had her hands full at that time. Both older siblings were "neurotypical;" and Chelsey seemed normal and healthy at birth, nursed well for a few months before being placed on a milk formula, and was an unusually quiet, well-behaved baby who didn't demand a lot of attention. However, we all noticed that she seemed quite serious; she would not smile or respond very much when one would try to play with her or talk to her. Actually, as she continued to grow, she began averting her gaze or wincing and covering her eyes if anyone focused on her too intensely. However, she seemed bright and very interested in toys, books, music, and playground activities.

I reside in Los Angeles and would call Liz every week at their home in Phoenix. In one conversation when Chelsey was almost four months old I recall Liz saying exasperatedly, "No, Mom, Chelsey is not smiling yet." Liz and my son-in-law, Jim, were not overly concerned about their youngest daughter. Jim is a very loving and devoted father, and he worked a lot of overtime as an electrical engineer to support their burgeoning family while leaving most of the childcare and home decisions to Liz.

I still had a full-time medical practice at that time, primarily as a psychiatrist, but I was moving more and more in the direction of anti-aging and alternative medicine by the early 1990s. In 30 years of solitary private practice in Southern California, I had not seen any autistic children and had encountered only a handful of adults with autism. These patients had been brought to me by their parents or caretakers, who were seeking psychotropic medication for behavior control. These inscrutable patients usually could not convey to me how they felt. For the most part, they were from institutions or group care homes, and they were continuously on various anti-psychotic medications. In other words, I was totally ignorant about autism. I remember learning in my medical training that the earlier notion about autism—that it was caused by "refrigerator mothers"—was gradually being replaced by the general belief that it was a rare genetic and untreatable disease. Anti-psychotic medication was used simply to control autistic individuals' "acting-out" behavior.



My slight concerns about Chelsey did not materialize until it became apparent that she did not exhibit the usual stranger anxiety at nine months of age. Actually she did not seem to notice who was caring for her. She had a series of ear infections during her first year of life, and received four to six courses of antibiotics. She remained a sober child, but physically she was very active and well developed. She also met all of her motor developmental milestones on time. Although she could walk, run around, and play on the playground equipment, she liked to be by herself. She had few sounds and certainly no words by 18 months of age.

Chelsey demonstrated a high pain threshold and seldom cried. After her first year, she stopped having ear infections, and she actually seemed healthier than her siblings. However, she started to become quite hyperactive. She appeared not to hear anything when we would talk to her, and I was becoming suspicious of retardation or a hearing problem. I was also in total denial, along with her parents, about the possibility of autism. I began encouraging Liz to seek an evaluation for her, but Liz felt she was just a slow developer and that her sisters, who were very talkative, were doing the talking for her. She did agree to have Chelsey's hearing tested because she thought that the frequent ear infections had injured Chelsey's hearing. The tests indicated that Chelsey had excellent hearing.

Finally, around two years of age, Chelsey was brought to her pediatrician for a complete assessment. The pediatrician assured Liz that Chelsey was fine and that some children just learned to speak later than others. He also was not concerned about Chelsey's persistent loose stools, and told her relieved mother it was just "toddler diarrhea," and she would outgrow it. (Actually, it did not clear up until we finally implemented the gluten- and casein-free or GFCF diet when she was almost five years old.)



Although the pediatrician's assurance put Liz's mind at ease for a while, I was not convinced that all was well. I knew I could only push my very independent daughter (who was studying to become a nurse) so far before she would remind me that these were her children, not mine, and she would take care of things. I was trying hard not to be a bossy doctor Mom. However, I became more and more convinced that Chelsey needed an expert evaluation, and Liz and Jim finally agreed to let me make an appointment with a child development specialist at UCLA when Chelsey was 33 months old. The expert observed Chelsey and after only a few minutes, said "classic autism," and matter-of-factly proceeded to advise us to get her immediately into applied behavior analysis (ABA) as the only available treatment for her disorder.

Needless to say, the shock of Chelsey's diagnosis sent us all reeling. Liz was mobilized into action, advertising for and procuring a group of women who were willing to be trained to do ABA. She had an ABA expert from California travel to Phoenix to teach her and her group of helpers the basics of behavioral modification training. Chelsey began the treatment 40 hours a week in her home, continuing for almost two years, with great benefit.

With my denial finally shattered, I also was mobilized into action. I was chagrined at how little I knew about autism. I first made the mistake of reading the leading book at that time (1996) on autism, which left me in deep despair about the chances of Chelsey ever having a normal life. The author, a psychologist, stressed the importance of early educational intervention, feeling that the only hope for these individuals was through behavioral training. She also estimated that 85% of autistics would need some kind of custodial care during their lifetime, and that only 15% would ever become well enough to live independently. There was no mention in this book about any kind of treatment for autism other than ABA, and the prognosis was grim.

Shortly after that time, I finally admitted defeat and reluctantly came into the modern technical age to learn how to use the Internet. That was where I discovered the Autism Research Institute's website and learned about Bernard Rimland's work with vitamin B6. His findings confirmed my growing sense that Chelsey suffered some kind of biochemical disorder. We started giving her vitamin B6 (in P-5-'P form) along with magnesium. Her hyperactivity almost abruptly stopped, and this made it much easier for her to sit and do her ABA work. When Chelsey was around four years of age, we once ran out of the B6 and forgot to replace it for several days. Her hyperactivity resumed with a vengeance, leading her to crash into the edge of the couch and knock out her two upper front teeth. Needless to say, we never forgot her B6 after that, and her missing front teeth continue to remind us of the importance of this nutrient for her daily functioning.



Not long after starting the B6, we started giving dimethylglycine (DMG) to Chelsey. I had also learned about DMG from Bernie's writings.

Soon after starting her educational intervention, we knew that Chelsey was bright because she would quickly learn how to identify shapes, colors, and letters. She did not utter her first word until shortly before her third birthday. She said, "Cold!" as she opened the doggie door once and a blast of cold wind hit her. We were jubilant, realizing that she actually could speak. However, no more words were forthcoming for weeks even though we had already started ABA. But words did start coming within weeks of starting the DMG, and her new language skills made her ABA training proceed rapidly. Although she could vocally identify objects, she still would not use spontaneous speech for social conversation. Gradually, she did learn to express what she wanted very clearly, mostly in one-word commands, e.g., "Chips!" "Swim!" "Trampoline!" Reading and spelling also came easily to her, although she did not comprehend what she was reading and handwriting was a difficult task for her.

Needless to say, Chelsey's improvements as a result of the nutritional supplements galvanized me into a frenzy to study everything I could possibly learn about the biochemical basis and nutritional treatment of autism. My search led me to start contributing posts to an autism support e-list, and I began receiving requests from parents to help them with their autistic children. In the beginning, I kept telling everyone that I was just learning, but many parents had had absolutely no luck in getting any other physician at all interested in any alternative approach. The parents who started working with me in 1998 were willing to participate in my early learning attempts and went along with many experiments with various nutritional approaches. Many of them brought information to help me investigate new research findings that were being reported more and more frequently as it slowly began dawning on us that our children and grandchildren were part of some sort of epidemic.

Chelsey received her autism diagnosis when I was 65 years old. At the time, my husband, Jack Zimmerman, and I had been planning to move to Hawaii to spend more time teaching and writing in our later years. We had planned to focus on the topic of "relationship" as a path for spiritual development. We conducted (and still do) relationship workshops for mature, committed couples. We also wrote a book in 1997 on relationship, *Flesh and Spirit, The Mystery of Intimate Relationship,* published by Bramble Books, in which we described techniques to develop deep and honest communication on all levels in a relationship. However, by 1999 my practice was becoming dominated by my work with autistic children, and I was busier and more "turned on" by medicine than I had ever been. I was inspired to help Chelsey and my other young patients gain as much health as possible. My pursuit was full of intensity and excitement that made every new discovery about the biomedical aspects of autism an adventure. This necessitated my going back to basic medicine much more than the anti-aging, hormonal, and brain chemistry issues I had already been investigating in the context of helping older folks (including us) stay healthy, active, and sexy indefinitely. My understanding of the importance of nutrient supplementation for aging placed me in good stead as I started applying these principles to the ASD kids.



I found myself running into a great deal of resistance in the medical community when I tried to enlist the aid of my patients' pediatricians or family doctors in my biomedical approach to the treatment of autism. When the news about secretin began coming out, we were all crazy with excitement that something really new was taking place in the treatment of autism. Bernie Rimland, as usual, was in the forefront of distributing information about secretin to all of us who were treating these patients, and he was extremely helpful in getting doctors to communicate with each other about their techniques and experiences in using this brand new treatment. Of course, traditional doctors, for the most part, equated secretin with "snake oil" medicine. Even though it did not turn out to be a panacea for the majority of children, at this point it has been shown to be beneficial to about 25% of the younger kids (under four years of age), and many parents continue to give secretin to their children even after using it for three years or more. Any treatment that can help 25% of kids without harm is cause for celebration as we continue to look for treatments that will help even more children. All of us working in this field have learned that there is no one "magic bullet" due to the incredible uniqueness of each person's biochemical status. A therapy that may help one child very much will often create no response or even a negative response in another child who may seem similar but biochemically reacts differently.

Since the time Chelsey was four years old, Jack and I have been bringing her with us to the Big Island of Hawaii every summer for a month. When in Hawaii, we live near a rain forest in a home that we timeshare with friends. Although we are 45 minutes from any "swimming" beach, we make that trek almost daily. The first year Chelsey flourished. She received undivided attention from us, and I was able to do what I had been asking Liz to do: get about 30 nutrients down her every day, apply transdermal secretin (and many other transdermals through the years), give her antivirals, antifungals, and endless probiotics, eventually start the GFCF diet, and help her listen to special auditory training tapes. I wondered how Liz got anything else done, especially after her fourth child came along when Chelsey was five years old. He was a neurotypical boy who, for sure, did not get vaccinations.



After our first stint in Hawaii, I understood why Liz had not been able to toilet train Chelsey: she had persistent, glue-like diarrhea. I then began a dialogue with Dr. Karl Reichelt, an autism researcher in Norway who is a parent of an adult autistic. He generously and patiently helped me understand that pizza and wonderful breads and cheeses (even ice cream!) may not be good for Chelsey. I began the task of talking Liz into trying a GFCF diet. This brought about the third miraculous result, after B6 and DMG, that demonstrated to me, without a doubt, that autism is a biochemical gut and immune disorder. Within several weeks she started to have formed stools; and within a short time, she was completely toilet trained.

Back on the mainland, a small group of autistic children's parents alerted our community to two issues: first, the cumulative amount of mercury in infant vaccines (found in thimerosal, a preservative), and second, the similarity between autism's symptoms and those of mercury poisoning. In response, the medical mainstream seemed to strengthen its resistance. Again, Bernie Rimland was in the forefront in aiding the autism community. In February of 2001 Bernie gathered 26 of the leading experts in the field of heavy metal poisoning and detoxification to develop a detoxification protocol. A protocol was hammered out after three intense days. The experts agreed upon the use of oral chelation therapy for children, using DMSA (trade name Chemet, 2,3-dimercaptosuccinic acid), which was approved in 1998 for the removal of lead in children. Since then, thousands of parents have used the chelation process and are continuing to use it with their children with great benefit. Unfortunately, for many physicians the word "chelation" conjured up the controversial IV treatments that adults had been using for arteriosclerosis. My patients would receive dire warnings from their doctors about this "very dangerous" procedure that I was inflicting on their children. Few, if any, of these doctors were willing to educate themselves about the DAN! Protocol and its information about DMSA.

Chelsey was as usual my little guinea pig and my first chelation patient. She was almost seven years old when we started, and she did not make the rapid improvement that I was observing in my patients who began the chelation process much younger. Also, Chelsey did not have any verbal or social development to go back to as had many of the children with late-onset autism, or "acquired autism." (Chelsey's disorder started at birth whereas these other children had experienced a year or more of seemingly normal development.) After learning that mercury is such a slow and deadly neurotoxin, we examined Liz's dental records and discovered that she had received amalgam work when she was four months pregnant with Chelsey. Of course, there is no way to ever know for sure what disturbed Chelsey's fetal development, but I remain highly suspicious that she got the first hit of mercury *in utero*. She was already set up for further toxic insults because she received all of her mandated vaccinations, including her newborn thimerosal-loaded hepatitis B, followed by all the required boosters. I, along with many others, did not have any idea back in 1994 that amalgams were so poisonous, nor did Chelsey's family or I have the slightest clue that all mandated vaccinations were not safe for all children.

After word got around that I was starting to use chelation in my practice, the applications for treatment began pouring in. Practicing alone in a small office definitely placed a limit on the number of children with whom I could work. Doctors Stephanie Cave and Amy Holmes in Baton Rouge, Louisiana had at least 800 children being evaluated for, or already using, the chelation protocol. They also had a long waiting list of anxious parents seeking this new biomedical treatment for their ASD children. This was true for many of the other DAN! doctors administering chelation.

By the middle of 2001, I was unable to add any more children to my practice even though the requests were increasing. I began to realize that the most useful thing I could do was to write a book describing what I had learned about the biomedical treatment of autistic children. I had desperately looked for such a book when I first started on this journey, but found none that could really help me set up a treatment protocol. An interminable list of possible tests that were listed in the DAN! Protocol did not direct me as to how and where to start, what labs to use, and how to proceed with treatment. More importantly, I had learned that most of the hard work of treating these children fell on the shoulders of the parents. In order to best help the parents, I wanted to teach them how to prepare their children for treatment that required professional help. For example, they needed to know how to change their children's diets and provide them with proper nutrients before chelation could even be considered. I decided to describe what I had learned—by trial and error in my practice—regarding how to best evaluate and treat these children. I wrote the book both for parents and for physicians who might want to start working with these families. My fantasy was that I could give this gift to the world and finally go off to my desert island and have my life of writing, teaching, conducting workshops, and continuing my private research on the biomedicine of autism.



I gathered information from October through December of 2001 with the help of intensive daily interviews with Dr. Maury Breecher, a public health professional who wanted to write a proposal to a publisher for a book on autism. When he could not get this proposal accepted by any large publisher, he moved on to another project. I began writing intensely in January of 2002 with lots of editing help from my husband, Jack, and from Teresa Binstock, who served as my scientific advisor. Each of them contributed a chapter plus articles in the appendix. Long talks with Teresa since 1999 had helped me realize that the brains of these children were malnourished—by ubiquitous gut problems, poor ingestion, and impaired digestion, absorption and utilization of nutrients. I entitled my book, *Children with Starving Brains, A Medical Treatment Guide for Autistic Spectrum Disorder.* As usual, Bernie Rimland was extremely supportive, and he wrote a wonderful endorsement for the book. When we spoke for the first time (when I called to ask if I could send him a copy of my manuscript), we had a great rapport and spent over an hour talking. I think parents and grandparents of autistic children have so much in common that others cannot ever really know. The bond is instantly there in many cases. It was also delightful to find someone older than me (by three years!) still passionately working in this arena.

The first printing of 5,000 copies of my book came out in August and was nearly sold out by November. It became clear that I had to include an index when it was time to publish an updated version of the book. The Second Edition, which I recently finished, contains new material that describes treatments that had been introduced to me a few months after completing the First Edition. This includes allithiamine (TTFD) to add to our detoxification treatments, concentrated injectable vitamin B12 to help the sulfation/methylation pathways, and oral immunoglobulin (OIG) as a new form of an already established substance (IVIg) to use in helping the impaired immune system. We can hope that many new treatments are discovered and that books like mine will need frequent updating, although after completing the Second Edition I surely want to try to enlist others for that job!

The popularity of the book in the autism community brought many requests for help from parents of autistic children throughout the country as well as abroad. After a number of presentations to parents, it became obvious to me that the most useful work I could do was to recruit more doctors to do this kind of work. The DAN! conferences had already been doing this for several years. The extent of the autism epidemic is causing a great shortage of knowledgeable healthcare workers for all the children who need help. My plan is to assist in physician trainings on my own and at DAN! conferences. I also plan to mentor practitioners who want to start specializing in the biomedicine of autism, many of whom are parents of children with autism. I am attempting to reduce my responsibilities for ongoing care, and I see patients primarily for evaluation and to outline a treatment plan that they can then take to their own doctors. My book gives guidance for many interventions that parents can do themselves. By the time they need a doctor, they need only medical help since they will already know about diet and nutrients, areas where most mainstream doctors are still undereducated.



My Chelsey is almost nine years old now. She is beautiful, sings like a bird, swims like a fish, and is adored and loved by everyone who knows her. She is wise and whimsical, creative, funny, and very, very willful. (Can't imagine where she got that!) She writes strange stories that leave us pondering for days as to their meaning. She loves music and meditation. On numberless councils with Jack and me, and on holidays with our very large extended family, she will sing songs that relate to the feelings that are being expressed in the circle. She has been my primary teacher about autism for the last five years and has been subject to ever-changing nutrient protocols; special diets; secretin infusions; six months of weekly FGF2 injections; nutrients and medications to control yeast and *Clostridium* infections; immune-enhancing substances, including transfer factor and oral immunoglobulin; too many blood, urine, and stool tests to count; interminable chelation for heavy metals; stinky creams; and daily vitamin B12 injections for weeks on end. In addition, she receives special schooling, one-on-one aide assistance until this year, cranio-sacral sessions, horseback riding lessons, auditory training, special healings, and evaluations by people of various persuasions. Since the publication of my book, I have received letters and posts from all over the world from parents telling me they are praying for her. Many tell me how grateful they are to her for inspiring me to write a book that has helped them understand, for the first time, what is ailing their children and how to help them feel better and start on the path to recovery. I feel enormously blessed to be able to serve in this way.



And yes—Chelsey still has autism. Although the mechanism of toxic injury is probably the same, clearly the earlier it happens the more damage it does. The children who have some language and social development before acquiring autism clearly have a head start in the recovery process. Yet, she has come a long way; and we are not by any means finished with our work with her. Although she can read and speak very well, she does not choose to do so very much (except for singing). I plan to continue to try new biomedical treatments on her (and myself) before I recommend them to others. I believe that she was volunteered into this role by something much greater than all of us, which I do not even pretend to understand with my ordinary mind. Her many talents continue to unfold as we all journey along this large learning curve about autism. I consider my husband, Jack, a relationship genius; and he has become one of Chelsey's primary teachers. He picks her up at school and works with her after school every day on her social interaction and other life skills. As I avidly pursue the biochemical approach, he avidly pursues the relationship path, and of course they are intertwined and both essential for optimum healing.

We feel strongly that Chelsey and all of the people on the spectrum need to be treated as real people instead of objects to be tolerated or catered to. They know much more than we usually give them credit for. I believe grandparents should be enlisted more and taught techniques to do this kind of regular interaction with these children—in my opinion they are a neglected and valuable resource. Jack has helped me to see that collectively our children are agents for waking us up to the changes that are needed in our relational, medical, educational, and political paradigms. They are especially helping us to see dangerous toxins that are injuring not only their bodies and brains but also our entire earth.

Bernie Rimland has been generous and helpful in promoting my work and my book. He is very supportive of all of us who are associated with DAN! and has helped us in our search for further knowledge in the biomedicine of autism. He has been in the forefront of every new biomedical approach to autism since he learned of his own son's diagnosis over 40 years ago, and he is still going strong. He says he will never retire until autism is "Defeated," and continues daily to present a wonderful role model for all of us who are aspiring to help children and adults with this disorder. As his son, Mark, has been for Bernie (he knew for sure that his wife was not a "refrigerator mother"), Chelsey has been an enormous gift to my life. I have made a vow similar to Bernie's, that I will never stop searching and learning everything possible to help her and all of the other autistic children so that they may have the best and healthiest lives possible. Bernie's dictum, "Do what works," has been a guiding beacon for me in the last five years, and he has continuously shown what an inspired and loving parent or grandparent can contribute to the hope for a better life and a lessening of pain for these incredibly interesting and wonderful children (who become wonderful adults) with autism.



To Bernard Rimland, THANK YOU!!! from the bottom of my heart.

*Update for Second Edition (September 2005):*

Grampa Jack began to work with Chelsey in the water when she was four. I watched her move from apprehension of the water to leaping in—accompanied by ritual cries that she repeated each time—and swimming (dog paddling) towards him across the pool. That was the first time we had ever seen her reach out to anyone. When Liz took her home in the evening to join the rest of the family, Chelsey cried in the car. She is a child who very seldom cries; we had not seen her experience or show separation pain before.

Their water relationship blossomed after that in Arizona and California pools—and most of all in the warm oceans and hot pools on the Big Island of Hawaii in her annual summer month with us there. I enjoyed seeing the two of them get to know each other in the water and then slowly evolve their connection out of the water primarily through music. Chelsey sings like an angel, with perfect pitch, natural vibrato and instant harmonic memory. By the time I knew it was imperative for Jack to move to Phoenix for six months to work with her after school each day when Chelsey was almost nine, they had developed quite a full musical curriculum that included listening to, singing, recording and making up songs. Her interests ranged from Kenny Loggins to Kitaro and Peruvian shamanic music to Gilbert and Sullivan. One afternoon late that spring when Jack descended into an unusual state of discouragement about her progress, she looked up at me as we put another CD on the stereo and said, "Grandpa sad?" We had never heard her really notice anyone else's feelings before that moment.

We have a complex relationship with Chelsey. We can get angry, sad, foolish, and very loving with her all in the space of an hour. As she began her approach to puberty in her tenth year, we noticed how awake and creative she became when the two of us were in a strong connected place ourselves—whether it was during council, meditation, listening to music, or in a particularly affectionate and happy place with each other. She would become noticeably agitated if we were angry at each other. We saw that the field of our heightened connection awakened her, and that inspired us to look for new ways of enhancing what we call the "relational healing field." Our two annual autism camps have come out of that inspiration. There have been times when we could almost see the dendrites growing. We anticipate that her emerging puberty will definitely enhance her interest in others.



During these past few years we have explored low-dose naltrexone*[Editors' note: Please see related article on page 427.]*, hyperbaric oxygen therapy *[Editors' note: Please see related article on page 413.]*, high-dose phosphatidyl choline, HEG (bio-neurofeedback), Namenda and galantamine, Actos, another year of transdermal chelation therapy, energetic mats, autism camps in the summers, and nutrients too numerous to list, all while observing the effects of onrushing hormones on her neurology. Chelsey's body is developing beautifully in response to these hormones, while she has a charming lack of self-consciousness about that, unlike most neurotypical girls. Yet like her two older neurotypical sisters, she is learning how to get what she wants with her unique blend of feminine wiles, humor, teasing, high intelligence, strong will—and impairment.

Yes, as she approaches twelve, Chelsey remains impaired, inexplicably destructive at times, sporadically seeming to lack any need for sleep, and needing to discharge a boundless amount of energy (trampoline, swimming, plus a variety of stims). Yet there are also increasing moments of deep affection and awareness of others, helping us to maintain an optimism about her future. We regularly meditate upon and envision her happiness in loving relationships. Her physical affection melts us; her grace and beauty at times move us to tears; and when we have a special moment of focused awareness with her, we feel blessed by the Goddess herself. And yes, we will continue searching for any possible aid to furthering her development, while appreciating fully the unique and wondrous being she already and always is.

## — Chapter 23 —

# Through a Glass Darkly

By Tory Shirley and George Mead

*George W. Mead and Tory Shirley are the parents of two children, Eleanor and William, who was born in May 1998. George is an attorney who at one time practiced medical malpractice defense (defending doctors and hospitals). Tory is a writer and advocate for special needs children. They both live in Portland, Oregon. This story was written in March 2003.*



"For now we see through a glass, darkly; but then face to face: now I know in part; but then shall I know even as also I am known."
*I Corinthians*

There is a Starbucks in our neighborhood that we sometimes visit to take our minds off our son's medical condition. On our last visit, there was a plastic donation box for children stricken with autism, and a little plaque that read, "Autism strikes one child in every 5,000." I ordered my double-latte and thought for a minute. Then I pulled out a red pen and deliberately defaced the sign, writing: "In Oregon, autism strikes one child in 150!"

Two years ago, shortly before his second birthday, our son William went to his doctor's office and received a standard set of "catch-up" shots, several of which contained a mercury-based preservative, thimerosal, which is 49% ethyl mercury by weight. Since that day, our lives have been profoundly changed in a way that none of us could have anticipated.

During the following summer William suffered from constant diarrhea, unexplained bumps and welts, reduced speech, bloating, binge eating, bloody lesions, "croup attacks," and lost interaction and eye contact. These conditions progressed into rocking, teeth grinding, eye squinting, spinning, hand flapping, gross motor problems, and a total loss of language. Twenty weeks after his shots, William, then two years old, was diagnosed with "regressive autism," perhaps the most devastating disorder a toddler can suffer.

But this is not a story of grief, it is one of hope. Through a combination of medical and educational treatments, our son has made great strides. He is talking, attending Montessori school with an aide. He falls squarely in the development range of a three-year-old. He is speaking six-word sentences, is potty training, singing nursery songs, and drinking from a cup. He can read 15 words, and is learning more. He shows every sign of making slow but steady progress toward recovery.

Although it will be a long and arduous process, we have one thing denied generations of parents before us: we have hope. With each passing day, the hopelessness of regressive autism is being challenged and overcome.

## When the Going Gets Tough

In the summer of 2001 we were losing the child we knew and loved. William, who was a nine-pound healthy baby at birth, was losing weight each day. Over the next several months William become progressively more withdrawn. He was unresponsive, and would sit at the bottom of the stairs in the corner, laughing at nothing.



Like many parents, we began our journey by having our son's hearing checked. We were told there was good news and bad news. The good news was that William's hearing was fine. The bad news was that we would need to go to the Oregon Health Sciences University (OHSU) autism clinic. Until that day, we had never heard of autism.

We believe in a cause-and-effect universe. We did not believe that our formerly normal child could be afflicted with a terrible psychiatric condition—without an identified cause. Science can clone pets and splice the human gene; science should be able to tell us what was happening to our child. Our family had to know what caused William's regression. We had to look autism in the face and learn why it had struck our son.

One of the doctors at the hearing clinic mentioned that some autistic children respond well to a casein- and gluten-free diet. We couldn't believe what we were being told. Could this mysterious psychiatric disorder be remedied by a change in diet? We went home and put William on a diet free from all dairy and all gluten (wheat, rye, spelt, oats, and barley). Within three days his eye contact improved. Within seven days his bowel movements improved, and within three weeks his self-stimulatory behaviors (stims) had dropped by about half. It was clear to us that there was a cause-and-effect impact. We started looking for more answers.

## The Battle of Autism: Finding the Root Causes

To live with autism is to do battle. When we took William to the public education specialists, we were told, "Autism is a lifelong disabling disease for which there is no cure." At his early intervention assessment, William was tested with an IQ of 55 and severe language apraxia, an inability to understand or respond to words. At the Autism Clinic, William was ranked smack in the middle of the DSM-IV psychiatric diagnosis of typical "late-onset" autism, in which normal children lose the ability to communicate and interact socially. The early intervention experts told us that we might have to institutionalize our son.

Shortly after our demoralizing experience with early intervention, we attended a DAN! conference in Portland. The Defeat Autism Now! (DAN!) movement started with a group of doctors and parents, led by Dr. Bernard Rimland of the Autism Research Institute in San Diego. Dr. Rimland's research showed that there was a medical component to autism. The DAN! conference focused on biomedical treatments for autistic children and the amazing progress being reported by parents across the country. After this conference, we met a truly courageous physician who had been thinking outside the box for years. He offered to take William as a patient, and our world began to change.



Our new doctor ordered laboratory tests of William's hair, urine, and blood. From these tests, we learned that something was terribly wrong with William's internal chemistry.

While William's earlier doctors had simply told us that he had a mysterious and incurable psychiatric disorder, we now realized that something very physical and very abnormal was going on inside him. He had seven times the reference range for mercury. He had an immune dysfunction and his body was devouring his nervous tissue. He had little IgG or IgA. He had terrible microbial infections from yeast and *Clostridium* in his stomach and his intestines were permeable. Most children with regressive autism are medically ill: they suffer from abnormal conditions that can be treated medically.

We began reading more research. Based on our pediatrician's recommendation, we flew William to the Pfieffer Clinic in Illinois for more advanced metabolic testing. Recent studies by this Clinic, led by Dr. Bill Walsh, indicated that 95% of affected children show significant deficiencies of metallathionein (MT). MT is a protein that, along with glutathione, is responsible for removing toxins, such as mercury, from the body. Many autistic children have reduced levels of MT. Whether that is genetic or the result of some environmental insult is still unclear.

The MIND Institute at the University of California at Davis has found that America's autism epidemic is genuine. Genetics do not cause regressive autism. There may be a genetic susceptibility within a child, such as an autoimmune issue in the family tree, but the regression is environmentally triggered.

All over the world medical scientists are improving their understanding of autism. There is enormous potential for using medical treatments to improve the lives of autistic children.

## Shaping an Appropriate Treatment Program

By that point we had enough medical evidence to begin work on William's recovery. We found a logical, science-based way to fight, and to hope, in the midst of despair. Gradually, we formed a team of supportive, forward-thinking doctors to help us with William's medical care. With each round of tests we came one step closer to an answer.



We moved William onto a high-protein, low-carbohydrate diet—a "yeast-free" diet based on gluten- and casein-free foods. Medical tests showed that William had a suppressed immune system. He had yeast and fungal infections. We started him on vitamin and nutritional supplements: vitamin A, cod liver oil, zinc (for seizures), Super Nu-Thera, vitamin B, selenium, omega-3 fatty acids, magnesium, *acidophilus* probiotics, and finally glycoproteins. They all helped him. We tried removing mercury and heavy metals from his system through a process called chelation.

We discovered several interventions that were to prove dramatic in William's recovery. We used vancomycin, and later Flagyl, to kill the intestinal bugs that had been plaguing him. We supplemented this with *Saccharomyces boulardii*, yeast that kills yeasts and *Clostridium*. The AIDS community has used it for years. We used glycoproteins, which are complex sugars. All of these interventions helped improve William's health and facilitate his recovery.

We also removed allergens from William's environment. We organized a "healthy home:" ripped up carpets, checked for mold and gas, and installed air filters and water filters. We purchased organic foods to decrease his intake of pesticides. We tried to ensure that his foods were antibiotic- and hormone-free, with no preservatives or dyes. We began using only the most natural cleansers, hygiene products, and hypoallergenic bedding products.

We began a home-based applied behavior analysis (ABA) education program and added speech therapy, occupational therapy, and auditory integration therapy to his schedule.

Over time we noticed several clear indications of recovery. William began to live in the present. He responded to his name and his interest in the world around him increased. He became more interactive and began to demonstrate imaginative play. Gradually, his sensory issues began to improve. He began to recover some of his early motor milestones, and to walk normally. His vision improved.

William is regaining speech and his cognitive scores are improving as he continues to make slow but steady progress.

## Mass General Hospital: Developing a Medical Protocol for Autism

We recently added a new chapter to our two-year search for medical answers.



In November 2002, a group of parents in Oregon, along with the Northwest Autism Foundation and the Autism Research Institute, raised $450,000 to fund a study in which Harvard University and Massachusetts General Hospital will collaborate in developing a medical protocol for the treatment of regressive autism.

The Harvard-Mass General study is remarkable. It is the first major study being conducted to establish a medical basis for treating autism. Within the first few months Harvard University and Massachusetts General Hospital have already made significant medical progress in treating autistic children.

Three months into the study, in January 2003, we flew William across the country to Mass General to be biopsied by their top pediatric gastroenterologists. Early findings from the study show that more than half of the children with autism have treatable gastrointestinal problems.

For two days we fed William soup broths and laxatives, preparing him for a gastrointestinal endoscopy. With his medical history of chronic diarrhea and severe food allergies, we needed to see what was happening in his stomach and gut.

The results of William's biopsy were not shocking for our family, but may be to many in the medical community, which still views regressive autism as a hopeless, lifelong disability. William was diagnosed with "nodular lymphoid hyperplasia," an intestinal inflammation affecting the lymph nodes. This finding is consistent with inflammatory injury to the intestines, and is a clear indication that William had an adverse biomedical reaction to a foreign environmental agent or toxin.

They say that a picture is worth a thousand words. Pictures of William's ulcerated lower intestine answered many questions for us. This finding explains how a child could eat all the time and suffer from malabsorption.

It explains the development of severe food allergies to inflammatory agents such as milk and wheat. It suggests how ethyl mercury might cause damage and create a porous intestine. Looking at pictures of our son's lower intestine, it seems very clear to us that William has a severe intestinal disease. While some autistic children's stomachs look like Swiss cheese, William's inflammation is mild and his lymph nodes are soft and healing. Our efforts to care for our son's digestive tract have been successful.

William's lab results were also dramatic. Some time before we took him back east, Will's gastric juices had not been sufficiently acidic, a condition that promotes yeast overgrowth. As result, we had put him on Betaine Hcl. But at Mass General, his stomach pH was shown to be extremely high (very acidic). Without the proper stomach acid, the pancreas doesn't function to produce enzymes to help the body digest foods. William is missing key enzymes that he needs to digest certain food products. He also has low levels of the amino acids that help to excrete heavy metals. We learned that William has low secretin, too low for his pancreas to function normally. He is missing several key enzymes: lipase (which digests fat) and amylase (which digests carbohydrates). This information is vital in shaping his treatment options.



The Mass General Hospital team is successfully treating autistic children by replacing enzymes and probiotics suspected to be deficient. Left untreated, these gastrointestinal problems will continue to cause increased neurological problems and exacerbate other symptoms of autism. Autistic children will continue to suffer and to regress without prompt and proper treatment.

## Timely and Appropriate Treatment: Giving the Children a Chance to Recover

Children with regressive autism need to have a thorough medical evaluation to determine what treatments are appropriate. Not all children's conditions are the same, but it is clear that many children have medical problems that need prompt attention.

There is no question in our minds that our son has a limited time for recovery. The fact that, in general, the medical profession, school systems, and insurance companies are doing very little to help these children is one of the darkest sides of our society. It is an epidemic of denial. Nearly 40% of all families with regressive autism believe their child's condition was triggered by vaccines. Most families realize that they have only a few precious years to recover their injured sons and daughters.

Parents of newly diagnosed children need to know they don't have to "reinvent the wheel." Meet and talk with other families. Don't lose hope. Don't believe that autism is just a mental illness. Investigate the role vaccines may have played. Get good medical tests and examinations from supportive professionals. Shape your own treatment program based on good, independent science.

When William was three, we were told that he might never talk and that we should ultimately investigate medication to sedate him and institutionalize him for his long-term care. Today, William has over 350 words. He can say, "I want more juice, please," "I want to go outside," "I love you," and "See you later." He plays with his sister, and he fights with her too.

We have made great sacrifices and incurred great costs in the two years since William was diagnosed but we have never lost hope. We have returned to William the gifts of health and speech—and those gifts are priceless.





*Update for Second Edition (November 2005):*

**Part II: The Glass Lightens**

When we wrote "Glass Darkly" several years ago, we had little idea how long the journey, or how apt the metaphor of a dark glass would be. The journey has been dark and at times terrifying, and the image of William, who he is and what he will become, has seemed at various points to be beyond reach and description.

Recently, a friend describing the ordeal, which he has observed firsthand for the last five years, said to a mutual acquaintance: "At first they tell you that the child you love is lost behind a brick wall, never to return. As a parent, you pick up your trowel and start picking away at the mortar between the bricks, hoping to loosen one brick at a time. Pretty soon, you notice there are people next to you with trowels, all working to tear down the wall. Then finally, you hear a sound from the other side. You work harder and harder, and slowly the sounds turn to vibration and ultimately words. Then you break through and see a face. The rest is pulling the wall down."

In 2003, William began or continued several therapies that have had dramatic effects on his recovery. First, we began B12 injections *[Editors' note: Please see related article on page 423.]* accompanied by folinic acid and

TMG, following the work of Dr. Jill James. Second, we put William on the specific carbohydrate diet (SCD), to promote gut healing and starve out the persistent gut bugs. Third, we have continued chelation with DMPS *[Editors' note: Please see related articles on pages 408 and 433.]*, and William's mercury levels after five years are now within the reference range! In addition to mercury, other heavy metals have started emerging, including lead.

We started RDI (Relationship Development Intervention) in 2004, as well as sensory integration. Both of these therapies have had dramatic effects on William's recovery. RDI is based on reconstructing basic emotional referencing and co-regulation development, interrupted by the toxic insult suffered by the children.

Since we began RDI, William has experienced a dramatic increase in referencing and language. Most importantly, he has learned to enjoy the benefits of co-regulation and play with his siblings.



William has continued to receive ABA therapy and has begun reading and is currently working on numbers. He is talking and tells us what he likes and doesn't like. He is very clear about what he wants.

Sensory integration, through the Sensory Center, is based on the recalibration of the body's three basic sensory channels: vestibular, proprioceptive, and tactile. Since we underwent an intensive SI regimen for two weeks in December of 2004, William's self-stimulatory behaviors, spinning, and humming have dramatically decreased.

William is currently in mainstream first grade with a "shadow." He has significant verbal delays, and continues to emerge emotionally and verbally. He plays with his siblings. He is interested in his world and tells us he loves us. He is continually emerging and growing up and developing. The wall is coming down. It may take awhile before it is completely gone, but the wall is coming down.

## — Chapter 24 —

# Improving Every Day

By Juliana Mendenhall

*Juli Mendenhall and her children, including son Conor, who was born in October 1996, live near Portland, Oregon. This story was written in March 2002.*



On October 26, 1996, I gave birth to my fourth child, Conor, an apparently healthy baby boy. He was tested and poked and prodded in the usual fashion, and handed back to my waiting arms. I put him to breast and laid him in the plastic "aquarium" crib next to my hospital bed. Exhausted, I lay back and fell into a deep sleep. I was awakened by my new angel's screaming. He had slept all of about 20 minutes and was now screaming for all he was worth! I picked him up and began a struggle that I did not know would last 3½ years. He screamed for 15 hours that night. For months after that, he would sleep for two hours and stay awake for six. My other children eventually learned that their needs would no longer be met instantly. They learned patience, and we learned to live around a very difficult child. The moments of happiness that we got from him were like glimpses into heaven! He was so beautiful. (I now consider that an autistic trait. They are all such pretty children.)

When Conor turned one year old, the grandparents gently told us that something was wrong. Friends would point out missed milestones and Conor's seeming inability to tolerate anyone's presence. Denial was my Siamese twin back then; I was attached to it and it comforted me. I finally allowed that he might have a hearing problem. The doctor backed my denial by telling me that boys are sometimes late bloomers, and not to worry. I had Conor's hearing tested three times during my 1½-year-long struggle to find out what was REALLY wrong with my littlest boy. Finally we were referred to Dr. Gene Stubbs at Oregon Health Sciences University (OHSU). He did diagnostic tests to uncover autism. The people there really bugged me; later I realized they threatened my denial. My safe state of ignorance was quickly becoming a thing of the past. "Mild autism" became the diagnosis. I felt as if someone had dropped me off a cliff. What could I hang on to? I had spun around so many times I wasn't sure which way was up anymore. I hardly felt the impact. I was too confused.

Once I got a grip on myself, I was ready to fight. I was given a piece of paper with a list of books and a flier on government therapy. Armed with these poor excuses for weapons, I went home. My husband (we have since divorced, another statistic for the parents of handicapped children) looked up autism and came across Temple Grandin. Reading about her world, and seeing her as an adult, made me realize that this was a lifelong struggle. Conor didn't just have the measles; the vacant look in his eyes wasn't going to go away like a rash would. My husband also found information on a gluten-free and casein-free (GFCF) diet. It looked interesting, but we were not there yet.

We found a company that did private ABA therapy, and began weeks and months of work. I had already taught Conor his ABC's, shapes, numbers, animals etc. My mother's foresight led her to tell me, "Work with him daily, Juli!" However, working with me and working with a therapist turned out to be two entirely different things. Conor screamed constantly. I would stand outside the therapy room with tears in my eyes. My two-year-old had a 30-hour-a-week job! He has worked at that job ever since, give or take some hours, and he has never liked it. It has taken time, but therapy has turned out to be wonderful. We switched to the Carbone method, and he is now answering questions and requesting all the time. Therapy has been a huge part of Conor's road to recovery.



Back when therapy started, Conor's therapist mentioned his odd reaction after I had given him a muffin for breakfast. The therapist explained that some parents believed gluten and casein caused a drug-like effect. I told my husband, and we learned everything we could about the GFCF diet. I began this impossible diet two years ago. It tasted so awful that I knew I would never be able to make decent food for Conor unless I acclimated myself to the taste. So, one month later I, too, began the diet. It has been two years now. My son went from a gastrointestinal nightmare to a once-a-day regular. He eats like a king. I make pop tarts, pizzas, donuts, spaghetti, soups, risotto, etc. After beginning the diet, Conor started to feel pain. He would look surprised when he bumped his head, as if wondering, "Hey, did you do that to me?" (This from a little boy who could previously drop a tool on his foot, and walk away with a cut as if it were a mark from a pen—no pain.) His eye contact went up, and he began verbalizing more often. There was never a magical day when he looked at me and said, "Hi mommy, I can talk now, thanks!" but he is healthy and more aware, no doubt about it.

After implementing the diet for Conor, I started looking into other biomedical treatments. I read Karyn Seroussi, Catherine Maurice, William

Shaw, Ph.D., and a host of others. I decided that yeast was next. Through a support group I began at the urging of Conor's therapists, I learned about a marvelous doctor in a nearby town. He would help me with these unorthodox ways to treat autism. In fact, he thought they were a good idea! This was a far cry from the sideways glances and patronizing nods I got from my son's pediatrician. We did Flagyl and nystatin. My son had a horrible die-off reaction that sent me calling the poison control center: vomiting, eyes rolling back in his head, crying. "Flu," they said. Hmmmmmm, then why was he eating fries one hour later? I never saw a huge difference from doing a yeast kill. We did it right—no fruit, no sugars of any kind. He did not test for a big yeast problem, either. Oh well. Next!



I began to go to DAN! conferences, and any other forum that would give me more information about my son's treatments. I heard about Dr. Mary Megson and her theories on cod liver oil. It made sense to me, so I began Kirkman's cod liver oil immediately. The results were amazing. The eye contact went way up. He began turning the lights on and off just like Dr. Megson had described. He was getting results!

Potty training was always such a problem, but I knew that Conor was not ready. I had listened to Dr. Megson describe bethanecol or urocholine as boosters for the cod liver oil. Some parents giving these supplements to their children were seeing results with potty training. I called my lovely doctor who had an open mind and kind heart, and he prescribed this for us. Conor was potty trained shortly after.

I now began to look into Conor's health more seriously. I had heard about mercury and how its symptoms matched autistic symptoms. I took my son to a naturopath close to home to have his blood and hair tested for minerals. What a nightmare. I had used a numbing cream on Conor's arms. Apparently, if you use too much of it, it shrinks the veins. Well, wanting my son to feel no pain during the blood draw, I—the uninformed—slathered it on. Still, the lovely naturopath was able to get enough blood to test.

Conor had high copper, elevated aluminum, and some mercury. However, at that point I rejected chelation. I am an extremely cautious caretaker, and this treatment had not been tested enough for me to trust it. Since then I have done three rounds of chelation on Conor. I have not seen results yet, but I do believe I will.

I had heard about secretin at the DAN! conferences, and felt it would benefit Conor. I did not, however, have the stomach to give him an IV. We began transdermal and saw no real effect. I discontinued that treatment and began transdermal glutathione. He gets a four-ml rub nearly every day. He is quite grumpy without it. He also gets a Super Nu-Thera supplement in an omega-3 fatty acid paste at lunchtime.

I have stocked my kitchen with dipeptidyl peptidase IV (DPP-IV), taurine, hemogenics (iron supplements), vitamin C, calcium, and probiotics. We use them all. I do believe these are a strong support system for my son.

Conor improves every day. There have been milestones. We went to a fair one time and my sensory-sensitive son wanted to go on a kids' roller coaster. We went, twice. He loved it! He came up behind me once and called me Mommy. I always told myself that I would believe in his recovery if he could call me Mommy. I get that reward a lot now. He sings songs he makes up. I enjoy seeing his imagination when he plays dinosaurs and animals. He watches Disney now, and screams appropriately. He has an autistic trait that he won't let go of, however: he raises my sleeve and rubs his face in the crook of my elbow. I don't really want to let go of that one.



*Update (February 2003):*

Conor continues to improve daily. I recently started him on Houston enzymes, which keep his bowels in order. His preschool is so happy with him that they ask if it is possible to have him come without a therapist. I am not ready for that. I like having a social advocate for my child at school. He still struggles with autism. It takes a minute but people see there is "something."

I took him on an airplane to Hawaii not long ago, and he was better than most of the kids on the plane, though he needed constant intellectual input, of course. We basically had a five-hour therapy session there and back! He loved Hawaii. I vacuum-packed individual meals and microwaved them for him. No infractions and a happy guy! We were even put into an Australian commercial with my nine-year-old neurotypical son. Now that's inclusion!!!

*Update for Second Edition (September 2005):*

Since this book was first published my life has taken many turns. I am newly married and my wonderful husband has turned out to be a great therapist! Conor is getting more athletic and plays with him. We have three dogs now and Conor loves to feed them.

Conor continues to progress. Our lead therapist, Nikki Deshane, has taught Conor reading, mathematics, writing (cursive too!), and to sit and listen in class. He has friends and is one of the best at academics in his class. The teachers and the director are amazing people. It makes you believe in Christian kindness again. This summer we took two days of school out of his scheduling and he regressed at home. (He never regresses for Nikki!) Nikki is teaching him to swim now, too. She has been a Godsend to our family. I defer to her for everything with Conor. She teaches him independence, telling everyone how smart Conor is and that he can do it, so they back off and let him (including me, although my head is thicker in this area than anyone else's). We owe her so much!

We continue with the GFCF diet and have dabbled in some other natural remedies. My support group is six years running now! The families have become close friends with whom we share everything. I continue to look for ways to help Conor, while always keeping his health highest on the list. He is a happy little guy with good buddies and a will of iron. Conor tries so hard at everything he does. Conor has brought so much happiness to us. He continues to teach the world grace.

# — Chapter 25 —
# Hope Renewed
By Kelli Miller

*Kelli Miller and her husband, Ron, live near Cincinnati, Ohio, with their daughter, Avery (who was born in May 1998), and their son, Austin. Avery, initially diagnosed with pervasive developmental disorder, now is re-diagnosed as having attention deficit disorder. This story was written in June 2002.*

## Introduction



*"Prepare yourselves for a life of institutionalization."*

Those words were absolutely devastating to us as proud parents of a beautiful 22-month-old little girl. As we walked out of the Child Evaluation Center in Louisville, Kentucky our minds were racing. How in the world were we going to deal with this? How could this happen to us? What were our friends and family going to think?

Avery Hope Miller was born on May 14, 1998 in Louisville. My pregnancy was normal but was termed high-risk because of a history of multiple miscarriages. She was a healthy 9 lb., 3 oz. female with a full head of hair.

Avery's development was normal, and she hit all the typical milestones: she held her head up at six weeks, rolled over at 10 weeks, sat at five months, and walked at 12 months. The only thing we noticed that was unusual was that she loved "Veggie Tale" videos. We really didn't think a lot about it, passing it off as an "inherited" characteristic from her father since he can watch an Indy car race in the middle of a tornado and not even notice that the weather is less than perfect.

We were actually quite concerned about our 34-month-old son's speech development. The words he used to communicate were unclear, and we were concerned because he had experienced recurring ear infections. Our pediatrician recommended that a therapist come into our home to evaluate Austin for a developmental delay; she also recommended that Avery be evaluated at the same time.

When the therapist came to our house, Austin was evaluated first because we were very worried about his hearing. After a two-hour workup, which came back normal, it was Avery's turn. The therapist asked Avery to do several things—stack blocks, string beads, identify pictures—but Avery just wanted to spin the wheels on a toy car. She really had no interest in what this stranger had to say. We, of course, felt that Avery wasn't relating to her because she was a stranger, and that Avery just preferred the toys she was used to. After all, she was less than two years old.

The therapist's words would change our lives forever. She announced to us that Avery was exhibiting signs of PDD-NOS. She told me not to research it—it would only scare me to death. She referred us to the Child Evaluation Center in Louisville to confirm her suspicions. Of course, the first thing we did was go to the Internet and search for PDD-NOS. The search came back "See Autism." The only thing we knew about autism was the movie "Rain Man." Was that the way my child was going to be, like Rain Man? We later found out that PDD-NOS stood for "pervasive developmental disorder, not otherwise specified." What did that mean? The more we read, the more confused we were. Our child did not injure herself. She did not cry all the time. She reacted quite normally to our showing of affection; as a matter of fact, she could not stand for her mother to be out of the room. We thought the diagnosis was obviously a mistake, but it would be confirmed later by the Child Evaluation Center. We also learned that PDD-NOS is on the "autism spectrum."



### Not My Child

The diagnosis of a child with a "lifelong disorder" is similar to the diagnosis of a child with a terminal disease, in terms of the grieving process that is involved. After the initial shock and anger, we decided that this was not going to happen to our child—she was going to recover. We would try every therapy, spend our last dime, and pour our whole existence into making her "normal." The Child Evaluation Center recommended one hour of speech therapy and one hour of occupational therapy per week, so we hired a therapist to work with Avery four hours a week. After three months of absolutely no progress, we were at our wits' end.

It was April 2000, Autism Awareness Month. While I was channel surfing one day, a caption on C-SPAN caught my eye: "Autism and Childhood Vaccinations." I had heard something about the MMR causing autism, but I never really thought that was credible. The U.S. government is here to protect our civil rights, protect our lives from harm … our government would never allow our children to be injected with something that could actually cause harm to them. C-SPAN was airing a Congressional hearing with parents testifying that their children were fine before their vaccinations, after which they were lost in the world of autism. The good news was that there was a doctor in Baton Rouge, Louisiana who was having success in helping children who were experiencing autism symptoms to become normal again. The next day, I made an appointment with Amy Holmes, M.D.

Dr. Holmes said that Avery acted a lot like her own son had at the same age. Upon reviewing test results, she found Avery had classic symptoms of heavy metal poisoning, specifically mercury. How could she have high mercury levels? We soon found out that the culprit was thimerosal. Thimerosal is a preservative used by pharmaceutical companies to make multiple-dose vaccinations. It has no use other than to allow these companies to package 10 doses to a vial rather than making individual-dose vials. Thimerosal is 49.6% ethyl mercury by weight, and in Avery's case it was injected into her body on day one of life through her hepatitis B vaccine, and then multiple times during her first year of life through other vaccines including the DTaP and HIB.



After further research, we discovered that by the time Avery was six months old, she had been given nine different vaccines with thimerosal, totaling 187.5 mcg of mercury. We compared the amount to the suggested safe limits for methyl mercury intake published by three federal agencies: the Environmental Protection Agency (EPA), the U.S. Food and Drug Administration (FDA), and the Agency for Toxic Substances and Disease Registry (ATSDR). Mercury intake through vaccination during the first six months of Avery's life *exceeded* the limit set by the EPA.[1]

## The Protocol

Dr. Holmes started Avery on a chelation regimen using the drug DMSA every four hours, seven days on, seven days off. The effectiveness of chelation was demonstrated when we viewed Avery's very first urine test. It showed a whopping 19 mcg of mercury dumped into her urine on her very first chelation trial (19 is at the far end of the "Very Elevated" column). This was proof to us that mercury was the reason for Avery's problems.

After three rounds of DMSA by itself, tests showed that her body was rid of loosely bound mercury, and it was now time to go after the tightly bound mercury that was located in the brain and other vital organs. To do that, Dr. Holmes prescribed alpha lipoic acid (ALA) to be given at the same time as the DMSA. At first we had the DMSA/ALA compounded into suppositories, but later we were able to give the combination orally. We did change her chelation schedule to three days on, 11 days off, dosing every eight hours. There is a lot of controversy about the dosing schedule, but Avery seemed to do equally well on either schedule. We stuck with the eight-hour schedule because it allowed all of us to get at least eight hours of sleep at night. Avery was on DMSA/ALA from November 2000 to February 2002. At that time, test results showed that her metals were in the normal range.

In addition to chelation, Avery has had 30 hours a week of applied behavior analysis therapy in our home. She has done exceptionally well with this therapy, and now has as much, if not more, academic knowledge than her peers.

### Progress



Avery is now four years old, and has been re-diagnosed with ADD—she no longer qualifies for the diagnosis PDD-NOS. Avery still has a speech delay, but is talking in full sentences and asking questions. Her social skills are growing every day, but she still appears to others as a little shy. She does have little girl friends, and enjoys it when they get together to play. Avery has no self-stimulating behaviors. Nobody would ever know the original diagnosis unless they knew her history. We are confident that Avery will function normally in her world, and will be able to lead a normal life. We are so thankful to Dr. Holmes for her dedication to children on the autistic spectrum. Avery owes the quality of her life to her.

We are also thankful for the many friends and family who could do nothing but pray for our family. It has not been easy—what started out as a life with only brightness ahead was interrupted by darkness, but thanks to prayers and the dedication of Dr. Holmes, Avery is a beautiful, normal little girl with a bright life ahead of her.

### Interesting facts (May 2002)

- Only two single-antigen pediatric hepatitis B vaccines exist on the U.S. market: Engerix-B (GlaxoSmithKline) and Recombivax HB (Merck). Both contain thimerosal and 12.5 micrograms of mercury per 0.5 ml dose. The American Academy of Pediatrics pressed CDC to agree to a delay of the hepatitis B vaccination series, usually started at birth, for children born to hepatitis B surface antigen seronegative mothers. The Academy argued that the delay would be only temporary because both Merck and GlaxoSmithKline had promised that they could quickly shift manufacturing to thimerosal-free vaccine, perhaps in just a few months (the FDA had already promised to review applications for thimerosal-free hepatitis B vaccine within 30 days).

- The FDA is moving in the pharmacological direction of "single-dose presentations of vaccines without preservatives," said the FDA's Dr. William M. Egan at the Third Annual Conference on Vaccine Research in Washington, DC, May 4, 2000.[2]
- Dr. Egan, acting director of the Center for Biological Evaluation and Research's office of Vaccines Research and Review, centered his talk on thimerosal, a common preservative in vaccines, including childhood vaccines. The American Academy of Pediatrics and the Public Health Service released a joint statement saying that the risks of not vaccinating far outweighed the potential risk of thimerosal. But the statement—as Dr. Egan pointed out—also recommended that thimerosal be removed from vaccines as soon as possible.
- As of May 2000, it is possible to get the entire course of childhood vaccines without thimerosal, as several manufacturers have developed thimerosal-free vaccines.



**References**

[1]Thimerosal and Neurotoxicity, written and overseen by Lewis Mehl-Madrona, Program Director, Continuum Center for Health and Healing, Beth Israel Hospital/Albert Einstein School of Medicine (www.Healing-Arts.org/children/index.htm).

[2]Washington, May 4, 2000 (Reuters Health). FDA endorses single virus vaccines without preservatives.

*Update (March 2003):*

Avery will be five years old in May 2003 and is fully integrated into her preschool classroom. She was re-evaluated in January 2003 and given the official diagnosis of ADD with expressive speech delay. Her speech is coming along very well. She is talking in sentences that are appropriate but somewhat immature. The important thing is that even though her speech is behind, she is developing now at a normal pace and at some point will catch up with others her age. We are convinced Avery will lead a normal life and are very thankful to the doctors in the DAN! movement who gave us hope and the courage to not give up on her.

*Update for Second Edition (February 2006):*

Avery is doing great! She is mainstreamed into Mason, Ohio, schools (one of the top public school systems in the U.S.) and in the second grade. She is a straight-A student and doing awesome. Her reading and writing are ahead of the second-grade schedule and she continues to amaze her teachers with her wit and charm.

She now is truly part of the peer group in her classroom. She is indistinguishable from her peers and very social. She is a cheerleader for her brother Austin's fourth-grade football team, the Comets, and has exceeded every expectation of her both in school and in a social setting. She is a blessing to everyone who comes in contact with her. We are truly proud of her and her accomplishments. There are many great things to come for Avery. We pray for your kids too!

## — Chapter 26 —
# Austin's Journey
By Jeri Parrott

*Brad and Jeri Parrott live outside Portland, Oregon, with their four children: Jen (1981), Adam (1983), Ashlie (1991), and Austin (1993), who faces the challenge of autism. This story was written in May 2002.*



Austin was born on April 27th, 1993. We had a few complications during labor: I needed oxygen, and Austin's doctors had to attach electrodes to his head while he was still inside. I received Pitocin to speed up delivery, and when Austin was finally born, his lungs needed to be suctioned because of the meconium that he had swallowed. Other than that, his delivery was unremarkable.

He came home two days later, and everything seemed perfectly normal. He was a very, very good baby. He was sleeping through the night at five weeks, was a good eater, and was hitting every milestone about the right time. When Austin was somewhere between two and three years old, however, we began to notice that he was losing language. He also started to talk with an English accent, which we found both amusing and strange. When he was 3½, we became more concerned about his lack of language skills, and noticed that he was becoming more and more difficult to console and wanted to be with Mommy most of the time. He stopped responding favorably to people he knew, and was beginning to retreat into his own world. He played relatively normally, but by himself.

Austin also started self-stimulating behavior, and began banging his head on the wall or floor, whichever was closest. We felt that he was doing this out of frustration, but this was unacceptable behavior, so we disciplined him. He stopped head banging, but another behavior would appear. Each time it was met with discipline, and each time it would stop, only to be replaced with another more interesting one. We also noticed that his hair, which was once "Shirley Temple" curly, had now become stick straight.

We took Austin to see a noted doctor. After testing him, the doctor said he believed that Austin was bright (he was being coy with the doctor, smiling and interacting). At the same time, the doctor was frustrated because he couldn't get a good sense of how Austin was functioning intellectually, as he was not cooperating fully with the testing. He would do very well and then lose interest, but when the testing resumed at a higher level he would become interested again. The doctor concluded that we just needed to find the "key" for Austin.

We took Austin home, not particularly worried about him, certain that he would continue to develop and be fine. Perhaps, we thought, Austin was just a quiet child and a slower learner. We started with speech therapy, which he enjoyed, and just hoped for the best.

From his therapist, we heard the possibility that Austin might have autism. But if he did, the therapist suggested, he was certainly on the mild end of the autism spectrum, and we felt okay with that.

When at four years of age Austin had no interest at all in potty training, we went back to the same doctor for help. With his guidance we had Austin trained successfully in one day—four hours, to be exact. We were all encouraged by this because it showed that Austin was capable of mastering a task that he had no desire to do, and all he might need was extra encouragement and motivation.



Austin started kindergarten in the fall of 1998. It was hard for him, and he was struggling. Although he seemed happy, he was not really interacting with his peers, and was keeping to himself. In the spring of 1999 we met with the staff at Austin's school to develop his individualized education plan, and again autism was mentioned.

Austin was given an aide for the remainder of the school year, and he has had one ever since. He is currently in mainstream second grade, although his work is modified for him.

We knew nothing about autism with the exception of what we had seen in "Rain Man," so we became avid readers. In the summer of 1998 I came across an article talking about the gluten-free, casein-free (GFCF) diet and its usefulness in treating autism. I immediately contacted the doctor mentioned in the article, and arranged to have Austin's blood drawn and tested. Sure enough, he had a problem digesting gluten and casein (wheat and dairy). Again, we were encouraged by this, and implemented the GFCF diet. I also hooked up with Dave Humphrey at Kirkman Labs. His expertise was invaluable; after directing me to Dr. Bernard Rimland's website so I could do further research and come up with a list of supplements that I hoped would be beneficial to Austin, he helped me get started.

We had the great privilege of meeting Dr. Rimland a few years ago. All I could do was give him a great big hug and thank him profusely for his knowledge, because it was helping our son on some level. I have spent countless hours scouring his website for every piece of information that I could find. I started with Super Nu-Thera vitamin supplements, and went from there.

About this time, we noticed an increase in Austin's language. He also seemed happier and brighter all around. Austin was becoming more aware of his surroundings, and actually telling us what he wanted instead of making us figure it out for ourselves—not an easy task when you have only a finger point to go on. After becoming a picky eater at around age three (we affectionately called him a grazer), he started eating very well.

Not satisfied with these results alone, we went to see a doctor in Florida, where another battery of tests was done. Austin had high levels of mercury in his system, so we decided that chelation was in order. We were baffled about where the mercury had come from, though as we look back now it is easy to link it to the vaccines, because it was around that time when Austin started to change. The new doctor also noted that Austin had a yeast/fungal overgrowth, which we treated with nystatin for a while; he did not react favorably, so we switched to Yeast Control.



We have been doing chelation since the fall of 2000, and continue it today. We have Austin's blood tested regularly, and have noticed that the mercury is coming down slowly.

In the spring of 2001 we put Austin on Dexedrine to help with his focus at school. This did help some, and more so when the dosing was increased in the spring of 2002.

In July of 2001 we had an EEG done. We found out that Austin was having almost constant seizures; they were not noticeable, but occurred frequently for two to 10 seconds each time. His doctor suggested that this could be getting in the way of Austin's learning because his thought processes were being interrupted on a regular basis. Again, we were thrilled at this information because it might help explain why Austin was struggling to learn. We started Depakote, and waited. We did see improvement again at first, but then he just seemed to stay at one level. Sometimes we'd see great gains and at other times we'd see nothing—very frustrating for parents.

In the winter of 2001 we hooked up with a doctor in Reno, Nevada, who did a complete biochemical analysis of Austin's blood and urine. Through this we were able to identify the specific substances that Austin's system was lacking, and were able to add them: amino acids, vitamins, and electrolytes. This has helped him greatly. As a side effect, Austin's hair has become quite curly again.

There are days at school when Austin is "right on," and wants to do his work, and has no problems. Then there are days when he struggles and is uncooperative, and Cheryl, his assistant, can't get him to do anything. Luckily, Cheryl is great at improvising, and has the patience of a saint.

We feel blessed that we have Austin. He has been challenging, to say the least, but he is a very sweet, lovable, affectionate child, and we love him like crazy. There is absolutely nothing that we would not do for him. I feel that we have been tremendously blessed with the people whom we have met and from whom we have learned so much.

While we definitely see improvements in speech and language, we have yet to see the tremendous breakthrough that we want for Austin. We will continue to advocate for him and pursue any and all therapies, tests, etc. that could be beneficial for him, without harming him.

Although we chose to take an alternate medical route in developing the best and safest protocol for Austin, with little or no guidance from his pediatrician, we are lucky to have hooked up with the people we have met. Without exception, each and every one is dedicated to helping children with this baffling spectrum of autism, and we are immeasurably grateful for their guidance.



*Update (March 2003):*

During the summer of 2002, Brad and I, along with Austin's neurologist, decided to wean Austin off his Depakote (he'd had a clean EEG and had begun to develop side effects from the high dosage). We cut down the Depakote over two months and really didn't see any change one way or the other with the exception of the side effects disappearing, and Austin was much happier and more animated.

In the fall we lowered his Dexedrine and he was eating everything with no problems. We had an amino acid plasma test done and found that Austin's body was extremely low in every single essential and nonessential amino acid (by low I mean they were virtually nonexistent). He was immediately started on free-form amino acids, and we began to notice changes for the better in his schoolwork—small changes, including more focus and attention to particular tasks. He also began to race through programs that he'd shown no interest in completing before.

In February of 2003, we took Austin to Massachusetts General Hospital for a colonoscopy and endoscopy. We found that Austin's pancreas was not manufacturing enzymes and that he had a major malabsorption problem.

He also has severe constipation, much worse than we ever knew.

Austin is currently being treated with digestive enzymes with every snack or meal, free-form amino acids, and regular enemas (such a pleasure, for both of us) and laxatives to help him become, and we hope stay, regular. We started secretin infusions, which he now receives every four weeks, and have seen great results.

At school he is doing amazingly well for him. He can write almost the whole alphabet, he can write his numbers and name, and he can copy sentences somewhat accurately. He also has started to read very basic books and is working with Tami (his tutor) on sight words, writing and reading four times a week after school.

This is a child who could not write his name last fall, let alone any numbers, and would not read with any accuracy or predictability. Things are far from where they should be; however, the improvements we have seen these past two months are phenomenal, and for the first time we see real hope for our beautiful little boy.



*Update for Second Edition (December 2005):*

Since we originally wrote about Austin's journey, we have tried several new treatments that have seemed to make a difference for him. We went to the Sensory Learning Center (SLC, www.SensoryLearning-Vancouver.com) in Vancouver, Washington, last April. Since completing the 30-day program, we feel we have seen improvement in Austin's spontaneous and meaningful language. With Austin we get to a plateau where it seems that no new changes are occurring; but then after a while, maybe a couple of weeks, Austin will do something new that will give us encouragement. Either he will have more imaginative, interactive, and creative play by himself or with others, or he will have more meaningful and spontaneous language.

In addition to going to the Sensory Learning Center, Austin attended Eden Institute's summer camp in Connecticut for two weeks. Eden works with the student's IEP, combining academics with social activities and peer interaction. The Institute also works with us to organize Austin's IEP for the coming school year. Austin also attended Mt. Hood Kiwanis Camp for a week this summer. All of this, along with tutoring provided by Tami Brester for three or four days a week, and a great program at school, has contributed to Austin's continued success and achievements.

We continue to seek information about new treatments or therapies that we could try with Austin. His happiness is our main priority. Seeing him take pride in himself, and give and receive love and affection within our family, makes us feel a tremendous amount of pride in being his parents.

## — Chapter 27 —

# Inspiration, Hope, Perseverance, and Success

By Susan and Garry Petrie

*Susan and Garry Petrie live in Portland, Oregon, with Conrad, who was born in December 1995. This story was written in October 2002.*

Our story has the familiar elements: fear, anger, denial, and sadness. There is also hope, determination, help, and love. We feel our story is successful, although we know the outlook for our son's future is guarded.



Conrad was born on December 18, 1995, and my husband and I truly considered him the most magnificent thing that ever happened to us. Before Conrad was born, I had only heard other mothers describe the miracle of birth and the love of a child. Until you have your own child, no words can ever describe the joy a child brings.

I am a very optimistic person by nature and always look at the positive side of things. After Conrad was born, I was in a blissful state. My bliss lasted a wonderful 39 months. Conrad was a happy, bright, warm, loving child. There were times when friends or family would comment, "Conrad needs discipline." I would always retort, "He is in his 'Terrible Twos.'" I gave him appropriate time-outs, and he appeared fine. However, looking back, I now realize that most of my friends, family, and Conrad's caregivers knew more than I did.

When Conrad was two, I thought he needed to be around more children and I enrolled him in a small daycare at a local church. Because I worked out of my home, Conrad only attended daycare for two mornings a week. I never realized that while he was at daycare he was just sitting in a corner by himself and not interacting with the other children. When I came to pick him up, he would be playing by himself, but I did not think much of the fact.

I had read about the Terrible Twos and knew that toddlers going through them have many tantrums because they have not learned adequate communication skills. Typically, as children learn to communicate, their behavior problems reside. I was just waiting for Conrad's tantrums and behavior issues to take their natural course. Conrad was our first child, and I had very little experience being around children. I had no knowledge of what the natural course was. I went happily along my way reading *Parent* magazine and being my optimistic self. Privately, I was dreading the thought of taking Conrad anywhere away from the house. He had terrible meltdowns and was becoming very difficult in unfamiliar places.

Then one day I mentioned to a good friend that it was time for Conrad's three-year checkup with our pediatrician. My friend had just taken her daughter to her checkup, and everything was fine. I mentioned that I had just taken Conrad to his pediatrician because he had an unusual cold and runny sinus, but now he was doing fine. I told her I did not think it was necessary to go for another visit, because I had just seen the doctor. She quickly explained that the doctor looks at childhood development during the exam, as well as health issues. She convinced me I should make the appointment and take Conrad. This was the start of the realization something was terribly wrong.



During the examination, Conrad would not interact with the doctor, making the exam very difficult. The doctor finally looked at me and said, "Do you understand what he is saying?" Of course he was yelling "Momma," because he was upset about being at the doctor's office. The doctor looked at me and said, "When a child is three, most people should be able to understand him 90% of the time, yet Conrad is still using baby 'jargon.'" The doctor referred me to a speech pathologist, who subsequently referred me to Washington County for further evaluations.

I made my appointment for Conrad's evaluation. Washington County sent their autism specialist to observe Conrad at his daycare setting. The daycare staff later told me they had thought something was wrong with Conrad. They felt it was not their place to talk to me about it. It seemed people around me knew, and I was in a state of denial. Because he showed significant delays, he qualified immediately for early childhood intervention.

Conrad's assessment was definitely a shock. I immediately called his pediatrician and made an appointment with the Child Development Clinic at Kaiser. After a long evaluation, Conrad's Battelle Development Inventory Scores were:

| | |
|---|---|
| Personal Social | 16 months (23 months behind) |
| Adaptive | 22 Months (17 months behind) |
| Cognitive | 19-21 Months |

All of his scores showed that he was over a year behind his peers. The doctors gave Conrad a diagnosis of autism. This was the worst news possible. My first response was one of complete denial. "No, my child is not autistic." The doctors countered, "Yes, and he is showing very pronounced autistic behavior." His behavior included the typical autistic traits: no eye contact, not responding to his name, not playing with toys in a typical manner, substantial language delay, etc. The staff of the clinic advised me that there was help available, and to use the diagnosis to get assistance. The doctors reminded me that there is no cure for autism. The clinic did not give us treatment recommendations, but merely referred us back to early intervention at the county.

I felt as if I were a terrible mother. How did I not notice that my child had stopped developing around the age of two years? Why was I in such a state of denial and blaming everything on the Terrible Twos? I will probably never know the answer to these questions. I could not consider why this misfortune befell me, but only consider how to fix it. Since Conrad was born, I had enjoyed a blissful life. Life was becoming much more of a struggle and Conrad's behavior increasingly more difficult. I needed to find a solution and restore harmony.



After we received the diagnosis, my husband and I went directly to the bookstore to look for books on autism. We searched the Internet and joined support groups. We met other parents with autistic children. We concluded that ABA (applied behavior analysis) was the most promising treatment.

**Treatment**

Our research indicated that ABA was promising, but it was neither guaranteed nor easy. Early intervention did not want to hear the words ABA—we had no idea about the controversy surrounding the treatment of autistic children. Early childhood intervention in the State of Oregon interprets ABA as meaning 40 hours per week of intensive one-on-one training and therefore too expensive to implement.

We became advocates for our son. This can be an overwhelming task, to say the least. We found help with a good attorney and a book entitled *The Effectiveness of Early Intervention* by Dr. Paul Guralnick. Chapter 14 of the book deals with early intervention programs. The chapter, written by Drs. Dawson and Osterling of Washington State University, compared different autism programs. This gave us a good place to start designing Conrad's recovery program.

We contacted Dr. Kathy Calouri of Project P.A.C.E. (Personalizing

Autistic Children's Education). She explained to us that if a child does not have eye contact and does not have imitation skills, the child cannot develop and learn in a typical fashion. She recommended a treatment plan for Conrad that included discrete trial therapy 2½ hours per day. This included working with noun and verb picture cards to teach Conrad how to associate verbal labels with objects and events. Conrad would work with PACE for the next 2½ years.

We continued with the early intervention program provided by the State of Oregon at the Westside Early Autism Program and Integrated Preschool. Early intervention preschool was from 8:30 am to 12:30 pm Monday through Friday. Therefore, Conrad's recovery program consisted of 6½ hours per day, five days per week. During the summer, we applied for extended school year services so he would not miss any educational opportunities. We also placed him in the Oregon Hearing & Speech Institute's summer program. For two summers Conrad participated in ACAP (Autistic Children's Activity Program). We filled Conrad's schedule with any meaningful program we could find. He was going to so many different programs I needed a spreadsheet to keep track of his schedule. Conrad was receptive and progressing at a steady rate.



We heard about secretin so I enrolled Conrad in a secretin trial at the Oregon Health Sciences University. This was a double-blind study where the children received two injections: one shot was secretin and the other was a placebo. The doctors told neither the parents nor the staff conducting the study which injection contained the secretin. The most astounding thing was that after Conrad's first injection, he actually came up to me with his hands extended and said, "Messy hands." This was his first spontaneous speech. I felt it was the secretin.

The study findings appeared to be inconclusive. However, most of the parents in the study felt that the secretin had helped in various ways. I do not know if Conrad's first spontaneous speech occurred because of the secretin or because he had been in therapy (during the period between the injections, Conrad had continued with his ABA program with P.A.C.E.). Should there have been more injections? I do not know. We were not about to stop a proven therapy on account of an inconclusive study. But I was happy that his spontaneous speech was developing and at a rapid pace.

During the secretin trial, the doctors asked us to collect a urine sample so they could test Conrad's intestinal system. They explained that many autistic children have "leaky gut syndrome." However, getting a urine sample proved impossible. We tried other regimens to address the leaky gut question. We started Conrad on a regimen of probiotics and colostrum from Kirkman Laboratories. We noticed that these products seemed to help boost his immune system. He did not have as many colds and sinus infections as in the past. We also put him on Super Nu-Thera, a vitamin supplement from Kirkman Labs designed for autistic children.

Parents always try to do what is best for their children, and I can truly say that we have tried many things. At this time, Conrad has just finished kindergarten without the special help of an aide. At the end of kindergarten, he tested in the average range for academics. This June I took him back to the Child Developmental Clinic and the doctors told us that we had done an "excellent job in closing the developmental gaps" of autism. My treatment program for our son was successful. He is doing great.

The future is guarded. Conrad may have particular behavior traits, but they are within the norm. All children, whether autistic or not, need guidance and love. The point is, that is your job.



*Update (March 2003):*

Conrad is doing well in first grade. His math skills are good but his reading, writing, and spelling skills are delayed. It is evident that Conrad can do the work but has terrible trouble focusing and staying on task. We had him tested at The Children's Program in Portland to try and understand more about his learning disabilities.

The child psychologist's tests showed that Conrad had significant ADHD. Because autistic traits can overlap with ADHD we are now looking at treatments for ADHD. We are having him tutored in reading and writing. However, I am confident that when we treat his ADHD Conrad will be successful in his academics.

Conrad currently attends a "relationship development" playgroup through PACE that follows Steven Gutstein, Ph.D.'s methodical approach to creating meaningful and lasting relationships. He has made huge improvements in his social skills. Conrad is invited to birthday parties and involved in Scouts and Tae Kwon Do.

I will always guard my son's future but I feel he has overcome the significant delays and behaviors of his autism. I wish for all parents facing the obstacles and frustrations of autism hope, perseverance, and success. Most of all, a cure.

*Update for Second Edition (November 2005):*

Conrad is now in fourth grade in public school in Oregon. He is in the regular classroom with an aide who helps him along with other children in the classroom.

He is academically with his peers in math and is pulled out to the resource room 40 minutes a day for reading. His reading is about one year behind his peers, but with tutoring and help from the resource room teacher (who is wonderful) this gap is closing. His meltdowns decrease each year. We strongly believe that intensive early intervention is the key to Conrad's wonderful success.

## — Chapter 28 —
# Love Never Fails
By Jason and Angelene Rowe

*Jason and Angelene Rowe live in Oregon with their autistic son, RJ, (born in 1993) and his younger brothers, Christian and Colby. They wrote this story in January 2003.*

Dedication: We dedicate this to our beloved son, our "R.J. Bear." You continue to broaden our hearts and minds as we continue to learn more about yours. You're an inspiration for all who know you and an incredible blessing from God. Always remember God never gives us more than we can endure. He has given you a great calling and the strength it will take to carry it. You are truly amazing to us, and you have taught us so much about the fortitude and endurance of the human spirit. We pray you will always follow your heart, for it is there that you will find strength and peace to continue your journey. "Good Job. Peace. We love you!"



* * * * *

We were married at ages 18 and 19; just one year later, we were preparing to bring our first child into the world ... the odds were against us. It seems now that our son, Ryan Jason Rowe II, was destined to face down the odds as well.

My pregnancy and RJ's birth were uncomplicated, yet hours after he was born on October 30, 1993, RJ faced his first challenge. His little lungs, fighting against amniotic fluid, were suctioned three times during his first day of life. RJ suffered from colic during his first four months, and from reflux as well. This caused constant projectile vomiting throughout his first year of life. Shortly after the colic subsided, our next fight began, with what seemed like never-ending double ear infections attacking his health, in addition to severe diaper rashes. Along with these prolonged ear infections came prolonged exposure to antibiotics, further weakening his challenged immune system.

Despite these challenges, RJ would light up a room with his smile. Though not entirely healthy, RJ was a typically developing, happy baby. His eyes were full of life and our home was full of laughter. He hit all of his milestones on time or early and had good eye contact with the people around him. RJ showed no signs or symptoms of autism for the first 18 months of his life.

By the time RJ was six months old he had received twelve vaccinations, and in each of our son's vaccines was a preservative called thimerosal, a mercury compound. Mercury is a known toxic substance that can cause behavioral problems, learning disorders, and many other medical conditions. Dr. Stephanie Cave's book, *What Your Doctor May Not Tell You About Children's Vaccinations*,[1] has been a great resource, educating us on the safety issues surrounding vaccines and recommended vaccination schedules.

In RJ's first six months, he was injected with approximately 200 micrograms of mercury. We believe this mercury was the trigger responsible for taking our son into the world we now know as autism. Shortly after his 18-month shots, RJ seemed to shut down right before our eyes. His first words stopped abruptly and he wouldn't do anything to communicate except point and grunt. He stopped interacting, smiling, and laughing altogether. He started banging his head on his bedroom wall, throwing temper tantrums, and staring at nothing instead of playing. When he had messy pants, he would take off his diaper and wipe feces all over his toys and the wall of his room. We couldn't connect to him the way we had before and we couldn't understand his sudden change in behavior. We wondered, "Where is our son in this little boy before us?"



We went to his pediatrician several times for his ear infections and behavior problems and it was always the same answer: "More antibiotics, but we're going to try something a little stronger this time," and, "Don't worry about his behavior, he just doesn't feel well." We were told constantly that we were "overprotective and worrying for no reason," that "it's just a phase—he'll grow out of it," and that "it's your imagination—your son is just fine." We received second and third opinions but the doctors always told us the same things. We thought it must be us if all of these doctors said RJ was developing normally. Yet I just couldn't shake the God-given maternal instinct that they were wrong and I was right. All I knew was that no one was helping our son, no matter what we said or how many appointments we made. The only conclusion I could draw was that I'd done something, somewhere along the line, to make my son like this. But what? I went over my pregnancy, his birth, and my mothering of him a million times in my head. I would search for these answers daily.

Finally, I found a pediatrician who listened to me (even though she thought some of the same things as all the other doctors). Her answer to our list of questions was, "Let's find out from a specialist and go from there." She referred us to a speech and hearing center to get RJ's hearing tested. The doctor told us that for the first two years of his life RJ was hearing as if he were under water. The way he learned to process sounds was therefore incorrect and would be an obstacle for learning correct speech. He underwent surgery to have tubes placed in both ears and his adenoids removed. This simple surgery gave us incredible results. He no longer had any ear infections and his persistent colds were now gone.

We will always be amazed at how many doctors it took to get to the one who recognized this problem. We have often wondered what RJ's speech would be like today if this option had been presented to us a year earlier.

Even though we saw dramatic changes in his health and a reemergence of his first few words, his behavior was unpredictable and alarmingly different from that of any other children we knew. We tried so hard to help him, but the truth was that we couldn't even potty train him. Who was going to help us with that?! (With the help of a wonderful neighbor and my mother, we finally got RJ completely potty trained at age 4½.)



Our doctor agreed to refer us to a behavioral pediatrician when RJ was still not progressing by the time he was four years old. Dr. David Willis at Emanuel Hospital in Portland, Oregon, finally gave us a diagnosis: pervasive developmental disorder, high functioning autism.

RJ was then put through a battery of different tests: MRIs, cognitive and adaptive tests, and a blood test for fragile X syndrome (that came back negative). Than we heard the most terrifying sentence of our lives, that there is no cure for autism and there was not much we could do to help our son. We were told we could only love him and teach him the best we could, even though we probably would not see much improvement. We were urged to enroll him in special education as soon as possible. So we put RJ into special education kindergarten, speech therapy, and occupational therapy soon after. His speech, however, was not progressing.

When RJ's communication did finally start to progress, his only language was a mixture of echolalia and gibberish that we couldn't understand. He only wanted to repeat parts of what others said to him instead of answering a simple "yes" or "no" to a question. Most of RJ's speech was learned from watching Disney movies. He used phrases and words that were usually out of context, but it was communication and we hadn't had that before. We celebrated every success RJ had, and learned early on that RJ thrived on praise. We also found that any negative feedback or response such as a simple "No!" would create a negative response from him that seemed to last forever.

Then there were the social challenges. Going out in public was always a stressful event, as we would never know what RJ would do or say to people, and it usually ended in frustration and embarrassment. There were countless times when we would get into a store and RJ would run away from me. Often he would be found growling in someone's face like a lion (Disney's "The Lion King"). There was even a time when he ran underneath an elderly lady's skirt to hide from me. Checkout lines were the worst because he would yell and throw tantrums, throw items out of the cart at people, and yell "No!" and "Go away!" as he swatted at the air between himself and the person in line behind us. I would explain my son's actions and strange behaviors to others, but it rarely mattered. The things people would say were very painful. On numerous occasions, I heard things like, "What kind of mother are you?" or, "What a brat! My child would never…" or, "Don't you discipline him?" Then there was my personal favorite, "Some people shouldn't be allowed to have kids."



Complete strangers would make these remarks as if I weren't even there. Did they really think they could do better than I was doing as a mother of a special needs child? Even when they wouldn't say a word, the looks and gasps I received were piercing. I dreaded going to the grocery store and would end up crying on the way home on almost every trip. Simple outings and errands were emotionally exhausting. I searched for answers on how to effectively deal with my child, but even then, most of the doctors I spoke with ignored or made light of our problems with RJ. We were never given any resources for the much-needed support we desperately sought. We weren't told of any books to read, conferences to attend, or alternatives to look into. It was the blind leading the blind, and it wasn't working.

A few years later when RJ was almost six (his younger brother Christian was four and his youngest brother Colby was almost two, both typically developing), we moved to the small Midwestern town of Ogallala, Nebraska. We immediately started looking for the special education services offered in the area for RJ.

We were told that the town had never really dealt with any cases of autism before and it would be a new area for them as a school system. This struck absolute fear in the hearts of my husband, Jason, and me. Had we made the worst possible decision for our son's future by moving there? When we met with the teachers, principal, and a special education team, we were assured that even though it would be new territory for them, they would put their energy, time, and money into learning the best way to teach our son. As good as this sounded, actions speak louder than words.

We decided to see how the school year started out before deciding whether to stay or not. We had never felt that any teacher or school system gave all they could for RJ's education, so we decided the school at least deserved a chance (even though we were prepared for another battle).

Then a breakthrough occurred when we were incredibly blessed with a teacher named Crystal Gerdes who immediately took on the full-time responsibility of working with our son. She gave RJ the gift of a real and complete education over the next two years, staying with him through a grade change and always going beyond the call of duty as an educator. Finally, RJ began to learn to read and do math. He learned important communication and social skills, which were his foundation for interacting with the rest of the world. RJ learned more with Crystal than he ever had before, on many levels of life. Few are blessed with such a wonderful, caring person in their lives. Crystal Gerdes made RJ's and our lives better and we count ourselves blessed to have such a lifelong friend.



During first grade, Crystal began using sensory techniques that worked well with RJ's behaviors. We later learned that these therapeutic techniques were similar to those used and taught elsewhere in the autism community. She would have RJ press his palms together for several seconds and then release or stiffen his body before relaxing again. Another technique involved having RJ sit in a rocking chair on another person's lap, facing forward, with the person's arms and legs mostly covering his limbs. The person in the rocking chair would squeeze RJ's entire body and then release. Sometimes we would do this with only his hands, while standing or sitting in front of him, face to face. These routines were performed every five to 10 seconds until he started to calm down and was able to focus. (The body responds to this constant stiffening and relaxing by releasing endorphins that make it possible to relax.) Additionally, weighted vests and spinning swings are calming tools that RJ enjoys. (We recently learned that Crystal is using these same "RJ techniques" with another autistic child in the Ogallala school system.)

RJ eventually learned how to implement these therapies independently when needed, and they've been great tools for self-regulation. In her books, Temple Grandin, a highly successful autistic adult, talks about pressure techniques and other tools that she has invented and used for years. We have found that her books are full of great insight and education as well as the details of her amazing life story,[2,3] and we learned even more from her in person when we had the honor of meeting her at a conference in Portland.

While still in Ogallala I decided that even though RJ's schooling was progressing, the answers that we were getting from doctors weren't good enough anymore. I dedicated my time to finding the answers for myself, diving into the Internet for every morsel of information I could find. It was then that I came across information about gluten and casein intolerances in some children with autism. I hounded our pediatrician until he referred RJ to be tested for these intolerances. Sure enough, he was slightly intolerant to casein and more so to gluten. I also asked about the instances over the years when RJ would "blank out" for several seconds (doctors had ignored our concerns about this for years). RJ was scheduled for an EEG, and the test showed that these "blank outs" meant something after all—RJ was having mild seizures. He was prescribed Depakene, which has worked well.

As mentioned earlier, we have learned much from reading books, attending conferences, and talking to autistic adults who have been able to articulate what it has been like for them throughout their lives. It has given us amazing insight into the mind of our son, and wonderful ways in which to deal with, communicate with, and teach RJ. After all, what better way is there to understand what RJ isn't able to tell us, than to converse with someone who has been there?



During my continued research on the Internet I also found a wealth of information on Dr. Bernard Rimland's wonderful website for the Autism Research Institute (ARI). There was an explanation or answer for almost every question I had (it was such a relief!). The site has provided information on many ways in which we can help RJ. I wondered why my son's pediatrician, teachers, and therapists hadn't known to refer us to this site and the other resources available to us that were so desperately needed.

The ARI site also introduced us to DAN! (Defeat Autism Now!). Our friend and frequent mentor, Dr. Steve Edelson, led us to additional invaluable reading material from DAN! as well.[4] We have since become involved with a DAN! doctor, Dr. John Green, outside Portland. He has walked us through several tests and biomedical approaches to help eliminate other issues and find ways to draw RJ out of his world and into ours. Dr. Green has initiated mercury detoxification for RJ, and we're hopeful for great results.

In the last two years the most significant improvements we've seen have come from a "team" of supplements RJ is taking from the Mannatech Research and Development Company. They have a patent-pending glyconutritional product called Ambrotose, derived from plant sources that provide necessary saccharides (sugars) for optimal cellular communication and immune system support. These products also contain dehydrated raw fruits and vegetables to support the immune system, and plant-based phytoestrogens to support the hormone system. These products have worked miracles with RJ's behavior and ability to focus. (They are listed in the 2001 and 2002 editions of the *Physician's Desk Reference*.)

Since RJ began taking these supplements, his teachers at school have noted many improvements and are now successfully able to integrate him into a regular education classroom. RJ's speech has improved, and his eye contact, concentration, and interaction with others are far better as well.

At one point, we ran out of the supplements and RJ was off them for three days. By day two, he was a mess. He was angry and lashing out, unable to sit still, and had very little eye contact. He also had reverted to using more echolalic speech instead of using his own words. As soon as we could, we got him back on the supplements, and by day two he was right back where he was before we had run out. This was astonishing to us! We knew that these products were good for him and that they were helping, but until he was off them we didn't realize how much of a difference they were actually making in his life. We have read numerous testimonials attached to these products and now have RJ's own story posted on their website.[5] We believe strongly in these supplements and the company responsible for them. In truth, they have been our miracle. Thanks to Mannatech, biomedical treatments, and education, we are excited at the promise of RJ's future.



I've learned most of my information regarding autism from countless hours of personal research. The health practitioners and therapists who contributed to our understanding and progress have been rare. It is our hope that one day, autism and other developmental disabilities will receive the same attention, resources, and dedication that are given to "normal" afflictions. We also hope that parents will be given clear and concise treatment and directives for their special needs children, just as they would if the symptoms presented were those of a common cold or the flu. We pray that someday those with autism and other developmental disabilities will have the same, readily available medical expertise at their disposal as the "rest of us" have. Until that day, my husband and I are dedicated to doing what we can to help make it so.

In the beginning, we started with a baby boy full of life and headed for a bright future. One day he was taken from us and in his place was a little boy who seemed void of any emotion, except anger; a little boy who wouldn't look at us, talk to us, smile, play, or interact in any form. He didn't seem to enjoy anything anymore, not even his family. Today we have a nine-year-old son who laughs and smiles again. He communicates, makes eye contact, and loves playing with his brothers. RJ can also play organized sports now. He has played T-ball and currently plays on a special needs ice hockey team through Special Hockey, USA. He is also in mainstream education and recently received his school's "student of the month" award.

We never gave up on RJ and we never allowed him to give up, either. We have been so blessed to have a strong family support system that helped us and encouraged us all along the way. We have wonderful friends and family who have given freely of their time and energy over the years in order to give RJ a chance at a solid, normal, healthy, and happy life.

Though research from books, the Internet, and conferences have been invaluable to our learning, the best way we have found to bridge the gap between our son and the rest of the world is to stay involved, to be active in the autism community, and to treat him like the rest of our children. If we treat him like he is a special needs child in every situation, than he won't be challenged to develop the skills needed to be involved with his family, his peers, and his community. Some things are harder for him and some things come easier, but we've found that if we focus on his strong points and find his interests, he is a happier child who enjoys life.



The most wonderful thing to watch as a parent is the growth of your child, but there is something a little extra powerful when it's the growth of your special needs child. Hearing RJ say simple sentences correctly, watching him deal with a stressful situation calmly, and seeing him initiate social interaction for the first time in his life brings a joy to us that cannot be measured or explained.

We are so proud of the tremendous strides RJ has made in these last seven years. Seeing our son, our baby boy, reemerge right before our eyes, has been breathtaking. We see life sparkle in his eyes, a smile on his precious face, and the most wonderful sound ... the sound of his voice and the beauty of his laughter! Even though our journey has been hard and full of emotion, we hope our family's story will help, inspire, and give hope to others. We've learned that you must persevere even when things look hopeless. There is no one in the world who will fight for the life of your child as you can.

The Bible says, "Love bears all things, believes all things, hopes all things, endures all things. Love never fails." It also says that when all else fades away, faith, hope, and love remain, but the greatest of these is love. We have faith in God, and in our son. Because of our faith, there has always been hope, no matter what we've had to face. Ultimately, it's the love of God and the love for our son that have seen us through. On behalf of our precious RJ, may love see you through, too.

## References

[1] *What Your Doctor May Not Tell You about Children's Vaccinations*, by Dr. Stephanie Cave, M.D., F.A.A.F.P., Warner Books, Copyright ©2001 Stephanie Cave, M.D.

[2] *Emergence: Labeled Autistic*, by Temple Grandin, Ph.D., Arena Press, Copyright ©1986 Arena Press

[3] *Thinking in Pictures and Other Reports From My Life With Autism*, by Temple Grandin, Ph.D., Vintage Books, Copyright ©1995 Temple Grandin

[4] *Biomedical Assessment Options for Children with Autism and Related Problems: A Consensus Report of the Defeat Autism Now! (DAN!) Scientific Effort*, by Jon B. Pangborn Ph.D. and Sydney Baker, M.D., The Autism Research Institute, Copyright ©2002 Autism Research Institute

[5] www.mannatech.com, Mannatech Research and Development Company



*Update for Second Edition (October 2005):*

As his 12th birthday approaches, RJ is currently in the fifth grade and having his best school year to date. Although he struggles with reading comprehension and math, he's insistent on trying to figure out his subjects all by himself. He'll tell you, "I'm a man, and I'm very big." Shedding his 'little boy' status is at the top of his priority list.

RJ's communication has improved dramatically as well. He still tends to become quiet and unsure of himself when confronted with discipline or when he finds himself in a tense situation, but when all is well we're hearing things like, "Guess what I did today!" and "I had a nice day!" for the first time in his life. RJ remains brutally honest and his improved communication has only enhanced that character trait, much to the chagrin of some. When being lectured by an adult recently after a brief "exchange" with another child, RJ sighed (exasperated) and announced, "I wish you would stop talking to me!"

The only new challenge to report is RJ's growing awareness of girls. Puberty is a trying time for typical children, so it's no mystery how difficult it must be to go through it unable to express yourself to the extent that you'd like. We're taking it in stride, however, as we're well aware of how many other parents are praying for the chance to experience any expression of affection from their affected child. RJ may be less subtle about expressing his feelings towards others, but we'll take his way of doing it every day of the week and twice on Sunday!

As for interventions, RJ continues to take supplements from Mannatech (Ambrotose, Phyt•Aloe, PLUS and a multivitamin) as well as supplements from Kirkman Laboratories (Super Nu-Thera, DMG with folic acid and vitamin B12, EnZym Complete/DDP-IV 2 with Isogest). We hope to implement a medical diagnosis/biomedical treatment regimen in the coming months, including chelation therapy and digestive/gut analysis and intervention (administered by a DAN! doctor).

With the work that we've done and are continuing to do, through our autism-based film and video production company, Puzzled Media, LLC (www.PuzzledMedia.com), we are learning new and valuable tools every day to help our son. It is our goal to get essential, usable information out to the autism community in a manner that is easily accessible and financially possible.



While the journey towards RJ's complete recovery continues, our little "man's" huge heart, tremendous courage, and unyielding will to be "a real boy (man) just like other kids," blesses us every day.

He'll never give up, and neither will we.

## — Chapter 29 —

# Matthew's Story

By Diane Savage

*Diane Savage's son, Matt, is a highly accomplished professional jazz musician, with many public appearances and several CDs to his name—and he's not even a teenager yet! Matt (who was born in May 1992) lives with his parents and his sister in Massachusetts. This story was written in September 2001.*

My son was born nine years ago. He was always different from other children, even from birth. He was colicky for four months, crying inconsolably every day for hours on end. None of the standard calming techniques worked. Matthew couldn't even ride in the car seat like most children—he would scream hysterically until we stopped and took him out of the seat. As you can guess, we never went anywhere. Changing diapers and giving baths were traumatic. All Matthew wanted to do was to nurse, in the dark, with nothing going on around him. He was very jumpy, never slept, and was very fussy. He would line up toys and do things over and over again. He would be traumatized if one of his rituals could not be followed exactly as he expected it should be. He always walked (actually, ran) on his tiptoes, turned his head sideways, and waved his arms. My husband and I couldn't understand how other parents could just let their children loose to play nicely with other children. Our son would not play with others. He'd usually be dismantling something he shouldn't be touching, or running away from any sort of interactive experience. Every outing ended in a tantrum. What misled us was the fact that Matthew had an extensive vocabulary (because he was echolalic), he was reading everything in sight (because he was hyperlexic), and he was highly intelligent. We thought his hyperactivity and distraction were due to his constant curiosity about how things worked.

Matthew was extremely defensive in response to sensory input. We couldn't watch television when he was around. Vacuum noise, popcorn poppers, any unusual sound would cause him to cover his ears and become agitated. He was also tactilely defensive and highly perseverative. His saving graces were his hyperlexia and extreme intelligence.

Needless to say, my husband and I searched for answers. We were told that Matthew had pervasive developmental disorder (PDD), possibly Asperger syndrome, with hyperlexia. After contacting the Autism Support Center for information, we followed through with extensive research and got into the "parent network" to find the best help for our son. Fortunately, we found a wonderful program for him, and he has blossomed in the years since his diagnosis. He has had the benefit of private speech, occupational, and psychological therapy, in addition to an excellent school environment flexible in balancing mainstreaming with separate classroom situations. You'd never know this was the same child.

One thing that was difficult for us was that although as a young toddler Matthew seemed to enjoy singing and quiet music, he lost this ability at approximately 18 months of age. He couldn't tolerate listening to music in any form and wouldn't sing. We couldn't sing "Happy Birthday," listen to music, or sing songs with him the way we used to. When he was approximately four years old, we heard about a controversial therapy called auditory integration therapy (AIT), created by Dr. Guy Berard in France. We spoke with many people about it, and came to the conclusion that it certainly wouldn't hurt for us to try it on Matthew, and it might possibly help. We had heard of other children who had shown positive results, ranging from speaking to focusing better to being less hyperactive. There was an individual who performed this treatment locally, so we decided to try it. Matthew had all of the classic symptoms of a child who might be helped by AIT, including extreme sensitivity to sounds and sensory defensiveness.



Even during the treatment, we noticed immediate and dramatic changes in Matthew. By the time he had completed the ten-day treatment, Matthew noticed the world around him ... the sound of birds singing, the hair on my husband's arm, plants in the garden, the texture of our carpet. Even more miraculously, his sensitivity to music and voices was greatly reduced. Suddenly, he was singing, loved math, and started asking questions! He had never asked questions before. He started making great strides in his development. We had not told his teachers that he had received the therapy, but suddenly we were receiving reports of new things Matthew was accomplishing. We were thrilled.

Not long after this, we started looking for other "nontraditional" therapies. We ordered a copy of the DAN! Protocol, and started testing for things like allergies, heavy metals, yeast, and intestinal problems. Matthew had always been very small for his age and had had constant diarrhea. We found several things we were able to address, including leaky gut problems, allergies, yeast, and absorption problems. We completely revamped his diet to become wheat-free, dairy-free, dye- and chemical-free, and as organic as possible, and we eliminated foods to which he had shown an allergy. We saw immediate results. Within 24 hours, Matthew started writing. He had avoided it entirely before this because it was so difficult for him. Now he was writing whole sentences, drawing pictures, and just HAD to get things down on paper, especially anything related to mathematics. Matthew started taking special supplements and vitamins to give his body what it needed: nystatin to combat systemic yeast, Super Nu-Thera (a B6/magnesium supplement created by Dr. Bernard Rimland and sold by Kirkman Labs), Creon5 (an enzyme) to help him break down food, and lots of other vitamins prescribed to him by his doctor. He started making even more progress. He had better eye contact, more energy, normal digestion, more desire to interact, and better focus. The only thing that was difficult initially was Matthew's adjustment to the changes in his body. Once he adjusted, the results were more and more positive.



Now that Matthew is nine, he has come very far. We tried a second round of AIT therapy when he was almost 6½ and found that he showed even more improvement. Suddenly he started playing music. He started with a toy piano, graduating to a keymonica and then to a piano. I taught him the basics and then gave him several beginner piano books. From there, he took off on his own. Before he took his first teacher-taught piano lesson, he could sight-read perfectly. He had absolute pitch, knew a great deal about piano terminology, automatically knew music theory, and could play anything "by ear."

He took one year of classical music lessons, flying through books and piano pieces that normally take years to learn. He loved playing, and especially loved playing variations on the music. He would transpose the piece to another key, play improvisations, turn the music upside down and play it. We were amazed at his great flexibility, and at his ability to cross midline with his hands and cross one hand over the other with ease. These are monumental accomplishments for a child with autism. The only issue with which Matthew sometimes struggles is his fear of "making mistakes." Sometimes he wants to avoid a piece because he looks at it and says he won't be able to play it perfectly. We are always reassuring him that mistakes are part of life, and that if he breaks the piece down into two parts (the right hand and left hand separately), he can learn each part and THEN try playing the parts together. He has become much, much better about this, and this step-by-step approach is starting to make its way into his life in general. Breaking down a big problem into smaller pieces will always be difficult for him, however.

We wanted to encourage Matthew's natural improvisational ability, so we contacted the New England Conservatory of Music and had him audition. They were amazed at his abilities and knowledge, and took him on as a jazz student for private lessons. Matthew can immediately tell the key in which a piece is written, can identify four notes played simultaneously, and plays everything from jazz to blues to classical to improv at a moment's notice. He just loves piano. I've even seen him face away from the piano, put his arms back, and play a blues piece! My husband and I love to listen to him play. He has played in several piano recitals, including one for gifted and talented students. He was the first autistic child allowed to play at this particular recital. I think half the people in the audience were people who have been involved in Matthew's life and wanted to see how far he has come.



Don't misunderstand me. There are many, many difficulties with which Matthew copes every day. He still shows signs of his autism. People immediately notice him in a group! He still has inappropriate behaviors and regresses in new situations. But he is making progress. We focus on how many things he has been able to accomplish, not on the things with which he will always struggle. He made the transition to a fully mainstreamed third grade class at school last year. And although there have been a few glitches, fourth grade this year has been wonderful. Matthew LOVES school. We are very proud of him.

To raise awareness (and funds) for autism research and support, we put together a CD of solo piano (jazz/blues/improvisation) on which Matthew performed. The title of this first CD was "One Is Not Fun, but 20 Is Plenty." The name was taken from a poem written by Matthew. The CD includes many elements—readings of my own poetry describing life in a "special needs family," interpretation and performance of these poems in music form by Matthew's professor at the New England Conservatory, readings of poems written and performed by Matthew, and many, many original piano pieces composed and performed by Matthew. It is really remarkable to hear Matthew being a child, and then hear him playing a magnificent piece. But that's the nature of autism. Different children have different levels of abilities, and different behaviors.

Matthew released a second CD (and first solo piano effort). You DEFINITELY will enjoy the CD. Matthew composed or improvised ALL of the piano pieces on it except for three tracks. The name of the new CD is "Live at The Olde Mill." It was recorded in two parts. The first part was recorded at a live performance given by Matthew last summer at The Olde Mill Restaurant in Harrison, Maine. The second part of the CD was recorded this past December in a studio. Matthew still sounds like a young musician; however, his emerging talent shines through and makes for a wonderful collection of music. Matthew listens to jazz and classical music constantly, and is composing increasingly impressive pieces. His most recent ventures have been into the world of jazz ensembles. You need tremendous awareness of other people and subtle interpersonal communication skills to play in an ensemble. Matthew is already making great strides. He is truly gifted … gifted beyond imagination.

The most recent news is that Matthew has started his own trio, The Matt Savage Trio. It is composed of two adult sidemen, John Funkhouser on bass and Steve Silverstein on drums. Both men are accomplished, world-class musicians who teach as well as perform.

The Matt Savage Trio has recorded their first CD as a group. It is entitled "All Jazzed Up," a name taken from one of Matthew's original compositions. It is a professionally recorded live performance by the trio during August of 2001 at The Deertrees Theatre in Harrison, Maine. Most of the pieces on the CD are original compositions by Matthew, although there are tunes by Charlie Parker, Miles Davis, and Billy Strayhorn. It is unbelievable to witness Matthew's musical accomplishments over such a short time.





*Update (February 2003):*

Matthew is almost 11 now. He continues to make daily progress, and I believe his music and the experiences he is having because of his music have contributed to this progress. He is still taking his vitamins and supplements and is starting to grow and put on a little weight, although he is still small for his age. He is also still on his GFCF diet, although we allow a bit more flexibility now as his most recent allergy tests indicated a great reduction in allergic reactions to foods. He is also getting stronger, and is more coordinated. He is able to do many things he wasn't able to do even a year ago, such as ice-skating. At the same time, he is beginning to show signs of preadolescent angst and emotionality.

Matthew is still the leader of his own trio, The Matt Savage Trio. And they have recently released their third CD, entitled "Chasing Your Tail." It was recorded at a live concert and contains mostly original material written by Matt.

We take everything on a day-to-day basis, and do NOT push the music. Matthew makes all of the decisions about where and when he performs. And I limit his travel. I believe that being with family is more important than performing gigs for both him and us! But we do encourage him and support him. We also encourage and support our daughter. I believe that both of our children are thriving because we love them no matter what they do, we accept them for who they are as individuals, and we listen to them. We listen to their needs, their fears, and their dreams, and help to guide them along their path. But we let them set their path, as winding as it may be.

You can order the group's newest CD (or any of Matthew's CDs), learn more about Matthew, or find out where Matthew is performing by visiting our website: www.SavageRecords.com.



*Update for Second Edition (October 2005):*

Matt has continued to thrive, as he has continued using the DAN! Protocol. He is still on the GFCF diet and still takes supplements such as Super Nu-Thera and other vitamins to help him maintain his health and energy level.

He continues with his love of jazz, performing worldwide and traveling.

## — Chapter 30 —
# Predetermined
By Kelli Schlapfer

*Kelli Schlapfer is the mother of Ryan, born in September 1990. She and her husband, Rob, live in southern Oregon. This story was written in May 2002.*

Dedication: This I dedicate to my beloved son who will always be the most precious child God could ever have given me. Never let anyone take away your hope; remain steadfastly determined, for you have been given a great calling.



* * * * *

I tell you the truth: this is the first time I've expressed in writing how I feel about my son Ryan's disability. I simply haven't devoted these past many years to thinking about it—in spite of its almost overwhelming weight. My time has been spent trying to fix it, cope with it, and fight it.

I find I'm not alone. I join a company of parents who've walked the same path and encountered the same obstacles—facing them with the same determination and resolve. These are my heroes—the people who inspire me to hope.

Here is the reality for those who have a child with autism: Shortly after having your child diagnosed, you come brutally face-to-face with what it means to have his future determined before you even get a chance to make a difference.

At its most basic level, parenting is about making something of your child's life. If he's a troublemaker we say, "I wonder what the parents are like," or "His parents don't discipline, spend enough time with, or encourage that child enough." It seems we approach childrearing as if there is an absolute correlation between how well a child turns out and the parenting skills—or the lack thereof—applied to the situation. I too fell into this way of thinking.

When a doctor tells you that your child has autism, the very next sentence is invariably, "We do not know what causes the disability, and we do not know how to treat it."

After recovering from the blow of this devastating news—hours, days or weeks later—you begin to yearn for an answer. Surely there is something out there, someone who can help your child. Thus begins the search.

The search brings more grim news.

Your child's life is "predetermined." There are myriads of statistics to prove it. The odds are that he will be placed in an institution when he grows up or, at BEST, placed in a group home.

A group home ... is that my dream for this child? What about your child? Imagine if the best home your child could have would be a group home. Is this your dream? For an autistic child it is predetermined.

More grim news: an autistic child's school life is usually limited to a self-contained special education room. For some it means never learning to talk, never having a friend, and never learning anything we typically consider valuable to succeed. Add to that a life full of odd behaviors that will render him, at best, socially awkward and, most likely, an outcast. Is this what you dreamed of for your child?



Imagine if the best education your child could have was a self-contained Special Ed room. I'm not talking about the merits of special education here. I'm talking about dreams. Nobody dreams about having their child's school years spent in special programs. For an autistic child it is predetermined.

It doesn't stop there.

It costs two million dollars to raise an autistic child through to adulthood. Insurance companies do not help; they don't cover your autistic child's treatment. Once they reach adulthood, autistic individuals most likely will never marry, never have kids.

If all this is not enough, you will probably end up raising your child alone: marriages that involve a child with special needs fail fifty percent more often than the national average.

Imagine if the best family life your children could hope for was filled with strife and stress. Is this the dream you dreamed for your family? In a family with an autistic child it is predetermined.

The statistics became the reality for me the day we received Ryan's diagnosis from the excellent team at the University of Oregon, in Eugene. It was the spring of 1996. I cried all the way home. I kept crying the rest of the night as I learned what my family's future held. The hope I had about raising our child was snatched from me in an instant. The dreams that I had for Ryan, what he would be like when grown, the hope of what might be, now met me not in sweet dreams but in startling black and white.

Imagine if the best future you could hope for was limited, not by your dreams, but by your diagnosis. For an autistic child it is predetermined. That's what they tell you.

What cost was I willing to pay to save Ryan from a life that was Predetermined? I knew I had to pick myself up from my despair and fight, no matter what the cost. Emotionally, physically, financially, spiritually it has been a huge cost, more than I first imagined. The weight of raising a child with autism is tremendous. There have been times when I wished I could put it all down and go the way of the statistic. But somewhere along the way I decided I could not give up; the very choice was the driving force to move me forward. I had come to the point where I believed that I could make the difference. I found tremendous strength in that conviction.

I am no longer Predetermined in my role as a mother—I am DETERMINED. Determined to, one day, look in my son's eyes and see a boy pulled out of the grips of what we call autism.



There are many metaphors associated with autism. One of the more poignant is robbery—the violation one feels when something precious has been stolen from you. Having a child with autism is like being robbed, for it steals what we hold most dear: the unique parent/child relationship.

I am especially drawn to Ryan while he sleeps. I have since learned that this is true of many parents with autistic children. While Ryan sleeps I can touch his head without him pushing me away. I can kiss his hair without being called a name. I can hold his hand and whisper all my hopes and prayers for him. I can snuggle next to him, gazing with the simple eyes of a mother looking at her beautiful son. These are precious times, yet bittersweet. As I sit there in the dark of his room, the self-doubt comes—the sheer panic as I look down at his face and wonder, "Will I have made a difference? Is being determined enough?"

There have been plenty of low points during our struggle to recover Ryan. But I've never lost my belief to remain steadfast. In the beginning I found it difficult to advocate for Ryan while encountering disbelief. Every doctor and every specialist said the same thing: "We don't know how to help him; he is just autistic." They would say "autistic" as though this answered all of my questions. They had no faith, no hope, and no belief. There were days that my belief was all I had. Somebody, something out there would be able to help.

Like so many others, we've run the gamut of therapies and tests: speech and occupational therapy, special preschools, prescription medicine, MRIs, EEGs, genetic tests, and many long years of ABA (applied behavior analysis). We've worked with 32 therapists, four junior therapists, countless peers, and classroom aides. At the end of Ryan's second grade year I'd come to the place where I thought I'd done all I could. I was still determined, but I realized there was more to the problem than I could answer.

Why was Ryan always sick, why so thin, why so allergic to the things around him, why troubled by digestive problems, why so hyperactive, and what in the world did this have to do with autism?

Searching for the answers, I began hearing about new biomedical treatments. They were being used to treat common problems among autistic kids. Our local doctors would not perform the recommended tests or treatments as outlined by the new DAN! approach. Once again, undaunted by others' disbelief, we flew Ryan to Florida to see Dr. Jeff Bradstreet. At that time he was one of the few doctors who would treat the medical problems that went along with autism. The biomedical treatments that Dr. Bradstreet and other DAN! doctors have used with Ryan address long-standing medical issues that had gone untreated for years.



We undertook the biomedical work as intensely as the ABA therapy. Ryan has been on a gluten-free, casein-free diet (GFCF) for many years. We added megadose vitamins and antifungal treatments to battle his out-of-control yeast problem. We did allergy testing, and relied on our own observation to determine what other foods should be removed. We did our first of many secretin infusions when Ryan was eight. For the first time ever, Ryan could go to school without worry that he would have a bathroom accident. As for his father and me, it gave us our first real connected conversation with our son. The use of secretin convinced us that Ryan's condition was a medical issue and not a mental health one. From that point we've never looked back—no stone has been left unturned. We have continued to pursue every viable medical option. Ryan has blossomed under this care, allowing all the work of the previous therapies to come to fruition.

For years we've fought to restore our son using the joint tools of education and biomedical treatment. The path has been difficult owing to the many obstacles that stand in the way for families that face autism. At times you have to fight everyone—the educational system for appropriate teaching, the medical system for healthcare, the insurance system for coverage, and society itself for understanding of our outrage and determination. Each system in its own way leaves you with the impression that autistic children are unlovely, not worth the determination.

My son is lovely. He has value and worth. Ryan has met every challenge presented, facing more struggles in his brief life than most adults have. He is now eleven years old and in the fifth grade. He looks and acts much like his peers. He has surpassed what the statistics had expected for him. He is one of the lucky ones—the system had to work for him … it was determined.

As I write today, I'm fighting for the other children I've met along the way—the ones who need someone to be determined for their well-being. As a society we need to be determined for the children behind the diagnosis. In the midst of all the statistics, research, and politics, it's easy to lose sight of the child. Every child must have the opportunity to receive the education and medical treatments that have proven successful to combat this disability. To families who are just starting out on the path toward recovery, there is one thing that will get you to the other side:

Determination.

I would be remiss if I didn't tell you that many people have given selflessly on behalf of my son and our family—some known, others unknown. To them we owe our deepest gratitude for their immense kindness. Ryan has exceeded our every expectation. They have helped Ryan find a way out of the darkness of autism, bringing him into a life full of brightness and hope.



Each time I watch Ryan laugh and play, each time our eyes meet and he tells me what is in his heart, each time I take him to school and he runs smiling from the car, I am grateful for those who came alongside and helped us provide ABA and medical treatments.

They have given us a great gift: the return of our son.

*Update (February 2003):*

Ryan has now matured into a teenager, so we have focused our intervention on developing his teenage social skills. His days are filled with older teens assisting him with the "typical" things teenagers do: music, girls, developing style, experiencing life, hanging with friends and—most importantly—acting "cool." There is an art to all of this, one that only another teen can model. This new intervention has had amazing results. Ryan is more mature, less self-centered, and more self-sufficient. Teens, even paid teens, have no time for residual autistic behaviors. They are merciless and achieve amazing results by just being themselves.

There is one thing I have found to be invaluable over the years: knowledgeable people. The most important piece of advice I can give a parent is this: *find someone who can be an educator for you*, a person who can guide you through the many complex medical and educational interventions you will need to learn, a person who has walked the road and can provide informed support—keeping you from wasting valuable time. It might be a parent who has gone before and had to walk the difficult terrain of the educational system. It might be a consultant who helps carry the burden, giving tirelessly, ultimately becoming a partner. It might be a school administrator who listens to you as an equal, isn't afraid to try a new approach, and teaches you along the way. It might be a mom who has done it all before—she knows first-hand your pain, and in the end her greatest gift is that she teaches you to laugh again. These people can help you make a difference in your child's life and if you are lucky, as I have been, some might end up being your best friends. In my case, Jeff, Erin, Rick, and Kathy share in the miracle of Ryan.

Hope and determination will always be with us.

*Update for Second Edition (February 2005):*



A family emergency has prevented the Schlapfers from preparing an update on Ryan's progress. They'd like readers to know that they continue to use DAN! treatments and to see improvements in Ryan. They added, "Ryan is happy. Ultimately, that is what we want for all our children."

— Chapter 31 —

# We Rescued Our Child from Autism

By Karyn Seroussi

*Karyn Seroussi is the author of* Unraveling the Mystery of Autism and Pervasive Developmental Disorder: A Mother's Story of Research and Recovery. *In addition, she is a cofounder of the Autism Network for Dietary Intervention (ANDI). Her son, Miles, has recovered from autism. Karyn's writings are referred to by other authors in this book.*

Adapted from the book, *Unraveling the Mystery of Autism and Pervasive Developmental Disorder: A Mother's Story of Research and Recovery*, published by Simon & Schuster February 2000, and in paperback by Random House/Broadway Books February 2002. Reprinted by permission of the author.



When the psychologist examining our 18-month-old son told me that she thought Miles had autism, my heart began to pound. I didn't know exactly what the word meant, but I knew it was bad. Wasn't autism some type of mental illness—perhaps juvenile schizophrenia? Even worse, I vaguely remembered hearing that this disorder was caused by emotional trauma during childhood. In an instant, every illusion of safety in my world seemed to vanish.

Our pediatrician had referred us to the psychologist in August 1995 because Miles didn't seem to understand anything we said. He'd developed perfectly normally until he was 15 months old, but then he stopped saying the words he'd learned—cow, cat, dance—and started disappearing into himself. We figured his chronic ear infections were responsible for his silence, but within three months, he was truly in his own world.

Suddenly, our happy little boy hardly seemed to recognize us or his three-year-old sister. Miles wouldn't make eye contact or even try to communicate by pointing or gesturing. His behavior became increasingly strange: he'd drag his head across the floor, walk on his toes (very common in autistic children), make odd gurgling sounds, and spend long periods of time repeating an action, such as opening and closing doors or filling and emptying a cup of sand in the sandbox. He often screamed inconsolably, refusing to be held or comforted. And he developed chronic diarrhea.

As I later learned, autism—or autistic spectrum disorder, as doctors often call it—is not a mental illness. It is a developmental disability usually thought to be caused by an anomaly in the brain. In 1995, the National Institutes of Health estimated that as many as one in 500 children were affected. But according to several recent studies, the incidence is rapidly rising: in Florida, for example, the number of autistic children has increased nearly 600 percent in the last ten years. In California, it may be showing up in as many as one in 130 kids. Nevertheless, even though it is more common than Down syndrome, autism remains one of the least understood developmental disorders.

We were told that Miles would almost definitely grow up to be severely impaired. He would never be able to make friends, have a meaningful conversation, learn in a regular classroom without special help, or live independently. We could only hope that with behavioral therapy, we might be able to teach him some of the social skills he'd never grasp on his own.



I had always thought that the worst thing that could happen to anyone was to lose a child. Now it was happening to me, but in a perverse, inexplicable way. Instead of condolences, I got uncomfortable glances, inappropriately cheerful reassurances, and the realization that some of my friends didn't want to return my calls.

After Miles' initial diagnosis, I spent hours in the library, searching for the reason he'd changed so dramatically. Then I came across a book that mentioned an autistic child whose mother believed that his symptoms had been caused by a "cerebral allergy" to milk. I'd never heard of this, but the thought lingered in my mind because Miles drank an inordinate amount of milk—at least half a gallon a day.

I also remembered that a few months earlier, my mother had read that many kids with chronic ear infections are allergic to milk and wheat. "You should take Miles off those foods and see if his ears clear up," she said. "Milk, cheese, pasta, and Cheerios are the only foods he'll eat," I insisted. "If I took them away, he'd starve."

Then I realized that Miles' ear infections had begun when he was 11 months old, just after we had switched him from soy formula to cow's milk. He'd been on soy formula because my family was prone to allergies, and I'd read that soy might be better for him. I had breast-fed him until he was three months old, but he didn't tolerate breast milk very well—possibly because I was drinking lots of milk. There was nothing to lose, so I decided to eliminate all the dairy products from his diet.

What happened next was nothing short of miraculous. Miles stopped screaming, he didn't spend as much time repeating actions, and by the end of the first week, he pulled on my hand when he wanted to go downstairs. For the first time in months, he let his sister hold his hands to sing "Ring Around the Rosy."

Two weeks later, a month after we'd seen the psychologist, my husband Alan and I kept our appointment with a well-known developmental pediatrician to confirm the diagnosis of autism. Dr. Susan Hyman gave Miles a variety of tests and asked a lot of questions. We described the changes in his behavior since he'd stopped eating dairy products. Finally, Dr. Hyman looked at us sadly. "I'm sorry," she said. "Your son is autistic. I admit the milk allergy issue is interesting, but I just don't think it could be responsible for Miles' autism or his recent improvement."

We were terribly disheartened, but as each day passed, Miles continued to get better. A week later, when I pulled him up to sit on my lap, we made eye contact and he smiled. I started to cry—at last he seemed to know who I was. He had been oblivious to his sister, but now he watched her play and even got angry when she took things away from him. Miles slept more soundly, but his diarrhea persisted. Although he wasn't even two yet, we put him in a special-ed nursery school three mornings a week and started an intensive one-on-one ABA program (a behavioral and language program recommended to us by Dr. Hyman).



We continued to see great improvements, but I'm a natural skeptic and Alan is a research scientist, so we decided to test the hypothesis that is was actually the milk that had affected Miles' behavior. We gave him a couple of glasses one morning, and by the end of the day, he was walking on his toes, dragging his forehead across the floor, making strange sounds, and exhibiting the other bizarre behaviors we had almost forgotten. It was a shocking revelation, and frightening to think that the improvements we had seen could be lost once again. A few weeks later, the behaviors suddenly returned, and we were relieved to be informed that Miles had eaten some cheese at nursery school. We became completely convinced that dairy products were somehow related to his autism.

I wanted Dr. Hyman to understand what we had observed, and to see how well Miles was doing, so I sent her a video of him playing with his father and sister. She called right away. "I'm simply floored," she told me. "Miles has improved remarkably. Karyn, if I hadn't diagnosed him myself, I wouldn't have believed that he was the same child."

I had to find out whether other kids had had similar experiences. I bought a modem for my computer—not standard in 1995—and discovered an autism support group on the Internet. A bit embarrassed, I asked, "Could my child's autism be related to milk?"

The response was overwhelming. Where had I been? Didn't I know about Karl Reichelt in Norway? Didn't I know about Paul Shattock in England? These researchers had preliminary evidence to validate what parents had been reporting for almost 20 years: dairy products exacerbated the symptoms of autism.

Alan, who has a Ph.D. in chemistry, got copies of the journal articles that the parents had mentioned online and went through them all carefully. As he explained it to me, it was theorized that a subtype of children with autism break down milk protein (casein) into peptides that affect the brain in the same way that hallucinogenic drugs do. A handful of scientists, some of whom were parents of kids with autism, had discovered compounds containing opiates—a class of substances including opium and heroin—in the urine of autistic children. The researchers theorized that either these children were missing an enzyme that normally breaks down the peptides into a digestible form, or the peptides were somehow leaking into the bloodstream before they could be digested.



In a burst of excitement, I realized how much sense this made. It explained why Miles developed normally for his first year, when he drank only soy formula. It would also explain why he had later craved milk: opiates are highly addictive. What's more, the odd behavior of autistic children has often been compared to that of someone hallucinating on LSD.

Alan also told me that the other type of protein being broken down into a toxic form was gluten—found in wheat, oats, rye, and barley, and commonly added to thousands of packaged foods. The theory would have sounded farfetched to my scientific husband if he hadn't seen the dramatic changes in Miles himself, and remembered how Miles had self-limited his diet to foods containing wheat and dairy. As far as I was concerned, there was no question that the gluten in his diet would have to go. Busy as I was, I would learn to cook gluten-free meals. People with celiac disease are also gluten-intolerant, and I spent hours online gathering information from celiac websites.

Within 48 hours of being gluten-free, 22-month-old Miles had his first solid stool, and his balance and coordination noticeably improved. A month or two later, he started speaking: "zawaff" for giraffe, for example, and "ayashoo" for elephant. He still didn't call me Mommy, but he had a special smile for me when I picked him up from nursery school. However, Miles' local doctors—his pediatrician, neurologist, geneticist, and gastroenterologist—still scoffed at the connection between autism and diet. Even though dietary intervention was a safe, noninvasive approach to treating autism, until large controlled studies could prove that it worked, most of the medical community would have nothing to do with it.

So Alan and I decided to become experts ourselves. We began attending autism conferences and phoning and emailing the European researchers. I also organized a support group for other parents of autistic children in my community. Although some parents weren't interested in exploring dietary intervention at first, they often changed their minds after they met Miles. Not every child with autism responded to the diet, but eventually there were about 50 local families whose children were gluten- and casein-free with exciting results. And judging by the number of people on new Internet support lists, there were thousands of children around the world responding well to this diet.



Fortunately, we found a new local pediatrician who was very supportive, and Miles was doing so well that I nearly sprang out of bed each morning to see the changes in him. One day, when Miles was 2½, he held up a toy dinosaur for me to see. "Wook, Mommy, issa Tywannosauwus Wex!" Astonished, I held out my trembling hands. "You called me Mommy!" I said. He smiled and gave me a long hug.

By the time Miles turned three, all of his doctors agreed that his autism had been completely reversed. He tested at eight months above his age level in social, language, self-help, and motor skills, and he entered a regular preschool with no special-ed supports. His teacher told me that he was one of the most delightful, verbal, participatory children in the class. By age six, Miles was among the most popular children in his first-grade class. He was reading at a fourth-grade level, had good friends, and acted out his part in the class play with flair. He was deeply attached to his older sister, and they spent hours engaged in the type of imaginative play that is never seen in kids with autism.

My worst fears were never realized. We are terribly lucky.

But I imagined all the other parents with children like mine who might not be fortunate enough to learn about the diet while their kids were young. So in 1997, I started a newsletter and international support organization called Autism Network for Dietary Intervention (ANDI), along with another parent, Lisa Lewis, author of *Special Diets for Special Kids* (Future Horizons, 1998). We've gotten thousands of letters and emails from parents worldwide whose kids use the diet successfully. Although it's best to have professional guidance when implementing the diet, sadly, many doctors are still skeptical, and other parents continue to be a powerful resource.

As I continue to study the emerging research, it has become increasingly clear to me that autism is a disorder related to the immune system. Most autistic children I know have several food allergies in addition to milk and wheat, and nearly all the parents in our group have or had at least one immune-related problem: thyroid disease, Crohn's disease, celiac disease, rheumatoid arthritis, chronic fatigue syndrome, fibromyalgia, or allergies. Autistic children are probably genetically predisposed to immune-system abnormalities, but what triggers the actual disease?

Many of the parents who wrote to me swore that their child's autistic behavior began after a vaccine, or specifically at 15 months, shortly after the child received the MMR (measles, mumps, rubella) vaccine. Mercury (used as a preservative in many shots) and the measles virus are known to impair immune function, and the measles-mumps combination is known to increase the risk of bowel disease. When I examined such evidence as photos and videotapes to see exactly when Miles started to lose his language and social skills, I had to admit that it had coincided with his MMR—ten days after which he had gone to the emergency room with a temperature of 106°F and febrile seizures. Repeated studies published by British researcher Andrew Wakefield, M.D., linking the vaccine to damage in the small intestine, might help explain the mechanism by which the hallucinogenic peptides leak into the bloodstream. If the MMR vaccine is indeed found to play a role in triggering autism, we must find out whether some children are at higher risk for a triple vaccine, and therefore should not be vaccinated or should be vaccinated at a later age, one shot at a time.



While working as a research chemist at Johnson and Johnson, Alan was able to positively confirm the abnormal presence of peptides in the urine of autistic children. He has continued that work independently, and plans to publish his findings as soon as possible. We have separated, but we share the same hope for the future of autism treatment: that eventually a routine diagnostic test will be developed to identify children with autism at a young age, and that when some types of autism are recognized as a metabolic disorder, the gluten and dairy-free diet will move from the realm of alternative medicine into the mainstream.

The word autism, which once meant so little to me, has changed my life profoundly. It came to my house like a monstrous, uninvited guest, but eventually brought its own gifts. I've felt twice blessed—once by the amazing good fortune of reclaiming my child and again by being able to help other autistic children who had been written off by their doctors and mourned by their parents.

*Update (March 2003):*

At age seven Miles was extensively evaluated by a team of specialists at Strong Memorial Hospital, and was found to have an IQ well into the gifted range, a mild ADD/inattention disorder (common in my family), and no trace of autistic behavior. At age nine he is admired by those who know him for his imagination and intellect, his warmth and humor, and his friendly, sympathetic disposition.

I have learned to take for granted that he is a "regular kid," and rarely remind myself that he once had autism, because that bittersweet remembrance comes with the knowledge that there are other autistic children and adults like my stepson, who were harder to treat or for whom treatment came later. But the memory comes back at unexpected moments, as it did last summer, from this little boy who once had a severe communication disorder.

"Mom, I love you more than I can express," he had said, thoughtfully. "In fact, I love you more than even a very expressive person could express."

I believe that all autistic children feel this way, whether they can express it or not.

*Update for Second Edition (September 2005):*

No update necessary.

## — Chapter 32 —

# The Twinkle in His Eye

By Rebecca Sytsema

*Rebecca Sytsema and her husband, Jack, live in Colorado, with their two children—their son Nicholas, who was born in July 1998, and his younger brother Sam. This story was written in January 2003.*

I remember the first time our son Nicholas said the word "shoe." While that may not be a big deal for most parents, for me it was one of the most joyful moments of my entire life!



For months upon end we had gone through the same ritual every day: I would show him the shoe, say the word over and over, and then say, "This is a sh…" I always paused hopefully, and yet many days I felt the tears well up as I finished the sentence myself. I felt lonely and confused, on occasion even devastated. "Please," I would plead with God, "Just let him say one word!" And yet, nothing. Day after day, nothing. The well of disappointment in my heart became deeper and deeper. Each day my husband, Jack, and I would try to reach into his world, only to feel the gap between us widen. Attempts to play with him or read to him met with no response other than annoyance. He didn't seem to know his own name. The only relationship he formed was with Steve and Blue, who were characters in a popular children's TV program. They could get our son to respond in ways that we could only dream of. Jack and I got only a dull, far off stare.

But then came that miraculous day when, true to our daily ritual, I said, "This is a sh…" and heard our son, who had been diagnosed with nonverbal autism, say, "Shoe." Everything within me jumped! I laughed, I wept, I shouted, I hugged him. I told everyone I knew and some folks I didn't. The joy I felt that day was intense. It was easily as intense as all the pain I had felt each day that he had not responded. Whether or not their child has spoken that first word, almost all parents of an autistic child can relate. There has been some breakthrough somewhere that they have struggled to see. And when it finally comes, the joy cannot be described.

But the breakthroughs often seem few and far between. There is nothing easy about having a son or daughter afflicted with autism. Everything in daily life is affected and hard. In our case, that included long periods of sleepless nights, continual ear infections, uncontrollable diarrhea, difficult meal times, hours of repetitive behaviors, and endless episodes of "Blue's Clues" ringing through our home. Many were the days when the effects of our two-year-old son's autism took over our home.

As we read and researched, looking for anything that would help our son, God's grace led us early on to read Lynn Hamilton's wonderful book, *Facing Autism [Editors' note: Lynn Hamilton's story is included in this book]*. In fact, we began reading her book before Nicholas was formally diagnosed. Through it we learned many things that have been vital to our son's recovery, not the least of which was becoming aware of Dr. Bernard Rimland and the Autism Research Institute (ARI). Some of what we read sounded too radical for us. But in retrospect we realize that through Lynn's book and through ARI, we found a wealth of information that would help our son begin to emerge from the devastating confines of autism.



Once we got a formal diagnosis, our first step in reclaiming Nicholas was educational. We set up an intensive in-home program based on applied behavior analysis (ABA). The first few months of our program revolved around getting Nicholas to respond and attend. It consisted of trying to get Nicholas to make eye contact, sit in a chair for a minute at a time, understand that his name was Nicholas, and reduce his compulsive, ritualistic behaviors. Progress was slow, but sure. Every once in a while we would catch a very brief glimpse of a twinkle in his beautiful blue eyes, rather than the dull, meaningless stare we had come to know.

Meanwhile, we began looking at what could be done for him medically. By now we knew there was no magic pill, and that conventional medicine as we knew it gave little to no hope for our son's future. We ran from doctor to doctor testing everything from hearing to brain wave functions, only to be left with a pile of test results but no real direction. Then our neurologist did us the biggest favor that any medical doctor had done for us up to that point. He found the phone number of a local mom of two children with autism and, pulling an old used envelope from his trashcan, scrawled her information on the back, suggesting that we contact her.

When we called her, we discovered that we were not alone. In fact, Nicholas was not the only child in our community with autism. There were many (far too many) others. Over the next few weeks and months we came to know many other parents who had faced the same horror we had. We learned that most of these children had sleeping problems, ate limited foods, and suffered from chronic diarrhea or constipation. We learned that many of these parents could pinpoint their children's troubles to a particular vaccine (and, come to think of it, wasn't the day that Nicholas got his last DTP shot the same day he stopped sleeping through the night? Yes, it was!).

We also learned that many of the radical interventions we had read about in Lynn's book had actually helped these children. It was then that we decided we had so little to lose and so much to gain by trying these interventions. Not long after, we came to realize that Nicholas was not helpless! We were not powerless! Using the information we gleaned, we embarked on a journey that continues to this day.

We began our biomedical treatment with the gluten-free, casein-free (GFCF) diet, which eliminates all wheat, oats, rye, barley, and dairy products. It took some weeks to get him on these foods as he had completely self-limited his diet to almost nothing but glutens and caseins in the form of grilled cheese sandwiches, toast, yogurt, and ice cream, occasionally allowing McDonald's french fries and potato chips in the mix. He showed little to no interest in any other foods and, in fact, gagged at the sight of any fruit, vegetable, or meat. If these foods were forced on him, he would vomit. Nevertheless, we were able to find acceptable substitute foods and slowly phase out the glutens and caseins.



After a few months on this diet, we had to admit that we hadn't seen significant changes and were beginning to wonder if it was really making a difference. But then came the fateful day when Nicholas found the dog food. Although he didn't eat any of the dog food, which was primarily made of wheat, he got the crumbs on his hands and proceeded to eat some chips before we realized what had happened. Within an hour his cheeks, ears, and chin turned fiery red. He began maniacal, uncontrollable laughter that we hadn't heard for a while. His balance wasn't quite right. In fact, he was acting drunk! For three days and three nights he bounced off the walls, unable to sleep for more than minutes at a time. His diarrhea was explosive and foul smelling, and he developed a severe diaper rash—like the ones that had disappeared months before. We needed no further convincing. This diet had made significant differences in ways we hadn't even noticed, but ways that we now saw were real and measurable.

We also began implementing many vitamin therapies. The first supplement we tried with Nicholas was Super Nu-Thera, which contained high doses of vitamin B6 and magnesium and was specifically designed for children on the autism spectrum. We began using this product after reading an article by Bernard Rimland in which he stated,

> All 18 studies known to me in which vitamin B6 has been evaluated as a treatment for autistic children have provided positive

> results. This is a rather remarkable record, since the many drugs that have been evaluated as treatments for autism have produced very inconsistent results. If a drug shows positive results in about half of the evaluation studies, it is considered a success and the drug is then advocated for use with autistic patients. ...[p]eople vary enormously in their need for B6. The children who showed improvement under B6 improved because they *needed* extra B6. Autism is thus in many cases a vitamin B6 dependency syndrome.[1]

Nicholas seemed to thrive on Super Nu-Thera. We began seeing many new and encouraging signs emerging in both his ABA therapy and his everyday life. It was not long after starting this course of treatment that Nicholas said his first word, "shoe," causing me the deep joy I described earlier. Also, prior to beginning biomedical treatment with Nicholas we could have thrown a party with 50 people in the room, and Nicholas would not have even noticed! But now, after beginning B6, we were seeing a new awareness of those around him and greater ease of eye contact with us. That twinkle in his eye was getting stronger and more noticeable.



One by one we began adding other supplements to his list, many of which produced new and favorable effects. One of the most outstanding of these was dimethylglycine (DMG). Again, this was prompted by an article written by Bernard Rimland in which he shared the following two stories of DMG use in autism:

> In some cases dramatic results have been seen within 24 hours: A Los Angeles mother was driving on the freeway, three-year-old Kathy in the back seat, five-year-old mute autistic son Sammy in the front. DMG had been started the day before. Kathy began to cry. Sammy turned and spoke his first words: "Don't cry, Kathy." The mother, stunned, almost crashed the car.
>
> A similar case: A Texas mother secured her six-year-old mute autistic daughter in the front seat, then, before driving off, turned to tell her husband, "I'll drop Mary at the babysitter's house first." Mary, on DMG for two days, startled her parents with her first words: "No! No babysitter!"[2]

Within days after we administered Nicholas' first doses of DMG, his therapists reported that he had a sudden surge in his expressive language. In fact, we had noticed the same thing. Up to that point every time he had labeled an object, his words had to be prompted by one of us saying something like, "This is a …," and waiting for his response. But now, for the first time ever, Nicholas was going around the house and spontaneously labeling objects! By the same token, we had noticed an increase in hyperactivity. But by reducing his dose of DMG and adding folic acid, we were able to eliminate this side effect and retain all the amazing benefits.

There have been other significant treatments that have made an impact on Nicholas, including melatonin (we *all* finally got some real sleep), mercury chelation, secretin, glutathione, Epsom salt baths, and many others. Each and every biomedical treatment that has been successful in Nicholas' life we have discovered either by attending the Defeat Autism Now! (DAN!) conferences, sponsored by ARI, through our DAN! doctor, or through publications that can be linked either directly or indirectly to the research and reporting of Bernard Rimland.



At the time of this writing, Nicholas is 4½ years old. He knows over four hundred words. He can express some of his needs and wants. He sight reads and can spell nearly 70 words. In addition to his ongoing home therapy, he attends preschool, where he is imitating his peers and making huge social gains. He has begun playing and interacting appropriately with his younger brother, Sam. Even though he is still on the autism spectrum, we have high hopes that he will enter grade school and someday be indistinguishable from his peers. In fact, just the other day on the playground, one of the teachers in his preschool asked his aide, "Which one is the boy with autism?" Thanks to dedicated people like Bernard Rimland and to God's mercy, our son is on his way to a productive and full life. And, by the way, the twinkle in his eye has all but overtaken the dull, autistic stare he once had!

**References**

[1] Bernard Rimland, "Vitamin B6 (and magnesium) in the treatment of autism," *Autism Research Review International*, Vol. 1, Issue 4; republished as ARI Publ. 34/September 2000, p. 1.

[2] Bernard Rimland, "Dimethylglycine (DMG), a nontoxic metabolite, and autism," *Autism Research Review International*, Vol. 4, Issue 2, p. 3.

*Update for Second Edition (September 2005):*

So much water has passed under the bridge for us since this book was first published. Time has passed, and, as children do, Nicholas has grown.

His little brother, Sam, just celebrated his fifth birthday; and we have been blessed with another beautiful son, Trey, who is now 18 months old. We have relocated to Melbourne, Florida, where my husband, Jack, serves as vice-president for the medical practice and non-profit organization of Jeff Bradstreet, M.D., an excellent physician focusing on children with autism and related disorders (for more information, please visit www.ICDRC.org).

With the time that has passed and all the changes for our family, I truly wish I could report that Nicholas is no longer on the autism spectrum. But in fact, he is still deeply affected by this terrible affliction. The road has been long, and the breakthroughs infrequent. He remains minimally verbal, and is not yet potty-trained. Even Dr. Bradstreet, who has been very successful in treating thousands of children with ASD, admits that Nicholas is one of his tougher cases.



Nevertheless, not all of the news concerning Nicholas is discouraging. Little by little we have seen him spending more time in "our world" than in his own. His ability to understand language has soared, and although he rarely uses language to communicate in return, he has a wonderful ability to connect with those around him. His sweet and gentle personality has captured the hearts of his teachers and therapists. His smile is stunningly attractive. And that twinkle in his eye has strengthened into a beautiful glimmer that even strangers have found compelling.

Somewhere in the sea of autism, we are making progress. In trying to keep him moving forward, we have explored many new treatment options for him, and each has played a role to some degree in his incremental improvement. Among the most notable was a course of IVIG of which he received 22 monthly treatments. We can say that the long-term effects of this treatment seem to be a marked improvement in his digestive system, and fewer obsessive behaviors.

More recently, we began a treatment of weekly IV infusions consisting of glutathione, vitamin C, and EDTA (a chelating agent). We have also begun intensive hyperbaric treatments and a round of the prescription drug Actos. We have high hopes that these therapies will make a significant difference for Nicholas. Will they? We don't know. Not everything we have tried has been helpful.

But our bottom line at this point is this: Never give up. Yes, the road is incredibly long and hard, but we have not reached the end yet! Even though there is much trial and error, new treatments and new hope for a full rich life are arising with remarkable speed. Yes, we are trying many treatments and, yes, we have done a lot of praying. But on those days when discouragement begins closing in, we have found our hope renewed by looking into our son's beautiful eyes. The twinkle is still there, stronger than ever. His hope and his destiny have not diminished simply because we don't see the improvement we want. He is on a different timeline than typical children, but we believe strongly that through medical breakthroughs and with the help of God, Nicholas will grow and develop, and fulfill his destiny—and do so with a beautiful twinkle in his eye!

# — Chapter 33 —
# Doctor, Can You Tell Me What's Wrong with My Baby?
By Kimberly Boyd Vest

*Kim Vest and her husband, Bryan, live in Springfield, Virginia, with their son Joshua, who was born in January 2001. This story was written in June 2002.*

Joshua Lee Vest was born on January 13, 2001, in Charleston, South Carolina. He was a healthy, beautiful boy who, to his father and me, was truly a gift from God. Staring at our little miracle, we felt that instant, unconditional love a parent feels for a child. During my pregnancy we read books about "attachment parenting" and decided that our child would be raised in this fashion. I was geared to breastfeed, co-sleep, wear my baby in a sling, and put aside my career as a massage and skincare therapist to be a full-time stay-at-home mom. We knew this would be a struggle, but we were willing to cut corners and live on a tight budget to give Joshua one of the most precious gifts a child can have: the devotion of quality time from his parents.



Picking Joshua's pediatrician was a no-brainer. The doctor came highly recommended, and the practice was even endorsed by the local children's hospital, which is ranked one of the best in the country.

It was at this pediatrician's practice, however, that my son's nightmarish dance with a yet-to-be-named beast began. My identification of my son's autism, and the treatments that I've discovered, have put my son on the road to recovery—recovery from a beast that tried to steal him from his father and me.

Joshua's problems started at nine days of age, when I discovered thrush in his mouth and diaper area. The doctor prescribed oral nystatin. This made the thrush worse (we learned later that the medicine was loaded with sugar, which fed the yeast). Then he was put on something stronger: oral diflucan (again, loaded with sugar). This killed the thrush in his mouth, but not in the diaper area. I, on the other hand, got thrush on my breast and developed mastitis. We played ping-pong for weeks with the thrush, but I was determined to continue breastfeeding.

Finally, after many weeks of medicine, Joshua and I both got the yeast under control. But he started showing other symptoms of illness, which (in looking back) seemed to coincide with his immunizations. I was calling Joshua's pediatrician on a weekly basis, insisting that Joshua's immune system wasn't developing normally. We battled not only thrush, but also constant, chronic congestion, eczema, and food sensitivities. It seemed that anything I ate affected him when he nursed. At each well-baby visit he was sick, but they still gave him his immunizations.

By his six-month well-baby visit he was getting worse, now with chronic rapid shallow breathing, hives, eczema, congestion, ear infections, and an ash color around his mouth, hands and feet. But his pediatricians didn't take me seriously and treated me like an over-reactive first-time mom.

Joshua had a severe reaction the evening after he received his six-month immunizations. He was running a fever of 104.5° and having convulsions, with his eyes rolling back into his head. When we called his pediatrician I was told that this was "normal" and to give him a double dose of Tylenol and monitor him. ***This reaction was never noted in his medical chart or called into the CDC's Vaccine Reaction Line*** *[emphasis by editor].*



Joshua continued to regress. He was now showing no appetite and was reacting negatively to the foods I was feeding him. I was very frustrated and anxious for help, so I started calling on asthma and allergy specialists. Joshua was put on a nebulizer of albuterol, and was diagnosed with a sinus and ear infection and more thrush. The doctor admitted him to the hospital with an IV and tested his heart via echocardiogram (EEG), finding that it was normal. A test for cystic fibrosis also came back negative.

Since my son was not improving I took him for a second, third, fourth, and fifth opinion. He had skin tests for food allergies, which were negative, and he was tested for celiac disease because he had developed dark-green oily stool or white and porous stool that smelled very foul.

Joshua basically quit growing and gaining weight, and by nine months of age he had fallen from the 50th percentile in height and 75th percentile in weight to less than the third percentile in both.

The pediatrician who attended Joshua's nine-month well-baby visit said to me, "This child has seen more doctors than Carter's has liver pills and they can't find anything wrong with him. To be honest, they all have told me that they think you're over-reactive and maybe *you* need to see a doctor yourself for some medication for anxiety. However, I am the only doctor who doesn't think you're crazy—you just need to feed your child more calories a day to get him back on the growth chart. I don't care what you put in his diet at this point—give him milk shakes, add lots of butter to his food—whatever it takes to get 900-1100 calories into him a day."

I was furious! How dare he tell me these things. To top it off, he gave Joshua another immunization, and all the while my son had a fever and an ear infection! This was the last time Joshua was seen by that medical practice.

The newest symptom to add to the list was his refusal to eat solid, textured foods—he would gag and throw up. His behavior was becoming strange, too: he had started a high-pitched constant scream, and would not sleep unless we swung him to sleep in his car seat. He also became a video addict—refusing any activity including eating unless it was during a "Baby Einstein" video. In addition, he was starting to bang his mouth on walls and floors, and no longer had an interest in playing with his toys—he wanted to put them into his mouth instead. We thought, "Oh, it's just teething."

I found another pediatrician and explained my story, sobbing all the while. I told the doctor that Joshua was in a loving home and we were big advocates for attachment parenting—where were we going wrong? I knew I wasn't crazy. My intuition told me my son was horribly ill and not developing physically or socially.



The new pediatrician sent Joshua for another cystic fibrosis test—negative; a pH probe for reflux—negative; a barium swallow—negative. Back to the E.N.T. who scheduled a laryngoscopy and bronchoscopy to see if there were any blocked airways, and surgery to put tubes in his ears (Joshua was now on his eighth ear infection). The morning of his scheduled surgery he was admitted to the hospital for dehydration and possible pneumonia, as well as the continued ear infection. Once he was cleared, the surgery took place, the tubes were placed in his ears, and other tests were done. Afterward, the doctor told us that Joshua's stomach opening showed a long leak and major irritation of the lining, consistent with reflux. Desperate for an answer, we bought it. But as we learned later, we were wrong.

Joshua's pediatrician consulted with the E.N.T. and told us that it all made sense: he was refluxing and it was taking a U-turn into his lungs, therefore causing asthma and immune responses (eczema).

"But this doesn't explain all the other problems," I told him. "His bowel movements and food sensitivities. His refusal to eat solids and his bizarre behavior." Joshua's latest issue was refusing anything but lactose-free whole milk, brown rice cereal, and fruit. The doctor prescribed Prilosec, which had to be made at a compounding pharmacy due to Joshua's corn sensitivities. (At this point, Joshua was reacting to corn, soy, gluten, most colored fruits and vegetables, and foods containing salicylates and phenol, especially apples, tomatoes, and bananas.)

We saw an initial improvement for about three or four days, followed by a dramatic regression. The holidays were now approaching and so was Joshua's first birthday. Instead of being excited about visiting family for vacation and celebrating Christmas and Joshua's birthday, I was dreading it. Fear that Joshua would get sick again overwhelmed me. Packing to take Joshua on a trip was almost like moving—we couldn't forget one thing for fear that he would have a meltdown.

When we got to my husband's family's house, there were a lot of people there. Joshua became over-stimulated and went on a food strike. Within three days the whole family was sick from a nasty bug that was going around. Joshua was horribly sick and very congested, was covered from head to toe with a bizarre rash, and had a high fever. That night we took him to the emergency room and were sent home with the answer we expected: he had a virus. Ten days passed and the virus got worse. Joshua's eyes were constantly dilated, we were giving him a nebulizer every four hours, and his nose was running, thick and green. We went back to the pediatrician and E.N.T., who ordered a CT scan of the sinuses that showed absolutely no air in Joshua's sinus cavities and a major sinus infection. We started another round of antibiotics.



THIS WAS ENOUGH! I had to get an answer, so I took Joshua to someone my own doctor had recommended: a woman with a Ph.D. in natural medicine who specialized in living blood studies. She took one drop of blood from Joshua's heel and put it on a microscope slide that was attached to a TV for us to see. The immediate look on her face told me something was terribly wrong. She started pointing to the TV and explaining what each particle in his blood was and how it worked in his system. She said, "Your son has a severe fungal infection in his blood—this is yeast, this is undigested food, this is a parasite, a blood worm. Your son has a leaky gut. However, although I have a Ph.D. in natural medicine, I cannot legally diagnose him. I can only tell you what I see and where it's coming from. This child is very sick and antibiotics are the worst thing for him as they're feeding the yeast. Also, you have to take him off dairy completely and start him on rice or soy milk instead."

Soy was out so we went with gluten-free rice milk. We also started colloidal silver, a natural antibacterial and antifungal. Within three days, Joshua's nose cleared up and he started to look better. This was a great leap in the right direction, but I was still concerned about his behavior and food sensitivities.

I was also concerned about his environmental sensitivities. We had experienced a lot of problems with mold. Right after we'd brought newborn Joshua home from the hospital, we had discovered mold growing in the HVAC system of our apartment. Our entire home became contaminated. (The mold lets off the same toxins found in chemical warfare. It is very neurologically debilitating, especially to autistic children, as we learned later.) We moved to another apartment, newly built, which also caused Joshua to have reactions because there was new material in the carpet and padding, and new paint that was "off-gassing." It was very toxic. We moved again. To our surprise, the third apartment had water damage that was not fixed properly—and we found mold growing on the inside of the walls (I discovered the mold shortly after we learned that Joshua was having "leaky gut" problems). Talk about bad luck, but we had learned something very important. We were finding answers to Joshua's health problems.



One night, three days after the naturopath told us about Joshua's leaky gut, I sat at my computer and said a prayer. "God, please, help us find out what's truly wrong with Joshua and help us cure him. He doesn't deserve this suffering. I need answers and so far we've only been given one that we know for sure. If this is part of a bigger puzzle, please guide me on this computer tonight and show me where you want me to go. I need you now, and Joshua needs you."

I typed in LEAKY GUT IN TODDLERS on the Internet. What popped up on the screen took my breath away. It was the Autism Research Institute's report on mercury toxicity from vaccinations, and its comparison to autistic symptoms in children. As I read the report, bits of terror crept into my heart and I felt breathless. I had an anxiety attack right there (just writing about it now puts knots in my stomach). This report listed EVERY symptom I had been complaining about to any doctor who would listen to me. This was my answer, and I knew it.

I went into my bedroom and woke up Bryan, my husband, and asked him to come into the computer room with me. Sobbing, I showed him the report. I said, "Joshua may have autism."

Bryan looked at me with disbelief and held me for the longest time while I sobbed. "Kim," he said, "you cannot believe everything you read on the Internet." I stopped him in mid-sentence and explained to him that this was divine intervention, that I had prayed to God before going online for answers. We looked at the report, and Bryan couldn't argue. We just held each other and prayed.

The next morning I called Dr. Bernard Rimland at the Autism Research Institute. He took my call and listened to my story. He told me that I was a "clever young woman to discover Joshua's symptoms and make a connection when he was only 13 months old." He also offered me hope, and the name of a doctor who practiced environmental medicine and was also a DAN! doctor. He gave me the number for Kirkman Labs, a leading distributor of gluten-free, casein-free supplements tailored to the needs of autistic children. "You'll need Kirkman," he said.

So our journey began. I had another daily talk with God. "If this is your answer, give us a cure," I prayed. "Give me the guidance to recover our son. Let me trust the instincts that put me here now." I picked up the phone and called the DAN! doctor, Allen Lieberman, M.D. But there was a problem; his office was unable to accept Joshua's insurance coverage, so I decided to wait. When I called again to make an appointment, Dr. Lieberman's office manager, Sheila, answered the phone. I asked for an appointment knowing that I was going to have to put his visit on a credit card, but I had no choice. I had to heal my son. Sheila remembered me and said that she had prayed that somehow we could get Joshua in to see Dr. Lieberman. She made the appointment.



During his first visit with Joshua, Dr. Lieberman took hair samples to check for heavy metal toxicity and urine samples to test for yeast. He also agreed that immunizations, as well as the environmental exposures, had played a part in Joshua's problem, along with the chronic yeast issues.

When Joshua's test results came in, they showed extremely elevated yeast levels as well as toxic levels of aluminum, antimony, arsenic, bismuth, cadmium, lead, mercury, silver, tin, titanium, and uranium. "First," Dr. Lieberman said, "we have to heal the gut. Second, we need to chelate him, but not until the gut is healed and the yeast is under control."

We started Joshua on Nizoral tablets to kill off the yeast. This coincided with the discovery of the mold in our last (third) apartment. When I called Dr. Lieberman about the mold, he told me to get Joshua out of the apartment immediately, and not bring him back. He said to avoid newly built homes, due to the "off-gassing," which is very toxic to autistic children.

We discarded all of our furniture and all of our belongings were sent away and cleaned with an antimicrobial for mold. We lived in a hotel for two months. The hotel environment, however, did wonders for Joshua. We started to see a great healing as the yeast died off and he was no longer exposed to the mold.

Because Charleston is one of the worst areas in the nation for allergies and has a very high mold count due to humidity, we decided to relocate to Northern Virginia to be closer to Bryan's parents and to provide Joshua with a healthier environment.

This is where we found Dr. Mary Megson, through the help of Kirkman Labs. Both are a true Godsend to the autistic community!

The moment Dr. Megson laid eyes on Joshua, who was not 14 months old, she asked, "Is he always pale around the mouth?" "YES!," I practically yelled. Finally, a doctor who noticed immediately what no other doctors did, the pale blue coloring around Joshua's mouth and his hands and feet. "I believe that this reaction is from the DTP vaccination," Dr. Megson said. I told her that Joshua had had 14 vaccinations by the time he was nine months old and that I had refused more. "No MMR for him," I said. Dr. Megson agreed: "You can't immunize a child who has no immune system."

Dr. Megson took Joshua's blood and explained her theory about the "cis" form of vitamin A and its healing properties. I explained that I had tried Kirkman's cod liver oil both orally and topically but Joshua couldn't tolerate it. As a matter of fact, at this point he was reacting negatively to almost all foods except chicken and brown rice, even though he'd progressed by leaps and bounds since Dr. Lieberman had tested him. His stools were still very foul smelling and loose, they were yellow to green and full of undigested food, and his skin was still very broken out with eczema and a rash. He was still at 17 pounds and not growing. His language was very delayed ("dada-dada" was his only sound, but not specific to dad himself). Dr. Megson explained to me that the yeast die-off could cause the foul-smelling stools and the skin rash, but the "blocked pathways" to his neurological system had to be "unblocked." I agreed, but how? He couldn't digest fats or oils, so cod liver oil was out; he couldn't handle digestive enzymes either. We were damned if we did, damned if we didn't. We had tried every organic food one by one with no luck, we were dealing with constant nebulizer treatments to cope with asthmatic reactions, Joshua still had skin rashes, and he wouldn't eat solid, textured foods without gagging and throwing up (we were having to puree and spoon-feed him his meals). He had also started banging his head and spinning and dragging his face across the floor again.



A couple of weeks later, Dr. Megson called to let us know that one of the tests was positive for *C. difficile*, bacteria that live in the intestines and thrive off the waste that yeast puts out. She prescribed Flagyl. This was a great help: Joshua calmed down and started becoming verbal. He said his first true words: "beep, beep," then "bye-bye," and "tickle-tickle-tickle" and "UH, oh!" His stools started to look a little better as well. One more small victory!

We found a new pediatrician in northern Virginia for Joshua's 15-month well visit. He is a very good doctor who is open to whatever treatments we want to try; skeptical, of course—conservative medicine has him under its thumb—but he's nice enough. I had to set some boundaries with him when he started checking off the immunizations Joshua was to receive on that visit. I made it crystal clear that until it was 100% guaranteed that my son's condition did not stem from immunizations, further immunizations were out of the question! Moreover, my son's immune system was too weak: he was fighting a cold that day and had a fever of 101°. We discussed Joshua's developmental delays and the doctor suggested that Joshua get occupational therapy as well as speech therapy. He also suggested that Joshua be seen at Children's Hospital in D.C. for his GI issues.

We made an appointment with the head of gastroenterology at Children's Hospital. After discussing Joshua's condition in great detail he suggested a pancreatic function test, a sigmoidoscopy, and an endoscopy to obtain some biopsies of tissue and to take a look at Joshua's GI system from top to bottom. I also requested a blood workup for food allergies to see if any antibodies would show, considering that earlier in the week the introduction of eggs to Joshua's diet had sent him to the hospital in an ambulance. The doctor was going abroad to attend a medical conference, so we waited to hear the test results from someone else in his office.



The results showed active colitis (inflammation of the intestine). However, they showed no food allergies. But eggs had sent him to the hospital just the week before—these tests are not reliable for these children!

Much encouragement came from my friend Jen, who has a very high-functioning autistic son, also named Joshua. Jen became my biggest support. When I got to northern Virginia and contacted her she came to me armed with books to read. I read Karyn Seroussi's book *Unraveling the Mystery of Autism and Pervasive Developmental Disorder* (this book became a bible to me—hats off to Karyn and her husband!). Jen was also trying to encourage me to check out secretin infusions, as they were the best thing she did to help her son recover. She showed me pictures and videos of before and after her son's infusions. He experienced better eye contact, communication and fine motor skills, and increased appetite. He had started coloring with crayons and stacking building blocks the day after his first infusion! He also started having formed stools for the first time ever.

Even though Dr. Megson couldn't help a great deal because of Joshua's restrictions, she recommended Kelly Dorfman, a nutritionist in Maryland who's among the "Who's Who" in helping children with autism recover through nutrition. Jen also encouraged me to contact Kelly. Kelly was very informative and pulled every trick out of the bag for me to try. She recommended a doctor in Maryland (who happened to be Jen's son's doctor) who had just come across a different form of secretin. Off to Maryland we went: me, Jen, and both Joshuas. The boys split a vial and each received an infusion.

I noticed a HUGE difference in my son within a week. His skin rash went away and in came more words—"E-I, E-I, O" from "Old MacDonald," "bubbles," "dada" (to daddy). His appetite soared and he started *feeding himself* solid, textured foods without gagging and throwing up. His constant need to watch videos disappeared, and he started showing interest in his toys. He also exhibited a great calmness. His stools were still not as formed as we'd like, and we were considering a drug called Dipentum to help with that. Jen's son also showed signs of progress with the secretin infusion: he was calmer, and went to bed willingly at 8:30 each night (previously it had been a battle for Jen to get him into bed and keep him there). He also showed better eye contact.



Shortly after the infusion, it got really hot outside and we started running the air conditioner. Within a couple of days, the HVAC system in our apartment (which I had insisted be inspected before we'd moved in, and which had seemed fine) started emitting a musty, "rotten onion" odor, and Joshua started to regress: skin rash and diarrhea, back to the nebulizer, spinning and dragging his head across the floor, and banging his head on everything in the house. He was extremely irritable as well. I started praying, "What now?" I went to our landlord and insisted they open the HVAC system because it was crippling Joshua. After putting up a fight, they sent someone out and there it was: the owner's manual that was never removed from the system when it was installed 15 years before, all molded completely through, lying across the blower and condenser unit. NOT AGAIN! Back to the hotel.

In the meantime, we started Joshua on Dipentum to help with inflammation of the intestine. This was a HUGE mistake. Dipentum is a member of the salicylate family (phenol), a huge problem for Joshua. He was so miserable: diarrhea and digging at his skin, scratching until he bled. At my wit's end, I decided to look into a tea that I had read about in Karyn Seroussi's book. It is a tea that the Ojibwa Native American Indians used for healing. It's now called Essiac tea, after a nurse, Cassie (Essiac is an anagram of her name), who received it from an Indian medicine man who used it to help heal women with breast cancer.

Being a firm believer in herbs (which are mentioned over 300 times in the Bible), I started knocking, seeking, and asking questions. What I got was an outpouring of positive responses. Parents of autistic children reported dramatic results in their children as well as themselves. The tea seemed to mimic a secretin infusion, naturally! I called and ordered it. The woman I ordered it from gave me the phone number of Jean Curtin, the parent of a 15-year-old recovering autistic son, Michael.

I called Jean, and God, once again, did his magic with divine intervention. I felt as if I were talking to the mother of Joshua's identical autistic twin, as the boys' symptoms and stims were identical (when Michael had been Joshua's age). Jean's knowledge, guidance, and two hours on the phone gave me more help than any doctor ever could have. She told me that phenols and salicylates are closely related, and told me about the Feingold diet, which eliminates foods containing them. She told me how amazing the tea was—a total miracle for Michael—and also told me to look into starting Joshua on vitamin B12. Neurological problems and digestive problems are often linked to a B12 deficiency.



She then put Michael on the phone. I felt so honored to speak to him that I cried. It was as if I were talking to my son—13 years later. Michael explained why autistic people stim, saying that banging his head felt great and it helped to ease a constant pressure, and that spinning kept him connected to life. He also suggested that Joshua might be dragging his head on the floor in order to reach a mold or a fungal source to feed the yeast in his body, or that the behavior may be due to yeast trying to escape. I was astounded to hear this, as Joshua was doing this only when he was exposed to a moldy environment. I hadn't told Michael about the mold sensitivity but he knew already. This young man was one of the most mature, intelligent, and informative human beings that I'd ever met in my life, and had a heart of gold. He is the Best-Kept Secret—a recovered autistic young man who could give answers to the questions that we parents always wonder about. Hats off to him and Jean.

I started Joshua on the tea when he was 17½ months old, and damned if it didn't mimic a secretin infusion. Within a week we saw solid stools and cleared skin, although his skin did break out when I upped the dose, due to the detox and yeast die-off. He's calmer, his appetite has increased, he's gained two pounds, and for the first time ever he ate white grapes and watermelon without a reaction. He's also showing an interest in other kids, which is a first. Just last night he hugged and kissed his cousin, Emma! I also contacted Larry at Kirkman Labs. We discussed B12, and he recommended doing a trial of it as he feels that B12 is much overlooked in autism. So look for more results coming soon!

Well, my friend, that's where we are with Joshua. WE WILL RECOVER OUR SON.

* * * * *

And finally ...

A point of interest: the head of the GI Department of Children's Hospital in DC finally gave me a call to let me know that he had looked over Joshua's test results. He said he couldn't do much for him, but he did mention that a speaker at one of the conferences he'd attended while abroad spoke of a connection between autism and the GI system, and that he had thought of Joshua. He started asking me what I was going to do for Joshua. I told him of the secretin and tea and my talk with Larry and Jean about B12 therapy, and the little miracles that we're seeing each day. He sounded genuinely happy for me, and asked me to keep him posted, saying that he would like to follow Joshua's recovery. He even offered to call in the prescription to have the vitamin compounded! Could this be a positive sign of the times to come? I hope so.



I hope my story can help you through this time as others' stories have helped me. From one parent to another, I will pass on to you what I discovered through this bittersweet journey:

1. Don't be afraid to follow your intuition. That's why God gave it to you. I believe that intuition can sometimes be God's voice.
2. Allow yourself time to grieve, but be careful not to get stuck there, as it does no one any good, especially yourself. You have to get busy—time is valuable. This time can be spent loving and recovering your child.
3. Escape denial and blame—just do it. *Move forward!*
4. Continue to knock, seek, and ask. You will meet some of the strongest, most amazing people in this network and they will be glad to help you and your child.
5. Most importantly, NEVER, NEVER, NEVER give up!

I will close with these words from Michael Curtin: "If you give up on your child, you will lose him forever, which would be a great injustice to you and him!"

May God bless you and yours.

*Update (February 2003):*

Since I wrote my story, the following changes have occurred with Joshua, who is now 27 months old. He is talking, singing, dancing, and putting sentences together. He shows a genuine interest in other children, has great eye contact, engages in pretend play, and is definitely in his terrible twos!

Behaviorally he is much calmer and more focused. We can take him out in public with greater ease. His "stims"—head banging, spinning, and dragging his face across the floor—are very few and far between and only happen when he is exposed to molds, phenolic foods, corn, dairy, or gluten. We have discontinued the Essiac Tea because he is now on a daily maintenance dose of SecroFlo secretin as well as bimonthly infusions. (Of the three different kinds of secretin we've tried, this is by far the best.)



We've also started using a line of digestive enzymes produced by a company called Enzymedica. That, along with the SecroFlo, has had a huge impact on Joshua's appetite, digestion (e.g., well-formed stools), and allergic response (both physiological and behavioral) to foods. He also has no more asthma attacks. This product line includes enzymes that are phenol-free. Of the many enzymes we have tried, these are the only ones that seem to work for Joshua. (It is important, however, that these enzymes be given BEFORE food is ingested. They can also be given between meals.) We use Lypo and Carbo for Joshua.

This company also carries an enzyme for yeast control that we have just started giving Joshua. Because the yeast can become resistant to the same daily treatment, we have found that it helps to vary the antifungals we use. We're trying to stick to natural antifungals because Nizoral affects the liver and crosses the blood/brain barrier. Probiotics mixed with *Saccharomyces boulardii* have done wonders thus far. We've started Kirkman's Colostrum to address Joshua's low immunity and slow growth and he is now growing again and slowly but surely gaining weight!

Another problem for Joshua has been a depletion of his essential fatty acids due to restricted diet. We have him on a product called "The Total EFA," made by a company called Health from the Sun. We mix the liquid form with YÜ Natural Organic Rice Beverage and add a Lypo enzyme to assist with fat digestion (www.YuBeverage.com; we have found that other brands of enriched rice milk contain carageenan and ascorbyl palmitate, which are not good for these kids). He is still taking Kirkman's Everyday multivitamin, Kirkman's Companion, extra B6 and B12 and magnesium, and 80 milligrams of zinc daily.

Joshua's doctors, dietician, and therapists are all amazed at his total turnaround in this past year. We truly have a much healthier, more normal child.

And finally, we continue to work on Joshua's gut-healing. We are still missing some pieces to the puzzle, but we have learned as a result of his blood work that his lymphocytes are "flip-flopped" (what should be reading low is reading high, and what should be reading high is reading low). We have made an appointment with Dr. Timothy Buie, a GI specialist at Harvard/Massachusetts General Hospital, who is currently doing much-needed research in this field. It is our hope that he can help us better understand Joshua's gut-brain connection so we can get him totally healed and recovered.

I'd like to close my chapter with a personal note and give many thanks to everyone who has been there for us on this bittersweet journey. Mostly we thank Christ Jesus who has carried us when we no longer felt we had the strength, whose grace and patience have humbled us beyond belief, and who has answered many prayers. We thank Joshua, for fighting this battle with us. We are grateful also to Dr. Richard Layton and his incredible staff, to our dear friends Teresa and Amy, and to all of our friends and family who held faith in us when everyone else thought we were crazy for taking a biomedical approach to healing Joshua. Thanks to Michelle at Ojibwa Tea, to the entire staff at Kirkman Labs, and to Tory and George Mead and Katharine Lawrence for all their time, love, encouragement, and moral support.

And lastly, a very special thanks to Dr. Bernard Rimland, the founder of the Autism Research Institute, whose research, guidance, and dedication have helped us and countless others to put our children on the road to recovery.

"And we know that in ALL things, God works for the good of those who love Him who have been called according to His purpose"... Romans 8:28.

*Update for Second Edition (October 2005):*

Hello Friends!

Joshua is just shy of five years old and he presents as a normally developing four-year-old child. His biggest setback continues to be immune dysregulation.

We have continued to stick to the diet, enzymes, and supplementation. We have discovered (with the help of Dr. Elizabeth Mumper) that Joshua's methylation pathways were not functioning normally, and he cannot process heavy metals or environmental toxins to which he is exposed. As a result, we've added methyl-B12 shots twice a week *[Editors' note: Please see related article on page 423.]* and have successfully completed twelve rounds of chelation with DMSA *[Editors' note: Please see related articles on pages 408 and 433.]*, along with careful monitoring and testing of his liver and kidney functioning, while keeping an eye on essential vitamin and mineral levels in his body.

So far, the chelation and B12 shots have been the "missing piece" to Joshua's puzzle. He has responded at an amazing pace, and we continue to see more and more improvement with him on a DAILY basis. Even his immune system is slowly but surely beginning to rebuild.

We couldn't be prouder to say that *WE HAVE OUR CHILD BACK!!!!!*

## — Chapter 34 —

# Against the Odds: A Story about Nikolai Young

By Robin and George Young, M.D.

*Robin and George Young live in Portland, Oregon, with their son, Nikolai, who has recovered from autism. Nikolai was born in June 1998; this story was written in February 2002.*

My name is Nikolai Young, I am 3½ years old, and I would like to tell you about my heritage and my life.



My father is of Russian heritage and was born in Poland while his parents were fleeing their native Russia and communism. He was born prematurely, with no resources; it was feared he would not live. He survived, however, and after his birth the family continued their journey into displaced persons' camps in Austria, where his sister was born. When he was four, the family journeyed to Santiago, Chile. From the age of four until he was 17, they lived in Santiago. His family, who had very little money, struggled for thirteen years, after which they emigrated to America in 1962. They had a total of $100 for a family of four when they arrived in North Carolina aboard a cargo ship. When they settled at their final destination in New York City, everyone worked and also struggled to learn English, as they had struggled to learn Spanish in South America. Eventually, my father would serve in the U.S. military (Vietnam veteran), work, graduate from Columbia University and then from George Washington University Medical School, and complete his internship and residency in radiology at the University of Minnesota. His is a true immigrant success story. He retains his fluency in Russian and Spanish, and continues his Russian Orthodox faith (my great grandfather was a Russian Orthodox priest).

My mother was born and raised on a farm in southwestern Minnesota. She, too, had meager economic resources. However, she had something far more important: a loving family who instilled in her a strong work ethic, and the kind of values about which Garrison Keillor sometimes speaks—Scandinavian honesty, kindness, and reserve (although the reserve has been replaced by a desire to express and understand thoughts and feelings openly). She was raised in the Lutheran faith, and is now searching for a worship community to join. Interested in the commonality of all faiths, she dreams of taking additional religious studies/comparative religion classes, as she did in college. She graduated from Macalester College in St. Paul, Minnesota, by virtue of scholarships, loans, and work. Before my birth, my mother worked for Hewlett-Packard in the field of Human Resources in St. Paul, attended graduate school in industrial relations/adult learning theory, and served as Human Resources Director for Clatsop County, Oregon.

My birth was a long-time dream of my mother, who over a period of years had endured several abdominal surgeries for severe endometriosis. My father had had a vasectomy after my two older half-siblings were born, and went through two reversal surgeries. I was a "high-tech" baby, conceived using *in vitro* fertilization and intracytoplasmic sperm injection (ICSI); my conception, especially on the first attempt, was truly against the odds.



My first 3½ years of life have been filled with both love and suffering. I was given my first vaccination at 12 hours of age in the hospital, for hepatitis B; it contained thimerosal (a preservative that is nearly 50% mercury). My parents believe this was the first assault on my intestines and my immature immune system. My mother thought it odd that I didn't seem to sleep very much in the hospital—my eyes were wide open most of the time. After I got home, I was increasingly fussy. I would pull up my legs and cry incessantly. I was hungry—I would go to my mother's breast to nurse, but I would pull quickly away, screaming. The terrible pain and cramps I experienced culminated in bright red blood in my diaper at three months of age. My stools were like oil, and obviously distressing. At my mother's insistence, a sigmoidoscopy performed at Oregon Health Sciences University (OHSU) showed severe colitis, which is not normal for an infant, but with a tissue biopsy insufficient to allow pathologists to diagnose the cause. My mother and father were left to their own deductive reasoning. My mother decided to eliminate all possible allergenic agents from her diet. Because I was breastfeeding, I got much better. It was only when my pediatrician started encouraging my mother to broaden my diet and introduce new foods, along with my continuing vaccination regimen, that I started a very slow and progressive process of becoming sicker. My parents believe that up to the time I was 33 months of age, my intestines were damaged by the thimerosal in the vaccines, the measles virus from the MMR vaccine (which also may have caused an autoimmune response in my brain), and the by-products of gluten and casein in my diet. Because my intestines were probably littered with tiny holes, gluten and casein molecules passed into my bloodstream, where they entered my brain as opioid-acting chemicals. Depending upon different theories, I was being subjected to either a heroin-like substance or a PCP-like substance every time I ingested gluten or casein. Because my digestive system was damaged, I was in effect malnourished—I was not absorbing the nutrients my parents were giving me. I was plagued by constant constipation, occasional diarrhea, terrible eczema on my hands and arms, a rectal abscess, and dark circles under my eyes. There were small welts on my face that you could see in the right light. My stomach was distended longer than the normal "baby tummy." I had unexplained episodes of high fevers and vomiting. Once I was hospitalized, because it was feared I might have meningococcal disease; there was never an explanation for the very high fever and red rash I developed at the end of that episode. I seemed to be developing a higher-than-normal tolerance to pain. I never slept through the night, and woke up frequently. I would sometimes laugh for a long time, for no apparent reason. Over time I continued to acquire words, but was not putting them together or answering questions. I was extremely hyperactive. My eye contact was becoming terrible—I was looking through or past people (I was probably seeing fragmented images at this point in time). I would not listen to a story or engage in play. I was covering my ears frequently. I would sometimes run into a different room, close the door, hide in a closet, and cover my ears when another child came to play. I was practically unmanageable in grocery stores and shopping malls; I would have ridden up and down on an elevator for hours if I had been allowed to, and would physically fight when I was made to stop. My palms and forehead were sweaty. I was a very, very sick little boy.



My parents continued to consult my pediatrician, visited an allergist in Seattle, saw a pediatric gastroenterologist at OHSU, and went to another specialist at Emanuel Hospital. My mother was told not to worry, that boys sometimes develop more slowly than girls. She was told to give me prune juice for the constipation.

Although my mother questioned the pediatrician about a report she had heard on CNN about the MMR vaccine being implicated in autism, and asked for alternatives, she was told that none were available, and that there was nothing to this report. She was asked if she wanted me to be able to go to school. In retrospect, she believes that the MMR vaccine was probably the final insult to my gut. After reaching all of my developmental milestones in my first year of life, I "slowed down" after the MMR at 12 months of age. I hit our big-screen television repeatedly that following summer. I became more and more hyperactive, and my language consisted only of naming concrete objects.

When I entered preschool in the fall after I turned two, my mother was concerned because I did not want to participate in circle time, preferring to play in the corner. I would frequently leave the room and run down the hall. Once, when another child came running up to hug me, I froze. I had "whole body" tension reactions if another child got too close. Although my mother didn't recognize it, I was echolalic (I parroted what others would say). My mother had to use suppositories all the time so that I could have a bowel movement after five or six days of constipation. Often she had to use several. I whimpered and cried pitifully when I saw the suppository, struggling to get away.

When I was 33 months old, I finally visited a developmental pediatrician whom my mother had heard about through my preschool. He reported that I was impossible to contain or control, that I was extremely active, that I did not respond to "no," and that I needed constant supervision. He noted my mechanical and manipulative skills, my "cause-and-effect" exploration, and the fact that I knew my letters, colors, and numbers. He also observed my short attention span and poor eye contact. He was struck by how autonomous I was, and how resistant I was to his trying to engage me in play and interact with me. He noted my rote counting, and also heard a considerable amount of immediate echolalia. He noted my nonspecific verbalizations. He noted that I smelled balls and plants. In summary, he told my parents that he was very concerned that I had autism spectrum disorder. He said that my delayed speech development with a disordered pattern of speech usage, characterized by frequent non-specific use of words, echolalia, and some appropriate use of words, concerned him. He noted that I didn't typically use words to indicate what I wanted or to communicate socially. He noted that my play with toys was very manipulative and mechanical, and that I had excellent motor and manipulative skills. He noted my obvious delay in social development and my difficulty in establishing normal peer interactions. He saw me putting my hands over my ears. He also reaffirmed my extreme hyperactivity and lack of inhibition to voice, requiring constant attention. He said, "Nikolai's behavior is such a concern that I suggest you see a psychologist privately." He told my mother she clearly needed help caring for me, because I was too much for one person to manage. He suggested the early intervention services through the public schools as my parents' only treatment for me. He told my parents that I had a lifelong disability, and that it would severely impair my quality of life.

My father sat in stunned silence. My mother immediately stood up and said, "What about the vaccines?" He responded, "There is absolutely no evidence that the vaccines have anything to do with autism." After returning home and experiencing an initial (but brief) period of extreme grief and fear, my mother got on the Internet. She discovered the websites for the Autism Research Institute and the Center for the Study of Autism. She somehow was able to get the home phone number of the Director of the Center for the Study of Autism, and called him on a Sunday afternoon. He was kind, encouraging, and extremely informative. She talked with other parents who were ahead of us. She printed articles for my father to read. As a traditional, conservative allopathic physician, my father initially did not believe that there was anything that could be done besides contacting the early intervention services program. He thought my mother was grasping for straws while she should have been accepting the situation. He started reading. He stayed up late many nights. He started searching the Web himself. He bought medical textbooks on immunology. He and my mother talked with the two designated DAN! physicians in Oregon. He scheduled himself for a DAN! conference in short order. He asked my pediatrician for the amount of mercury that had been in my shots, and she gave it to him. She stopped speaking to him, although my father did not express any antagonism toward her.



As of this writing, ten months have passed since I was at my worst. I was put on a strict gluten- and casein-free (GFCF) diet. This seemed to produce almost immediate results for me: my mother thought she heard me say, "I love you Grandma" in an extremely garbled voice; I pointed to an airplane in the sky for the first time; I told my mother, "Hurt toe" when I had never verbalized previous pain; I put on a new jacket my mother had gotten for me, and admired myself in the mirror—and I wore it to bed. My mother also eliminated foods to which I was allergic (as determined by specialized blood tests) when I was first on the GFCF diet. These foods have since been reintroduced with no apparent contraindications. My mother also started buying organic and additive- and antibiotic-free foods. I was given vitamin and mineral supplements to address my deficiencies and bolster my immune system. These supplements are hypoallergenic and purchased primarily from Kirkman Laboratories. I take 35 different supplements and vitamins a day. At first, my mother had to chase me and hold me down to get them into me. Although they don't taste very good mixed in banana baby food, now I say "Oh, gross," and "I don't like it" when I take them. I was given two courses of nystatin to kill fungus discovered through stool sample tests. My Grandma prays for me constantly. I have ABA therapists who have worked with me to help me make up for the developmental time I lost. I have "made up" over two years of expressive language skills in those 10 months. I have no more eczema, no more welts, no more distended belly, no more constipation, and my eye contact is normal. I speak in sentences and answer questions. My activity level is now normal, I am very social, and my imaginative play is wonderful. I love it when people read to me. My cognitive and motor skills are at or above average for my age, though my expressive language is still five to six months behind the norm for my age at this time.

My therapists tell my parents that I am very gentle, well behaved, easy to engage in conversation, and eager to learn. I am also very loving and sensitive. I seem to have unusual empathy and compassion for a child my age. A short while ago I was with one of my therapists visiting a pet store before going to my preschool. While in the shopping mall I noticed plants for sale. I asked Beth, "Can I get the purple one for Mommy and the yellow one for Grandma?" Needless to say, I arrived home carrying purple and yellow primroses, which I proudly gave to Mommy and Grandma (I did not ask for anything for myself). I need to continue to develop my conversational language skills and my use of pronouns (this is developing quickly). I am working on grasping more abstract concepts (concrete things come easily for me: I knew the alphabet, identified individual letters out of sequence, and counted to 20, even when I was very sick). I need to work on my attention and focus skills, especially in a larger group setting. This is also developing quickly. In short, I now have mild delays in language and social interactions with peers. I would no longer be diagnosed as on the autism spectrum. One of my therapists, who has a Ph.D. in psychology, has said that in her 19 years of working with children she has never seen anyone move so far so fast.



Although the developmental pediatrician did us an enormous service by correctly diagnosing my illness, he was not informed about how to help me get better. This denial and ignorance of the mainstream medical establishment regarding this illness is very shocking and disturbing.

I have beaten the odds more than once in my short life. My mother says it is hard for her to accept my suffering and struggle, but now she is looking for the gifts that this might have given me. Recently she asked another of my therapists what she would project as my strengths in years to come, and what good may have come from what happened to me. Beth said, "I think Nikolai clearly has a love of learning and of succeeding, he has a phenomenal memory, he is a very sensitive and gentle child, and he will probably always be the kind of person who will want to know everything possible about a given subject. Nikolai will perhaps have a slightly different perspective to bring to bear on things, and this can be a real advantage, not only for him, but also for others around him. He seems to love music, and will probably pursue that. He will probably be very good in math and science. He loves the creative process and artistic endeavor. I can see him performing in plays when he is in high school. He will probably be a very early reader. He is a very smart little boy."

Although my mother and father sometimes feel crushing sadness and guilt ("if only" is a phrase my mother often uses), I was lucky that they didn't think I was misbehaving or being naughty. I was never spanked or hit. My mother worries about the countless children affected by this horrific holocaust whose parents are uninformed, unwilling, or unable to invest the effort and resources necessary to help their children heal.

My mother has always had nicknames for me: "pumpkin," "muffin," "Pooh Bear" were some of her favorites, along with the typical "baby," "honey," "sweetheart," and "love." Now she usually calls me angel. But sometimes she holds me close and calls me her hero. She says she is so proud of me. She says that this is for the way I have borne my suffering with such grace. All of the frightened, sick, and innocent children involved in this tragedy are her heroes, she tells me, and someday I will understand.



I am blessed. I have a loving family that wants to give me the support to be whatever it is that I want to be. They have been able to afford the expense of the intensive ABA therapy, the special diet, and the supplements. My mother lives in our second home in Portland, Oregon, where the therapy and foods that I need are available. My father works half of the time in Astoria, Oregon, which is 100 miles distant from Portland. He has a medical practice and owns an MRI center there. He and I miss each other when he is in Astoria, but I need to be in a large metropolitan area to continue my recovery. My parents believe in me and want what is best for me. I have come so far, yet my journey has just begun.

*Update (February 2003):*

It has now been 22 months since Nikolai started the journey of recovery from autism. He is now in preschool with his typically developing peers. He has no aide. One of his teachers (who has years of experience teaching special needs kids, including children with autism) told us that she sees nothing that would even hint of autism. Another teacher just told us how he is initiating play with peers, expressing unusual concern and empathy when peers are hurt, and participating fully in the classroom. This teacher also told us that she wishes that all of her students were like Nikolai. He is cooperative, polite, helpful, and loving, and he is ahead of his peers cognitively. He is without a shadow of any kind.

We recently returned to see the developmental pediatrician who diagnosed Nikolai originally. These are his words: "This is the third time I've seen Nikolai. I first saw him on two occasions when he was 2½ years old, at which time I made a diagnosis of Autism. He had a very characteristic developmental pattern, and also seemed to be quite bright. In the interim, he has received several forms of complementary and alternative biomedical interventions, including a casein-free, gluten-free diet, various types of supplementation, and intensive therapy, and he's made remarkable progress. At the time of this reevaluation, Nikolai appears to me to be a normal 4½-year-old boy. He interacted nicely with me, showed good speech and language development, and played appropriately with toys. His attention span seemed short, but he wasn't otherwise particularly hyperactive. In summary, despite an earlier concern about Autism, Nikolai has made excellent developmental progress and currently shows no clear characteristics of that developmental disorder. In addition, he appears to be at or above age level in terms of his general development." (That Nikolai was coming down with a cold that day may have explained his shortened attention span.)



We are continuing to test to ensure his physical recovery is complete. We feel that the GFCF diet is essential and that the DAN! Protocol supplements helped him overcome his nutritional deficiencies. We feel that the glyconutrients (Ambrotose, Phytaloe, Plus and Immunostart), as well as the probiotic Primal Defense, were real contributors to Nikolai's recovery. We did not chelate; we argued about this. Although we were afraid to leave the mercury in his body, Dad was afraid chelating would make him worse. Dad (the M.D.) prevailed. The intensive ABA therapy helped him catch up and develop those skills and abilities that he had no opportunity to develop when he was so sick.

But without question, Nikolai's determination and motivation have been a wonder, a blessing, and a joy to behold. He had the support, the love, and fortunately the resources for his recovery. He is a remarkable child. He stands out in a crowd in a wonderful way.

We wanted our child back; we have him now.

*Update for Second Edition (September 2005):*

Nikolai is now in the first grade at a private, academically challenging school. He was "evaluated" at the same school in his kindergarten year for admission to first grade. He passed with flying colors based on his academic readiness, his social skills, his emotional development, and his behavior. More than a quarter of his year-end kindergarten progress report grades showed that he was exceeding expectations—not an easy achievement at a school that considers satisfying expectations the norm. Nikolai also was given the Stanford Achievement norm-referenced test, which measures challenging academic standards appropriate for each grade level. He scored in the upper 5-10% in the national grade percentile band across the board. His principal said, "I'd be very pleased; not only did he score very high, he did it across the board. He's also very articulate, well-behaved and socially astute."

Nikolai has a particular love of language. He is always learning new words and incorporating them into his conversations. Some of the most recent additions are "illustrate," "delightful," and "inappropriate." It is wonderful to hear these rather sophisticated words used in the correct context in a conversation.



Nikolai is taking private piano and musicianship lessons. He has close to perfect pitch and his ability to sing and play by ear is a gift. He is also enthusiastic about his swimming and golf lessons. If only there were more hours in the day!

Nikolai continues to take the supplements that our whole family takes: the glyconutrients, as well as some extras such as magnesium, calcium, Omega Brite, Indebenone and royal jelly. We do this because we think it is good for all of us, not to correct a problem. We are also considering an infrared sauna. We think we could all benefit from its detoxifying effects, given the daily insults that we are all exposed to in our environment.

On May 12, 2004, our son Christian was born. He is an almost identical likeness of Nikolai in every way. The difference is poignant though; he has not had one vaccine, and he is the healthiest, happiest baby that everyone who meets him remembers. He has had one ear infection in his 16 months, shortly after a vacation involving airline travel. Nikolai's early life was marked by far too much pain and suffering. He, too, should have had the happy, carefree start that Christian is now enjoying. But we go forward from here, thankful that we have our wonderful son Nikolai fully present in our lives and our world.

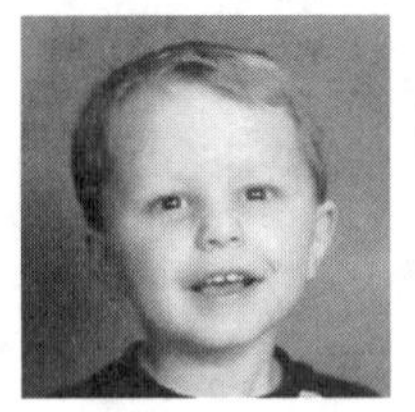
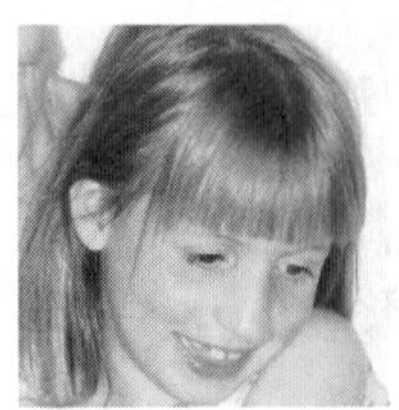

## PART III

# HOW TO HELP YOUR CHILD:

## A QUICK START WITH VITAMIN B6/MAGNESIUM AND DMG



Of all the biomedical interventions used to help autistic children, the use of high-dose vitamin B6 (always given with supplements of the mineral magnesium) has the longest record of safe and effective use, as you will see on the following pages. Another B-vitamin, dimethylglycine (DMG), has also helped thousands of autistic children, without a single report of any harm. These nutritional supplements are inexpensive and do not require a prescription. They have been the first steps taken by many parents toward bringing about significant improvement.

## — Chapter 35 —

# Vitamin B6 (and Magnesium) in the Treatment of Autism

By Bernard Rimland, Ph.D.
Autism Research Institute, San Diego, California

*Autism Research Review International*, 1987, Vol. 1, No. 4, page 3

All 18 studies known to me in which vitamin B6 has been evaluated as a treatment for autistic children have provided positive results. This is a rather remarkable record, since the many drugs that have been evaluated as treatments for autism have produced very inconsistent results. If a drug shows positive results in about half of the evaluation studies, it is considered a success and the drug is then advocated for use with autistic patients. However, despite the remarkably consistent findings in the research on the use of vitamin B6 in the treatment of autism, and despite its being immeasurably safer than any of the drugs used for autistic children, there are at present very few practitioners who use it or advocate its use in the treatment of autism.



Research on the use of vitamin B6 with autistic children began in the 1960s. In 1966 two British neurologists, A. F. Heeley and G. E. Roberts, reported that 11 of 19 autistic children excreted abnormal metabolites in their urine when given a tryptophan load test.

Giving these children a single 30 mg tablet of vitamin B6 normalized their urine; however, no behavioral studies were done. A German investigator, V. E. Bonisch, reported in 1968 that 12 of 16 autistic children had shown considerable behavioral improvement when given high dosage levels (100 mg to 600 mg per day) of vitamin B6. Three of Bonisch's patients spoke for the first time after the vitamin B6 was administered in this open clinical trial.

After my book *Infantile Autism* was published in 1964, I began receiving hundreds of letters from parents of autistic children throughout the United States, including a number who had tried the then-new idea of "megavitamin therapy" on their autistic children. Most had begun experimenting with various vitamins on their autistic children as a result of reading books by popular nutrition writers. I initially was quite skeptical about the remarkable improvement being reported by some of these parents, but as the evidence accumulated, my interest was aroused. A questionnaire sent to the 1,000 parents then on my mailing list revealed that 57 had experimented with large doses of vitamins. Many of these had seen positive results in their children. As a result, I undertook a large-scale study, on over 200 autistic children, of megadose quantities of vitamin B6, niacinamide, pantothenic acid, and vitamin C, along with a multiple-vitamin tablet especially designed for the study. The children were living with their parents throughout the U.S. and Canada, and each was medically supervised by the family's own physician. (Over 600 parents had volunteered for the study, but most could not overcome their physicians' skepticism.)

At the end of the four-month trial it was clear that vitamin B6 was the most important of the four vitamins we had investigated, and that in some cases it brought about remarkable improvement. Between 30% and 40% of the children showed significant improvement when the vitamin B6 was given to them. A few of the children showed minor side effects (irritability, sound sensitivity and bed-wetting), but these quickly cleared up when additional magnesium was supplied, and the magnesium confirmed additional benefits.



Two years later two colleagues and I initiated a second experimental study of the use of megavitamin therapy on autistic children, this time concentrating on vitamin B6 and magnesium. My co-investigators were Professors Enoch Callaway of the University of California Medical Center at San Francisco and Pierre Dreyfus of the University of California Medical Center at Davis. The double-blind placebo-controlled crossover experiment utilized 16 autistic children, and again produced statistically significant results. For most children dosage levels of B6 ranged between 300 mg and 500 mg per day. Several hundred mg/day of magnesium and a multiple-B tablet were also given, to guard against B6-induced deficiencies of these other nutrients. (In all probability, the temporary numbness and tingling resulting from B6 megadoses, reported by Schaumburg et al., were the result of induced deficiencies of other nutrients caused by taking B6 *alone* in enormous amounts—a foolish thing to do.)

In both studies the children showed a remarkably wide range of benefits from the vitamin B6. There was better eye contact, less self-stimulatory behavior, more interest in the world around them, fewer tantrums, more speech, and in general the children became more normal, although they were not completely cured.

People vary enormously in their need for B6. The children who showed improvement under B6 improved because they *needed* extra B6. Autism is thus in many cases a vitamin B6 dependency syndrome.

After completing his participation in our study, Professor Callaway visited France, where he persuaded Professor Gilbert LeLord and his colleagues to undertake additional B6/magnesium research on autistic children. The French researchers, although skeptical that anything as innocuous as a vitamin could influence a disorder as profound as autism, became believers after their first, reluctantly undertaken, experiment on 44 hospitalized children. They have since published six studies evaluating the use of vitamin B6, with and without additional magnesium, on autistic children and adults. Their studies typically used as much as a gram a day of vitamin B6 and half a gram of magnesium.

LeLord and his colleagues measured not only the behavior of the autistic children, but also their excretion of homovanillic acid (HVA) and other metabolites in the urine. Additionally, they have done several studies in which the effects of the vitamin B6 and/or the magnesium on the brain electrical activity of the patients was analyzed. *All* of these studies have produced positive results.



LeLord et al. recently summarized their results on 91 patients: 14% improved markedly, 33% improved, 42% showed no improvement, and 11% worsened. They noted that "in all our studies, no side effects were observed...." Presumably, no physical side effects were seen.

Several recent studies by two groups of U.S. investigators, Thomas Gualtieri et al., at the University of North Carolina, and George Ellman et al., at Sonoma State Hospital in California, have also shown positive results on autistic patients.

While no patient has been cured with the vitamin B6 and magnesium treatment, there have been many instances where remarkable improvement has been achieved. In one such case an 18-year-old autistic patient was about to be evicted from the third mental hospital in his city. Even massive amounts of drugs had no effect on him, and he was considered too violent and assaultative to be kept in the hospital. The psychiatrist tried the B6/magnesium approach as a last resort. The young man calmed down very quickly. The psychiatrist reported at a meeting that she had recently visited the family and had found the young man to now be a pleasant and easy-going young autistic person who sang and played his guitar for her.

Another example: a frantic mother phoned me to ask for information on sheltered workshops in her city, since her 25-year-old autistic son was about to be expelled for unmanageable behavior. I knew of no alternate placements for the son, but I suggested that the mother try Super Nu-Thera, a supplement containing B6, magnesium, and other nutrients. Within a few weeks she called again to tell me excitedly that her son was doing very well now and his piecework pay had risen dramatically from the minimum pay of $1.50 per week to $25 per week.

In view of the consistent findings showing the safety and efficacy of the nutrients B6 and magnesium in treating autistic individuals, and in view of the inevitability of short- and/or long-term side effects of drug use, it certainly seems that this safe and rational approach should be tried before drugs are employed.

# — Chapter 36 —
# The Most Air-Tight Study in Psychiatry? Vitamin B6 in Autism

By Bernard Rimland, Ph.D.
Autism Research Institute, San Diego, California

*Autism Research Review International,* 2000, Vol. 14, No. 3, page 3



"Your psychiatric colleagues are a bunch of bigots!" I said. "They are not really interested in helping autistic children—all they want to do is downplay the value of vitamins and keep using those stupid toxic drugs!"

"No, you're wrong! Psychiatrists are ignoring your study because it was conducted by your small institute, which they've never heard of. Besides, you used that innovative computer-clustering design, rather than the usual double-blind, crossover design that psychiatrists like. If your study had been done at a major medical school, like this one, and had used conventional methodology, rather than the new one you created, they would really pay attention to your work."

"I don't really believe that, Noch," I said to my friend Enoch (Noch) Callaway, M.D., who was then (in the 1970s) Professor of Psychiatry and Director of Psychiatric Research at the University of California Medical Center in San Francisco.

"Let's design and carry out a really well-designed study, the best possible study, and do it from here, and you'll see—if the results are positive, they'll be accepted."

"I don't believe that," I retorted.

"Let's try it," Noch insisted. "I'm sure we can get a grant to do it. I am very familiar with the grant procedures at NIMH, and I'll be glad to write the grant application. It will be the best-controlled, most air-tight study ever conducted in the field of psychiatry."

I was still skeptical, but I agreed, and we went to work on a grant proposal. Noch enlisted the assistance of Professor Pierre Dreyfus, the Chairman of the Department of Neurology at the University of California Medical School at Davis, near Sacramento.

I had recently completed a study of over 200 autistic children, using high doses of several vitamins, including vitamin B6, which turned out to be the most effective of the several vitamins in my study. About half of the children were found to have responded well to the vitamin B6, and I selected 16 of the responders for the new study. The sixteen were divided into two groups, matched on age, sex, weight, and severity.

Each of the 16 children was to be put through a five-phase procedure as follows: Phase One—baseline; Phase Two—test period A (B6 or placebo); Phase Three—baseline two; Phase Four—test period B (B6 or placebo); and Phase Five—baseline three.

To measure changes, if any, in the children's behavior, a special "Target Symptom Behavior Checklist" was to be developed individually for each child after several visits, telephone calls, and mail contacts with the child's parents and teachers.

To help guard against the possibility of human error, urine specimens were to be collected at the ends of Phases Two and Four, and the remaining contents of the B6 and placebo bottles from Phases Two and Four were also saved for laboratory analysis.



All three members of the research team, Callaway, Dreyfus, and I, were experienced researchers with many publications. Despite that, we requested the Research Design section of the National Institutes of Mental Health to review our design and make any suggestions that might improve the study. The NIH research specialists made several minor suggestions, all of which we accepted. We intended it to be the most air-tight, double-blind, placebo-crossover study ever conducted in the field of psychiatry.

The study was conducted in the form of a giant triangle, with myself and our San Diego Institute being the anchor of the triangle, and Callaway and Dreyfus, each 500 miles north, being the other apexes.

After matching the 16 subjects into two paired groups of eight, I sent the two lists of names and addresses to Dreyfus, in Sacramento, who decided in each case whether the child would receive the vitamin B6 in Phase Two or Phase Four. Neither Callaway nor I knew which child was given the B6 first.

The Target Symptom Checklists were completed by the parents, teachers, and local physicians, and sent to our Institute in San Diego. When all of the data had been collected, Callaway came to San Diego and he and I went through the completed data file for each child to determine, if we could, when the B6 had been given. We then telephoned Dreyfus with our decision for each child, except for child 16, for whom we could find no difference between the placebo and the B6. Dreyfus compared our reports with his list, and informed us that we had correctly classified the B6 periods for 11 of the 15 children. In the case of the sixteenth child, the code said that bottle B had contained the B6. However, on analyzing the contents of the remaining capsules in the A and B bottles for child 16, it was discovered that *both* bottles contained B6. Furthermore, the urine samples showed high levels of B6 in the urine for both phases. The source of this error is unknown, but the data for child 16 were removed from subsequent analysis. Lab tests showed no discrepancies in the urine or remaining tablets for all but one of the remaining children.

A discrepancy did appear in the case of child 14. This was one of the four children whom supposedly misclassified as being on placebo when according to the code he should have been on B6. However, the urine tests showed higher levels of B6 in the urine when he was supposed to have been on the placebo. The data for this child were left in the analysis, since they militated *against* the hypothesis.

Statistical comparison of the behavioral ratings for the 15 children while they were on the B6 versus while being on the placebo showed a statistically significant difference: P<.05, thus confirming the value of the B6 and supporting the results of our previous research study.



Callaway was surprised at the results of our study. He had felt that somehow my previous experiment, involving some 200 children, in which I had used the new computer-clustering procedure rather than the typical control group method, must have been in error. He was sufficiently impressed with the results that the following summer, when he started his year-long sabbatical at the Tours University Medical School in France, he brought with him a supply of vitamin B6 and magnesium and convinced his colleagues in France to undertake studies of B6 and magnesium in their population of hospitalized children. The French research group was extremely skeptical They argued that B6 was so "weak" you couldn't kill someone with it if you wanted—so how could it do better than drugs powerful enough to be fatal? Callaway persisted, and the Tours researchers, under the direction of Dr. Gilbert LeLord, undertook a study on 42 hospitalized children, including some who were autistic. The results were so favorable that even the skeptics changed their minds. They began a series of 12 studies, conducted over the next 10 years, during which the vitamin B6 was tried with children, with adults, with B6 alone, with B6 and magnesium, using behavioral criteria, electrophysiological criteria, biochemical criteria, and conditioning criteria. All of the studies, including 11 double-blind, placebo-crossover studies, provided positive results.

Several subsequent studies, by researchers in Venezuela and Italy, also yielded positive results. Two-time Nobel prize-winner Linus Pauling stated,

"My opinion, based on these Rimland studies and others, is that … treatment with vitamins and minerals should be tried for every autistic child…."

Despite positive results from (probably) the most air-tight study in psychiatry, and an unbroken series of 17 additional studies of B6 and magnesium in autism over a three-decade period, all yielding positive results, skeptics continue to insist that there is no evidence that B6 and magnesium are effective in autism.

Closed minds never change.

## — Chapter 37 —

# Vitamin B6 in Autism: The Safety Issue

By Bernard Rimland, Ph.D.
Autism Research Institute, San Diego, California

*Autism Research Review International, 1996, Vol. 10, No. 3, page 3*

There is no biological treatment for autism that is more strongly supported in the scientific literature than the use of high dosage vitamin B6 (preferably given along with normal supplements of magnesium). Eighteen studies have been published since 1965, showing conclusively that high dose vitamin B6 confers many benefits to about half of all the autistic children and adults on whom it has been tried. While B6/magnesium is not a cure, it has often made a big, worthwhile difference.



Included among the 18 studies are 11 double-blind, placebo-crossover experiments, eight experiments in which abnormal substances appearing in the urine of autistic children have been normalized by the B6, other studies in which brain waves have been normalized, and a wide range of other improvements: 18 consecutive studies showing megadose B6 to be effective and no studies failing to show that megadose B6 is effective. No drug even comes close.

None of the studies of B6 in autism has reported any significant adverse effects, nor would any significant adverse effects be expected. I conducted an intensive analysis of the literature on B6 safety before embarking on my first study of B6 in the late 1960s. A review published in 1966 by the American Academy of Pediatrics confirmed my own conclusion: "To date there has been no report of deleterious effects associated with daily oral ingestion of large doses of vitamin B6 (0.2 to 1.0 grams per day)."

Tens of thousand of people, including thousands of autistic children and adults, took large doses throughout the '60s, '70s, and beginning '80s with no reported signs of any adverse effects. However, in 1983, a paper by Schaumburg et al. reported significant, though not permanent or life-threatening side effects in seven patients who had been taking 2,000 mg to 6,000 mg per day of B6. The side effects, peripheral neuropathy, were numbness and tingling in the hands and feet—the sensation one gets when one's hand or foot "falls asleep." The foot numbness in some cases interfered with walking. These patients were not taking magnesium, the other B vitamins, or any of the other nutrients that should be taken if one is taking large amounts of B6. It is at least possible that the adverse reactions were due not to B6 "toxicity" but to deficiencies of magnesium and the other B vitamins induced by taking large amounts of B6.

It should be noted that the Schaumburg study covered only seven patients and had seven authors from several major medical centers throughout the United States. It would seem that a national search had been done to locate these patients, once the first case had been identified.

In the ensuing years, a few other patients have been reported in the literature who showed similar symptoms of peripheral neuropathy.

In my own experience, covering almost 30 years, and many thousands of autistic children and adults, I have, to the best of my knowledge, encountered only four cases of peripheral neuropathy. In these cases the numbness in the hands and feet was noticed by the parents, who reported that the child would: a) shake the hands as though to try to get the circulation back, b) have difficulty in picking up objects, such as bits of food, or c) have difficulty walking, because of numbness in the soles of the feet. When the B6 was discontinued, or the dosage was markedly reduced, these symptoms went away very quickly and completely.



It seems that some individuals are exceedingly sensitive to larger than normal amounts of B6. These cases are very few and far between, and discontinuing the B6 seems in all cases thus far to resolve the problem.

If you contrast these findings with the findings reported on a daily basis on the drugs that are used for autism, it becomes instantly clear that the B6 is immeasurably safer. There has never been a death or serious illness associated with ingestion of even very large amounts of B6. Deaths and permanent disability from prescription drugs are commonplace.

My own son, now 40, has been taking about 1 gram per day of B6 (along with 400 mg of magnesium, and other nutrients) for some 30 years. If there is a healthier person in North America, I would be surprised. Mark's only health problem to date occurred in his early 20s, when a dentist found one small cavity in one tooth.

Despite the extraordinary safety of B6, I have been told, over the years, by thousands of parents, that their physicians have warned them against giving their children high doses of B6, because of the supposed risks involved. It is unfortunately very typical of most of the medical establishment (which of course makes its money by prescribing drugs) to denigrate and exaggerate the dangers of taking nutritional supplements.

A case in point: recently the national news media gave heavy coverage to a paper from the University of Michigan which warned the public against the dangers of taking vitamin B6. This report was given national television coverage, and we received a number of alarmed inquiries in our office from parents who were frightened by the warning, "B6 is toxic!"

When I read the study, I was truly appalled. The authors, from the University of Michigan Medical School, were supposedly investigating the value of vitamin B6 in the treatment of carpal tunnel syndrome (a painful malady of the wrists, which has become very common in recent years, and is usually considered a repetitive motion injury). The conventional treatment is surgery, which is often ineffective, as well as being disfiguring, expensive, and painful. There have been a number of well-documented reports that high doses of vitamin B6 successfully treat carpal tunnel syndrome, in the majority of cases, so that over a six-week period people who were scheduled for surgery no longer need such drastic treatment.

The Michigan researchers had not given even 1 milligram of B6 to even one of their subjects (not patients)! Their warning was based primarily on the 1983 Schaumburg report. Further, they had not included even a single subject who actually had carpal tunnel syndrome! They did blood and nerve conduction studies on people who were "potentially" at risk for carpal tunnel syndrome, but did not in fact have carpal tunnel syndrome. The anti-vitamin B6 bias in the report is very evident when you read, in their review of research, that "several" studies have reported B6 to be effective in treating carpal tunnel syndrome, while "numerous" reports have failed to confirm the finding. If you look at the actual references in their study, you will see that there are 12 favorable reports, and only seven negative reports. So, to them, "several" equals 12 and "numerous" equals seven!



The University of Michigan study, with its highly publicized and totally irrelevant conclusions, is certainly one of the worst and most appalling studies I have ever read. Alan Gaby, M.D., author of *The Doctor's Guide to Vitamin B6,* referred to it as a "disgusting" display of bias, and I certainly agree with that assessment.

Nothing is perfectly safe, but B6 is exceptionally safe, particularly when compared to the alternative, drugs, which are infinitely more likely to cause severe illness, injury, and even death. An autistic person will improve on high dosage B6 *only* if that person's body *requires* extra B6. The benefits of B6 often start within a few days. If no benefits are seen in three to four weeks (in about 50 percent of cases), or if any signs of peripheral neuropathy appear (very rare), stop giving the B6.

A 1995 paper by Ellis and McCully reported that elderly patients who had been taking 100-300 mg per day of B6 for some years experienced only

27% the risk of heart disease, and among those who died of a heart attack, the average age at death was 84.5—eight years longer life than control group patients from the local area. In a 1993 study of epileptic newborns, Pietz found 300 mg of B6/kg/day—18 times the dosage used in autism—to be superior to seizure drugs. And B6, in amounts as high as 50 grams per day, is used as an antidote for victims of certain poisons. Is vitamin B6 toxic? Hardly!

*For a list of references and information on the use of vitamin B6 in autism, write to ARI (4182 Adams Ave., San Diego, CA 92116).*

## — Chapter 38 —

# Dimethylglycine (DMG), a Nontoxic Metabolite, and Autism

By Bernard Rimland, Ph.D.
Autism Research Institute, San Diego, California

*Autism Research Review International, 1990, Vol. 4, No. 2, page 3*

DMG is a rather sweet-tasting substance that was described in a recent article in the *Journal of Laboratory and Clinical Medicine* (1990, 481-86) as a "natural, simple compound with no known undesirable side effects." The article did not pertain to the use of DMG in autism, but instead described an experiment in which DMG was used to try to enhance the function of the immune system of laboratory rabbits. It worked—the immune systems of the animals given DMG showed 300% to 1,000% better response to infection than the controls.



DMG is readily available in many health food stores. It is legally classified as a food. It does not require a prescription. It is manufactured by several companies, and comes in various forms, most commonly in tiny foil-wrapped tablets about 1/3 the size of an aspirin.

The taste is pleasant and children chew the tablets readily. At about 25 cents per tablet, the cost is minimal, since only one to eight tablets a day are usually taken (eight for adults).

"So far so good," you may be saying, "but what does this have to do with autism?"

In 1965, two Russian investigators, M. G. Blumena and T. L. Belyakova, published a report showing considerable improvement in the speech of 12 of a group of 15 mentally handicapped children who had not been able to use speech to communicate. The children had been treated with a substance variously known as calcium pangamate, or pangamic acid, or "vitamin B15." In addition to enriched vocabulary, the children began to use simple sentences, their general mental state improved, and there was better concentration and interest in toys and games. Subsequent research has shown the essential factor in calcium pangamate to be DMG.

Soon afterward psychiatrist Allan Cott visited Moscow and brought back a small supply of pangamic acid, which he tried on a number of children in his practice, some of whom were autistic. Many of Cott's patients responded in the same way the Russian children had. One mother wrote, "It's the most exciting thing I've ever experienced. He was repeating words and he answers questions now…."

At about this time pangamic acid, or B15, entered the U.S. market. Chaos ensued. Every manufacturer touted his product as "the original Russian formula." There were at least four different formulas on the market, partly, it is believed, as a result of deliberate deception and obfuscation on the part of the Russians. DMG, in small amounts, was a component of some of the formulas. The FDA stepped in and lengthy legal battles ensued. One outcome is that the term B15 was outlawed. (Although DMG resembles the B vitamins in many ways—it is found in the same foods, for example—there are no known overt symptoms characteristic of a DMG deficiency.)

The significant outcome of the legal battles is that the sale of DMG is now permitted, as long as it is not referred to as a vitamin, and as long as it is sold as a food and not a drug.



I have been following the pangamic acid-DMG situation for almost 25 years. I have mentioned it in some of my lectures, and told parents and professionals about it in conversations and correspondence. Always I would ask, "If you try it, please let me know what results you see, even if *no* improvement is found."

I am now so firmly convinced that DMG is helpful to a substantial proportion of autistic children and adults that I have decided to "go public" in the *Autism Research Review International*—to tell people about it freely and openly, so they may try it if they wish.

Some who hear of this boldness may be aghast: "Where are the double blind placebo-controlled scientific studies showing it to be effective in autism?" they will ask. My reply is simple. "There aren't any, and none are needed." There are, of course, numerous double-blind non-autism studies of DMG in the scientific and medical literature, using not only humans, but many kinds of laboratory animals, often given very large amounts of DMG. As noted earlier, no adverse side effects have been found with even massive intakes of DMG. (I say "intakes" rather than "dosages" because "dosage" implies that DMG is a drug, which it is not.)

Since no company has the exclusive right to make DMG, competition keeps the price—and profits—down. Thus there is almost no chance that anyone will sponsor a $200,000 double-blind study of DMG on autistic children. A parent can buy 30 tablets for about $8.00. That is a sufficient supply, even for an adult given five or more tablets a day, to determine, in most cases, if it will be helpful. If it is felt to be helpful, fine. If not, you have wasted $8.00 (except for the boost given to the immune system).

To help the parents receive unbiased input, I usually tell them to refrain from mentioning to teachers, grandparents, and others in the child's environment that DMG is being tried. I have numerous letters in my files saying, "Johnny's speech therapist says he has made more progress in the last two weeks than in the last six months. As you suggested, we had told no one at his school that we were trying DMG."

I am 100% in favor of double-blind studies on drugs with considerable potential for harm, such as fenfluramine, Haldol, or the like. However, it doesn't make sense to insist on such refinements before trying a perfectly safe substance such as DMG, apple pie, or chicken soup.

If DMG is going to work, its effects will usually be seen within a week or so, though it should be tried for a few weeks or a month before giving up. In some cases dramatic results have been seen within 24 hours: A Los Angeles mother was driving on the freeway, three-year-old Kathy in the back seat, five-year-old mute autistic son Sammy in the front. DMG had been started the day before. Kathy began to cry. Sammy turned and spoke his first words: "Don't cry, Kathy." The mother, stunned, almost crashed the car.



A similar case: A Texas mother secured her six-year-old mute autistic daughter in the front seat, then, before driving off, turned to tell her husband, "I'll drop Mary at the babysitter's house first." Mary, on DMG for two days, startled her parents with her first words: "No! No babysitter!"

Although speech is the most notable positive change in those children helped by DMG, behavioral improvement is also often reported. One father gave his son one DMG tablet per day without mentioning it to the school. He later requested a copy of the school's detailed record of his son's day-by-day behavioral transgressions. The correlation between outburst-free days and the use of DMG was unmistakable.

An article in the *New England Journal of Medicine* (October 1982) reported that a 22-year-old mentally retarded man who had 16 to 18 seizures per week on standard anticonvulsants, experienced only three seizures per week while on DMG. Two attempts to remove the DMG dramatically increased seizure frequency.

Last year I sent information on DMG to Lee Dae Kun, Director of the Pusan (Korea) Research Center on Child Problems. He tried the DMG on 39 autistic children, ages three to seven, for three months, with the following (summarized) results:

**Benefits seen:**

Yes: 31 (80%
No: 8 (20%)
(Improved speech, eating, excretion, willingness, etc.)
Eight children had difficulty sleeping for weeks one and two.
Six children became more active for weeks one and two.

Lee Dae Kun wrote that the parents, usually skeptical, saw the improvements clearly. He concluded that DMG is very beneficial for children with autism, even if it is not a cure.

Information about the use of DMG with older persons is also encouraging. One mother of a 26-year-old who squeezed things (people, TV sets, etc.) very hard when frustrated, tried DMG, quite skeptically, to see if it would stimulate his very sparse speech. It didn't, but brought remarkable improvement in his frustration tolerance. "Even my husband, who was even more skeptical than me, now is a believer," she wrote.



DMG certainly doesn't always help, and it certainly is not a cure, but it is certainly worth trying, in my humble opinion.

If you try it, let me hear from you.

## — Chapter 39 —

# What Is the Right 'Dosage' of Vitamin B6, DMG, and Other Nutrients Useful in Autism?

By Bernard Rimland, Ph.D.
Autism Research Institute, San Diego, California

*Autism Research Review International, 1997, Vol. 11, No. 4, page 3*



I place quote marks around "dosage" because "dose" typically refers to drugs, and the nutrients to be discussed are definitely not drugs. A drug acts by *blocking or interfering with* a natural bodily process, while a nutrient permits or *enhances* these processes. That is why drugs are so often harmful, while nutrients are characteristically not only safe, but beneficial.

We are very often asked, "What is the right dosage of this or that for our child?" The answer is, for nutrients as it is for drugs—no one knows. Each person is very different from everyone else, and only by experimenting—trial and error—can it be determined if a substance will be helpful and in what amounts it should be given. Given that as a base fact, here is what I have learned over the last 30 years:

**Vitamin B6:** Vitamin B6 (must be given with magnesium) was found to be helpful in almost half of all autistic children and adults included in 18 consecutive studies between 1965 and 1996. In our own studies, the *average* amount of B6 found to be beneficial was around 8 mg of B6 per pound of body weight, per day. (This is about 500 mg/day for a 60-pound child.) Gilbert LeLord and his group of researchers in France arrived at an almost identical amount: 17 mg/kg/day. *But*—this is just an average. In *ARRI* 9/2 we published a letter from a father whose son did very well on about 40 mg/day. We suggest starting with one-quarter the target amount and increasing slowly over a 10- to 14-day period. If too much is given for that child, or if the dosage is increased too quickly, there may be minor side effects, such as hyperactivity, nausea, or diarrhea—but this is rather rare. In such cases, the dose should be cut back and increased again slowly, to try to find the right levels. We advise the parents to refrain from mentioning the experiment to teachers, therapists, relatives, and neighbors, so they can benefit from unsolicited comments.

The upper limits advised for adults or those above 120 pounds is 1,000 mg/day, although some have been on 1,500 mg/day. I added 500 mg/day to my own son's 1,000 mg/day for one year, but saw no improvement beyond the 1,000 mg that he had taken for 20 years, so I reverted to 1,000 mg/day.

Last year a Florida mother phoned to tell me that on visiting her adult son's group home she was appalled at his deteriorated behavior. On investigating, she found they had run out of his supply of B6/magnesium, which should have provided 1,000 mg/day of B6. She then ordered three times the usual supply of the powdered B6/magnesium formula, to protect against running out again. On her next visit she was amazed at the improvement in her son. He actually showed affection toward her for the first time! She then learned that her instructions had been misunderstood and her son was now getting 3,000 mg/day of B6—three times the recommended amount. Despite the improvement, the physicians in charge stopped the B6, claiming it was dangerous. He is now on a drug that *is* dangerous.



The only known harm from megadoses of vitamin B6 is peripheral neuropathy—seen as a tingling and numbness in the hands and feet. It is very rare—I have encountered only four cases in 30 years, and the problem went away when the B6 was stopped. A few people are supersensitive to B6.

The B6/magnesium will often produce benefits within a few days. If no improvement is seen in about a month, I suggest stopping it.

**Magnesium:** Giving about 3 or 4 mg of magnesium per pound of body weight, up to 400 mg per day for adults, enhances the effects of the B6 and protects against possible B6-induced magnesium deficiency. This is not a megadose of magnesium, but rather the amount that many researchers, including me, believe that *everyone* should take for optimum health. Almost every type of food processing depletes magnesium, so supplemental magnesium is essential to avoid a deficiency.

**Dimethylglycine (DMG):** The best suppliers of DMG provide it in tablets or capsules of 125 mg each. Determining right dosage really depends on trial and error experimentation. Young children are generally found to do well—if they respond to DMG—on anywhere from one-half tablet to three or four tablets a day, although one mother, a physician, found that her five-year-old son needed 16 per day! (He did well for several hours on four tablets, then regressed, so was given four more. This happened every few hours, so he reached 16 per day.)

Another physician, also the mother of an autistic son—a 170-pound man in his late 20s—ended up giving her son 26 DMG per day, for the same reason. It seems that a few people metabolize the DMG very fast, and thus need more per day than most.

Radio talk show host Gary Null of New York City told me that many marathon runners take one DMG every mile they run—26 in all. They perform better and suffer fewer physical problems. There is ample scientific research showing such benefits to be highly expectable.

Although there is a very wide range of dosage levels reported by those who use DMG, the usual dosage for children ranges up to about four per day, and for adults to about eight per day. As with B6, the differences between individuals are *huge*.

A small percentage of autistic children become hyperactive when given DMG. That is their way of telling you they need more folic acid. Folic acid, a B vitamin, may be bought in 800 mcg tablets or capsules. Two of the 800 mcg folic acid tablets with each DMG will usually solve this problem.

**Folic acid:** Folic acid itself has been reported to be helpful in autism (*ARRI* 8/4). The great French researcher Jerome Lejeune reported that supplements of about 250 mcg of folic acid per pound of body weight per day brought on major improvement in several autistic children. Dr. Lejeune gave thousands of retarded children (mostly Down syndrome) 20 mg of folic acid per day in his various studies, with no harm, nor would any harm be expected.



**Vitamin C:** In 1991, Lelland Tolbert and his associates reported that giving 8,000 mg/day of vitamin C to adolescent and adult autistic persons brought about significant improvement (*ARRI* 6/1). Since vitamin C is found in very high concentrations in the brain, this is not a surprising finding. A number of the world's leading experts on vitamin C, including Nobel Prize winner Linus Pauling, recommend that most people take *at least* that much vitamin C each day for optimal health. I have studied vitamin C for some 30 years, and own almost every book ever written on the subject. I take about 12,000 mg of vitamin C daily (three level teaspoons), in the form of sodium ascorbate powder (only about $18 per pound, from 800-325-2664). A small percentage of people get diarrhea on such doses—for the rest of us, especially those with autism, there is much to gain.

As the many benefits that nutrients can and do confer become more widely known and accepted, increasing numbers of parents will turn to these natural and healthful substances in preference to harmful drugs. *ARRI* will keep readers informed about research into these valuable treatments.

## — Chapter 40 —

# B6 and DMG Letters to the Editor, *ARRI* Newsletter

By Bernard Rimland, Ph.D.
Autism Research Institute, San Diego, California

The Autism Research Institute (ARI) has over the years received hundreds of letters from parents, and sometimes professionals, reporting the results of their trials with autistic children and adults of the nutritional supplements that the ARI has been advocating since the late 1960s. Many of the more interesting of these letters have been published in the "Letters to the Editor" section of the *Autism Research Review International (ARRI)*, the quarterly newsletter of ARI.



Following is a selection of some of the letters (and occasional responses from the newsletter's editor) regarding the efficacy of the vitamin B6 and magnesium that have been published in the *ARRI*. The letters are arranged, generally, in order by age of the child, with the letters concerning young children first, followed by school-aged children, and then adults.

All of the letters that follow were printed with the permission of their authors, although some requested anonymity. (These letters appear as "Name withheld," "A Florida mother," etc.)

It is particularly noteworthy, as has been observed elsewhere in this book, that some of the best results have been seen in adults, despite the widespread belief that the younger the child, the more positive the outcome.

Three other points also should be noted while reading the following letters:

1. Benefits cover a very wide range of improvements, including speech, sleep, reduction in self-injurious and assaultive behavior, learning, awareness, etc.
2. Benefits are seen in children with a very wide range of disorders, including Rett syndrome, fragile X syndrome, cerebral palsy, and Angelman syndrome.
3. A number of letters report that the parents followed the suggestion repeatedly made by ARI that they implement the nutritional supplements without mentioning their use to the child's teachers and other professionals working with the child. The result is that supplement trials become mini double-blind experiments.

# A. Young Children

To the Editor: *[1992, Vol. 6, No. 3, Page 6]*

Desperate to try something to help my (two-year-old autistic) son, I went to the health food store and bought DMG. I started him on one tablet a day and I immediately noticed an increased desire to talk. Before DMG, my son's speech was basically limited to the names of characters in his favorite videos. Within a few days he started to use some meaningful speech—asking for "juice," "cookie," "open." Further, we saw an increase in eye contact and cooperation.

Besides DMG, the only treatment my son has received has been attendance at a two-hour, once-a-week early intervention class (total of three classes so far). At the second class the speech therapist who had originally thought my son's behavior was too poor for him to benefit from individual speech therapy, said she had changed her mind. At our third class the physical therapist said to me that she had seen the whole spectrum of autistic children from the least to the highest functioning, and that she was surprised by the progress that my son had made in such a short time. I believe that the DMG is responsible for this improvement.

—Maureen Monihan, Belleville, NJ



To the Editor: *[1994, Vol. 8, No. 2, Page 6]*

My husband and I decided not to tell anyone about (starting our 2½-year-old son on B6/magnesium therapy) in order to conduct our own "blind study." Within one week of receiving the full dosage, five of the six therapists who work with my son commented on his increased attention span, ability to focus, and increased eye contact.

One very special moment occurred only a few days into the treatment. I had come home from work and greeted Erik in my usual fashion, kneeling down next to him. For the first time since he was 12 months old, Erik looked directly at me, put his hands on my face, and gently touched my entire face, looking at me as if seeing me for the first time. Since then, he has "looked at" and acknowledged five other people who have come into our home (friends, relatives—even my mother for the first time) and (this) has continued over several days.

Erik's purposeful use of words had been increasing before we administered the vitamins, and that has been enhanced as well.

—Kathy Fuller-Nordberg, Minneapolis, MN

To the Editor: *[1994, Vol. 8, No. 3, Page 6]*

I'm writing to tell you about (my son) Anthony and his vitamin therapy.

For the first 2½ years of his life, Anthony never slept a full night. Every hour or two he would wake up screaming. After countless trips to emergency rooms, pediatricians and neurologists—having heard everything from colic to teething and night terrors—I contacted your office.

Two days after starting him on DMG and (vitamin B6 and magnesium), Anthony began sleeping peacefully all night long. In addition, his eye contact has improved as well as his attention span.

I could never thank you enough for your help and hope you will share my story with other families.

—Mrs. Rose Giangiabbe, Maspeth, NY

To the Editor: *[1996, Vol. 10, No. 3, Page 7]*

My husband and I were concerned about the recent articles circulating in the media about the use of "mega" doses of B6 and magnesium. Our concern is for our two-year-old-son who is autistic and uses a B6 and magnesium supplement. He has been on the vitamins for two and a half months and we have notice such improvements as:

- an increase in verbal abilities
- a reduction in self-stimulatory behaviors
- an improvement in his alertness and focus.

Also, his therapists, who were not told he was taking the vitamin, noticed marked improvements. They also noticed and told us of his regression when we temporarily took him off during our concern with the recent media articles.

We have put our son back on the B6 and magnesium because of the drastic change in his behavior. However, our concern remains—are we doing something that can harm our baby?

—Concerned parents in Monroe, NY

Editor's Note: No! You are using nontoxic nutritional supplements.

To the Editor: *[1997, Vol. 11, No. 3, Page 6]*

I have a 28-month-old son diagnosed with autism and considered high functioning. I started him on DMG on May 31, with the following results:

- Within three days he started sleeping through the night again (which he hadn't done for a month before).

- His teachers at an early intervention program (two hours a week), who are unaware of his intake of DMG, have commented on his increased eye contact and say that he stays on task longer, he's calmer at group time, and (exhibits) increased verbalization.
- He amazed his aunt and uncle by greeting them with a smile and running to them.
- I have noted an increase in vocabulary from 10 to about 50 words.
- In the month that we tried DMG, I don't recall any tantrums at all.

I stopped using DMG on July 2 after reading an article which strongly suggests that this product may be carcinogenic.

The first day without DMG my son screamed and had tantrums frequently. He woke for an hour or two each night for a week. He is frequently frustrated, but his progress remains.

I know that it is up to me to weigh the risks/benefits of using DMG. I was hoping your institute could provide me with more information, as it has been very difficult to find anything written about DMG.

—Lisa Rider, Monmouth Junction, New Jersey



Editor's Note: The above letter is similar to many we have received over the years from concerned parents who have read the section titled "Pangamic acid/DMG (vitamin B15)" in the *Doctor's Vitamin and Mineral Encyclopedia* by Sheldon Hendler. DMG is NOT carcinogenic. Much to the contrary—DMG has been shown to protect against cancer.

The study that led to the false assertion that DMG might be carcinogenic was done by researchers who have made many false claims against vitamins before, including the nonsensical claim that vitamin C destroys vitamin B12. (It does not.) A study was published by A. J. W. Hoorn in *Mutation Research* (1989, pp. 343-350), which was designed to investigate the idea that DMG was carcinogenic. Dr. Hoorn thoroughly refuted the earlier study, and pointed to errors in the way the study had been done. Sheldon Hendler, M.D., Ph.D., the author of the *Doctor's Vitamin and Mineral Encyclopedia*, who has been a personal friend of mine for many years, now says "The report which claimed to show carcinogenicity was false. There is no evidence whatsoever that DMG can cause harm."

Many studies have shown that DMG enhances the effectiveness of the immune system, and it is therefore not surprising that DMG has anti-cancer activity. For example, E. A. Reap and J. W. Lawson, of Clemson University, studied the effects of dimethylglycine on melanoma in mice. Their report showed that "DMG may play a role in inhibiting or slowing down the metastic process (the spread of cancer)."

To the Editor: *[1997, Vol. 11, No. 4, Page 7]*

I started giving my two-year-old autistic daughter DMG, and within days, there was an amazing change. Better eye contact and speech. For the first time in her life, she came to me wanting me to pick her up and hold her facing me as I sat! Then she said, "patty cake." Truly amazing. She had never exhibited these behaviors before.

Also, she went to speech therapy, and the therapist said she was better than she'd ever seen her, spoke, and wanted to be held. The therapist did not know about the DMG.

—A mother in Kentucky



To the Editor: *[1993, Vol. 7, No. 3, Page 6]*

Let me start by telling you that I am skeptical by nature. I am a practicing attorney in Los Angeles and have also acted as a Judge Pro Tem for the Los Angeles Municipal Court. I have heard every possible story, excuse and fabrication imaginable. I do not believe in single solution answers or magic bullets to complex problems.

I am also the father of a 3½ year old autistic son. During my son's short life, I have never had a single meaningful one-word conversation with him other than his definitive "no." I could never understand what, if anything, was going on inside his beautiful head. It has been the most discouraging and frustrating event of my life.

To get to the point, my wife and I started Matthew on a regimen of DMG last Thursday. As instructed by the literature, we told no one of our doing this. We would then send him off to preschool as always.

Yesterday, I was summoned away from an important matter when a telephone call was received from Matthew's preschool director. She said it was very urgent and had to speak to me immediately. When I finally spoke to her, she seemed out of breath and I was bracing myself for some type of terrible revelation that Matthew was either injured, missing, or something equally nightmarish.

Matthew was observed walking by himself on the play yard. The director approached him and asked (knowing full well he would not answer)

"Where are you going, Matthew? I heard her stop for a deep breath, and then she said, "—your son stopped, looked me straight in the eye and said, "I'm getting a towel for swimming.'"

Of course, I could think of nothing else the rest of the day. So when I got home I went directly to my son to see if he could answer a simple question. I asked, "Did you eat dinner?" He gave me that blank look I've come to know so well. I asked again, "What did you have to eat?" This time, he looked at me and said, "Chicken," I asked, "Anything else?" He said, "And grapes."

(Today) my wife called from her car to say that she and Matthew were on their way to my mother's when they saw my office building from the freeway (a distance of approximately one half a mile). All of a sudden and out of nowhere, Matthew came to life and started saying, "Look, Daddy's office. I want to go see Daddy." My wife said that she was near tears and had to pull onto the shoulder of the highway to regain her control.



Once more, I am not a believer in a magic bullet or single solution answer to my son's dilemma. I'm still not sure what to make of this sudden change. My wife and I are doing nothing except adding the daily dosage of DMG to Matthew's intake.

—Los Angeles attorney

To the Editor: *[2001, Vol. 15, No. 3, Page 6]*

Last May, my 3½ year old son was diagnosed with autism. At this time, Nicholas could only say 10 words, was terrified of people, had many repetitive behaviors, didn't know how to play, and had very little eye contact. I had two doctors tell me, "There isn't much you can do with him except early intervention." After many hours of researching the Internet, I found your site. I started him on B6, DMG, magnesium, and vitamin C, plus I soaked him in Epsom salt baths for an hour every night. To my amazement, he started to have eye contact and less repetitive behaviors after a week! After three months, his vocabulary increased to about 200 spontaneous words. He also has about 30 percent eye contact, and is becoming very social. It's a blessing to see him come out of his shell and know that he will be able to function better in the world. He still has a long road ahead of him, but I have a lot of hope now.

—Robin Dooley, San Jacinto, CA

Editor's Note: Epsom salts benefit many autistic children because they provided needed magnesium and sulphur.

To the Editor: *[1991, Vol. 5, No. 2, Page 7]*

I cannot begin to tell you what a difference there has been in my four-year-old daughter since taking DMG. My little girl, who was frustrated and impulsive, with a very short attention span and very little speech, is now speaking with some sentences, is less impulsive, has a much better attention span, and is less frustrated and overall calmer and happier.

I strongly urge any mother considering DMG use to try it on your child. With little to no side effects, you really have nothing to lose and a happier child to gain.

—Nancy Jelen *[Editors' note: A chapter by Nancy Jelen is included in this book.]*

To the Editor: *[1992, Vol. 6, No. 4, Page 6]*

In December my husband and I (began giving our son) DMG. We had a "nothing left to lose" attitude. Matt was four years and non-verbal for the most part.



Two to three weeks (after starting DMG) he began to babble, then use jargon. Two months later, he began to make many word attempts. By June he was speaking true words. Today, he speaks well over 200 words. He puts together about 50 or so two-word phrases. He can write his alphabet, upper and lower case, and his numbers 0-30, and knows the quantity of numbers 1-10. He can spell his full name and his address, and many other words, and can draw simple pictures and is toilet trained.

When I tell people about DMG, they ask, "do you really think the DMG did all of this?" I reply that I think it really helped. It's cheap, very easy to get and administer, and is a (nutrient) that can't hurt. It may not work with your child, but it's worth trying.

—A New York Mother

To the Editor: *[1994, Vol. 8, No. 4, Page 7]*

My son Michael was seen on the B6 and magnesium video released by ARI four years ago. Today at age eight Michael has normal social skills, above-average intelligence, and reads on a sixth grade level with full comprehension. Vitamins gave us a toe-hold in his world without which this miracle would not have been possible. Keep sending out the message: recovery can happen. I pray every day that there will be many more Michaels.

—Jean Curtin, Newark, NY

To the Editor: *[1995, Vol. 9, No. 4, Page 6]*

We are the parents of autistic twins, four years old. One of the twins was accepted into an early intervention program here in Oslo that is connected to Dr. Lovaas at UCLA. (The other) twin started behavior modification in daycare, with help and guidance from his brother's program.

After about four months, the boys had not progressed as well as we had seen with other children. We met a British boy who had been in the program for about as long as our boy, but performed much better. Although they had similar scores on testing, the British boy had much better comprehension, spontaneous language, and "normal" behavior. From his parents, we heard about megavitamin supplements (mainly B6), to which they attributed the difference. Their boy had had dramatic improvements after starting on megavitamin supplements.

We ordered megavitamins from the U.S. and started these as soon as we could. After three weeks on megavitamins, we discovered a marked difference in both the twins' behavior. We observed more normal play, less self-stimulation, and better attention and comprehension. At that point we were unsure whether to attribute this effect to the behavior treatment program or the vitamin supplement. However, about three months later, we inadvertently ran out of the megavitamins. After about a week, we started to notice a marked difference in our boys' behavior. The higher functioning twin's "stimming" increased dramatically, his attention span decreased, and he became more difficult to train. The other twin's behavior also changed, with much more self-stimulation and a reoccurrence of behavior-induced vomiting episodes which had disappeared after starting on the vitamins. When the vitamins arrived, it took another 1½ weeks for (their behavior to improve). After this episode, we vowed to never run out of vitamins again.

Our primary physician is a neurologist and primary pediatrician for southern Oslo. He was very skeptical at first. However, after seeing the result in our boys, and having received similar information from France, he has changed his mind, and is currently recommending megavitamin supplements to other autistic children.

—Ketil and Sarah Stokke-Johnsen, Oslo, Norway

To the Editor: *[2001, Vol. 15, No. 2, Page 6]*

(Our son) Brandon is four years old. At this stage in his development, his teacher noticed that his hyperactivity level was not diminishing as she might expect. She uttered the word ADHD, which I was always prepared to hear some day. His behavioral therapist suggested that vitamin therapy was worth a try and gave me the phone number of your Institute. Once I received the paper regarding (vitamin B6 and magnesium) therapy, I was very impressed by the statement that this therapy is just as effective as Ritalin, with no or little side effects.

Here is a list of the way this vitamin has helped to improve my son's ability to cope with the world around him: little or no attention-getting behaviors, activity level has decreased, language clarity and depth of use of language, sequencing of events, focusing in class, can be reasoned with regarding his negative behavior, need to control diminished, sits on mom's lap to eat, no longer urinating on his bedroom floor. My husband and I cannot thank you and your Institute enough for this incredible therapy suggestion.

—Ann and Randy Schimka, San Diego, CA



To the Editor: *[1990, Vol. 4, No. 4, Page 7]*

I started my daughter, age five, on DMG 2½ months ago. The results are amazing. She has not spoken, except to say "daddy," but her behavior has dramatically improved. On days I forget to give it, which is rare, there is a noticeable difference.

She has newly stopped temper tantrums, poop smearing, responds almost always to a first command, is more cheerful, seems to be "into" people more.

My mother, who had not seen Kathryn since we began DMG, was astonished at the difference in her. So was a good friend. This is no little thing. The results are very substantial. I highly recommend trying DMG.

Kathryn's nutritionist says DMG works because it enhances oxygen supply to the brain, and helps utilize oxygen supply…

—Susan Stittgen

To the Editor: *[1993, Vol. 7, No. 2, Page 6]*

My daughter has been on DMG for almost 1½ years. In that time, we experienced miracles. At age five, her speech was almost totally echolalic, with constant pronoun reversal. She had never said "yes," and her attention span was very poor. Her muscle tone was very low. We had been told that many motor skills, such as jumping and bike riding, would never be achieved. At this time, we have independent speech, and she can answer most questions. She started saying "yes" after 10 days on DMG. Abby's teacher noticed an improvement in her attention span within two weeks. Her motor skills have improved dramatically. After six months on DMG, her muscle tone reached normal levels. She still has motor delays, but she can jump, and has recently learned to ride a two-wheel bike with training wheels!

—Karen Reznek

Editor's note: We continue to receive letters from parents who report that the nutrient DMG produces remarkable improvement. In a recent phone call, the mother of an almost six-year-old autistic girl told me she had given her daughter one DMG tablet at 6 p.m. The girl had spoken only a few words in her life. Yet the next morning, at 7 a.m., rather than turning on the TV, she went to her mother's room, shook her, and said, "Wake up mommy, it's time to get up." The mother told me that if she had not been lying down, she would have fallen down. The girl's teachers immediately noted greater awareness, eye contact, and language. Remarkable? Yes. Unprecedented? No.



To the Editor: *[1993, Vol. 7, No. 4, Page 6]*

Our 5½ year old son, Harrison, was diagnosed with PDD-NOS. Although he functioned in the normal range of IQ, Harrison's behavior was so severe he has always been placed in special education classes for severe communication and behavioral disordered children, because of his behavior and extremely poor gross and fine motor skills. He has been placed on several types of medication for hyperactivity and behavior control.

I started Harrison on B6 and magnesium. The following days showed dramatic decreases in Harrison's tantrums and whining and increases in symbolic play and talking about feelings. Before the B6 therapy, he would lash out at anyone who made him angry and now he is beginning to talk about his feelings and say: "You hurt my feelings," instead of screaming, pinching and biting the other family members. While he used his imagination somewhat before the therapy, he really uses it now. Almost every game he plays, he plays appropriately.

The most startling of all is a sudden spurt of development in fine motor skills. Harrison had been in occupational therapy for over a year and still couldn't draw or trace a letter. Suddenly, he picks up a crayon and draws the entire solar system to scale!

Finally, Harrison is going to be "included" full time in regular kindergarten starting in a couple of weeks. He has been mainstreamed in first-grade reading since the school year started. He is no longer taking any Mellaril and doesn't eat an inordinate amount of bread now. His doctor is very excited about the B6 therapy.

—Susan Murray, Memphis, TN

To the Editor: *[1992, Vol. 6, No. 2, Page 6]*

My son Jude, diagnosed with Pervasive Developmental Disorder before beginning a regimen of vitamin B6 and magnesium and DMG, has now improved so much that he is attending regular kindergarten! He is making steady and rapid progress toward normal speech, socialization and fine motor abilities.

—Darlene Hart, Metairie, LA

To the Editor: *[1992, Vol. 6, No. 4, Page 6]*

My son, though not autistic, has been diagnosed by an audiologist as having hypersensitive hearing. Only certain tones and frequencies bother him; the suddenness of noise also seems to contribute to his degree of reaction and sensitivity. Therefore, we're not sure if the hypersensitive hearing is the predominant cause of his hyperactivity and behavior problems. I just know that since taking B6 and magnesium, he appears to control his reaction to noise much better than before. His kindergarten teacher was absolutely amazed at the difference in him! She hadn't known he was on the vitamins until I had phased him off, and then after he restarted them, she was so surprised at the difference they made.

—Pam Parsley, Manchester, TN



To the Editor: *[1993, Vol. 7, No. 3, Page 6]*

Our son has been on DMG for one month now. Jack's eye contact has improved remarkably as has his speech. He also has stopped completely the teeth grinding and toe walking. His day care teacher noted his "babbling" and also said for the first time when she said "Good morning Jack," he turned, looked her in the eyes, and smiled. At therapy for the first time, he pushed a car across the floor and made the "brmmmmm" sound … he also said "bye bye" to Big Bird when I said it was time to leave. This happened all at one session…

Thanks for your help because we face "brick walls" here with the exception of our pediatrician who has been very open-minded…

—Sandy Valentine, E. Peoria, Illinois

# B. School-Age Children

To the Editor: *[2002, Vol. 16, No. 3, Page 7]*

My son is six and has cerebral palsy. I was very excited when I read your article on DMG, and went out immediately to buy the tablets. My husband was the only other person who knew that I was giving our son DMG. Twenty-four hours after I gave him DMG, the teacher's aide at his school was so excited to report the huge improvement in his work. She said he had improved from about 30 percent to about 70 percent with his work. She was so excited and said the other teachers were commenting on the huge improvement from the day before.

I'm not sure if it will continue, I hope and pray it will. His speech is basic, about 5 to 8 words. He seems to be trying to babble more. I will update you on how he improves, but so far, I am pleased with the results. I thank you very much for your article as it has given us hope.

—Frances Mayes, Dana Point, CA



Editor's Note: DMG helps individuals with autism, Rett syndrome, Angelman syndrome, and now cerebral palsy.

To the Editor: *[1998, Vol. 12, No. 2, Page 7]*

We have a seven-year-old son who was diagnosed three years ago with high functioning autism. He had progressed slowly, and we started searching for ways to help him.

We started (giving our son) DMG in February, and did not say anything to family, friends, or teachers. Within two weeks his teachers were telling us how much his speech had improved. That is when we told them what we had been giving him. They were astounded!

Since then, his speech has continued to improve, he has become more social, and is more receptive to being touched. The biggest improvement, though, is that he is finally toilet trained, albeit only during the day, but what a relief, and you should see how proud he is of himself!

The nicest remark came from one of our friends, who said that seeing our son's improvement was like watching a butterfly evolve from a cocoon.

—A Colorado mom

To the Editor: *[1994, Vol. 8, No. 4, Page 7]*

I am the mother of an eight-year-old boy who is a high-functioning autistic. Even though he can communicate, he has not been able to develop friendships. Last March, I tried vitamin B6, magnesium and B complex on my son James. After about two weeks, we introduced DMG.

The results were amazing. He used to walk around people in the school yard as if they were snakes. Now he seems at ease and stops to talk to some kids. His teacher was not informed about this treatment but she said he gives her hugs, waves goodbye to people he knows, and plays tag with the others....

James is a lot more talkative and sociable. He is actually having fun with other kids.... I know James is not cured and we still have some problems to handle but it is so much easier now.

—Renelle Turuba, Hearst, Ontario, Canada

To the Editor: *[1992, Vol. 6, No. l, Page 7]*



My daughter has slept through the night from the first dose of vitamin B6 and magnesium starting 2½ weeks ago. She is also noticeably calmer. She has never slept all night in 9 years!!!

I am recommending vitamin B6 and magnesium to all parents of autistic kids.

—Aileen Wolff, White Plains, New York

To the Editor: *[1990, Vol. 4, No. 4, Page 7]*

I am the lead instructor of a program for children with autism (ages four through twelve). Last summer I sent copies of your editorial about DMG to the parents and guardians of our 15 summer school students. I didn't see the students for seven weeks. When we started school in September I noticed significant difference in four of the students. I later found out that all four had been taking DMG.

Of the children who took DMG, three showed significant improvement in verbal communication and language skills. Three showed improvements in their ability to concentrate and focus on activities. Two appear calmer, showing less anxious and hyperactive behavior. All showed some improvement, and no negative effects have been noted by school staff or parents.

—Karl L. Dunn, Autism Specialist
Otter Lake Elementary, White Bear Lake, MN

To the Editor: *[1991, Vol. 5, No. 1, Page 7]*

We started our son Isaiah on DMG the day after we received your newsletter. He has become more alert and interested in interacting with his environment.... I have had several people at church come up to me and tell me how much better they think he is doing in terms of being "with it" or paying attention to what's going on around him.

—Ruth Shade

To the Editor: *[1991, Vol. 5, No. 2, Page 7]*

On behalf of the mothers in our parent support group in Rochester, New York, I urge you to continue to spread the message about vitamin B6. Twelve parents in our group have tried vitamin B6 on their autistic children. Of these 12 children, 11 showed considerable improvement on the vitamin. Only one child showed no change, and he ironically, was the least severely affected of the 12. The most consistently observed change was a marked improvement in awareness of surroundings and sociability. Several started looking at things around their homes as if they were seeing things for the first time. One little boy who rocked, hummed, and waved his fingers in front of his face all day long now sits down with his family and has real conversations with them. None of these children had any adverse effects. Several parents have taken their children off the B6 for a few days to a week. Every child who benefited from B6 regressed when it was withdrawn. In our minds, the evidence is crystal clear. Vitamin therapy does make a difference!

—Jean M. Curtin

To the Editor: *[1991, Vol. 5, No. 2, Page 7]*

Our son Danny had been on vitamin B6 and magnesium since December. When we took him off to do some testing, in April, there were some very noticeable changes, confirmed for us by other people who deal with him. He was more "hyper" and agitated, less attentive and compliant, and more likely to self-stimulate, cry and cover his ears. His eating inconsistencies increased, and he showed regression in this ability to settle down and go to sleep.

—Lorretta Boronat

To the Editor: *[1991, Vol. 5, No. 2, Page 7]*

I am writing to let you know that we have tried DMG on my son Aron and I can tell you it has brought about positive effects. He is rarely violent now, and tantrums have almost ceased completely. When he does start to tantrum he is able to pull it together quickly. I've received positive reports from school also.

—Loni Joss

To the Editor: *[1991, Vol. 5, No. 3, Page 7]*

Some of our parents have been trying DMG (dimethylglycine). It has been having very beneficial effects in the area of improving speech and concentration and interest in toys and games. I have tried it myself over about a month, and it does help my son's concentration, and his speech, although repetitive, is coming on. Even his teacher says how verbal he has become.

—Brenda O'Reilly
Allergy Induced Autism Group, Reading, Berks, UK

To the Editor: *[1992, Vol. 6, No. l, Page 7]*

(After starting my son on DMG) I noticed in less than 48 hours that he was much easier to handle. His one- to two-hour "whiny" period in the morning ceased and he was able to get over disappointments in a couple of minutes. Previously, any upset in his plans would set off a good 15 minutes of repeating. "that's okay, that's okay," until it drove us crazy. These are subtle changes, but they tremendously increased the harmony in our home.



—Nicole Shultz, V.M.D.
Greenville, NC

To the Editor: *{1992, Vol. 6, No. l, Page 7]*

I am writing to share with you my experience of adding vitamin B6/magnesium to my son's diet. His useable vocabulary has tripled. His awareness and eye contact have increased. He has added several new foods to his diet and will try new foods that are offered to him. Everyone who comes into contact with him, including teachers, family members and friends, have remarked on the fact that he is more alert.

The most miraculous change is that he now lets me know that he understands almost anything that is said to him. (Before there was no reaction.)

He is interested in his classmates for the first time and craves affection at home. Even when he retreats to his "other place," he doesn't seem to be so far away as before!

—Monica Rourke Palmer, Cheshire, CT

To the Editor: *[1993, Vol. 7, No. 1, Page 7]*

We learned about the potential benefits of vitamin B6 through the ARRI. After one week on the vitamin, our son showed signs of improved attention, less aberrant behavior at home and in public and more interest in his environment. Over time, these beneficial effects extended into his dietary and personal habits, communication skills and interaction with people. There is a diminution in the amplitude of emotional swings and aggressive actions directed towards family members and teachers. He is more receptive to constructive ways in which to deal with anger, frustration and disappointment.

Objectively, he is doing better in school compared to one year ago at this time. He is also followed by one of the major child study centers in the United States, which has confirmed through observation and testing marked improvement in many areas of behavior and knowledge. We can do many things together, including bicycle riding, bowling and other activities which were almost impossible before starting B6.

There is no magic cure for autism, (but) vitamin B6 helped our son dramatically by reducing the degree of negative behaviors, which in turn, has encouraged him to explore and benefit from his environment in a way never before possible.

—Deborah Berliner
Steven H. Berliner, M.D., F.A.C.S., F.A.C.O.G.



To the Editor: *[1993, Vol. 7, No. 3, Page 6]*

I have some good news! The vitamin B6 and magnesium powder from Oregon now tastes good! My son Ricky has been on the Super Nu-Thera powder for eight months, and it really helps him, but it was a struggle to get it down him. They are now using a better method of flavoring, so now I just mix it with juice and he drinks it right down. If you tried Super Nu-Thera before and had to give it up because of the poor taste, you can call the company and they will send you a free sample so you can try the new taste. Their number is 1-800-245-8282.

—Nancy Harrington, New Jersey

To the Editor: *[1994, Vol. 8, No. 2, Page 6]*

I started my daughter on DMG approximately five weeks ago. I give her two tablets in the morning and one in the afternoon. I have found that she seems more "organized" and focused. She doesn't seem to become restless and frantic as often, or at least as intensely, as before. She is more aware of her surroundings and people, or more tolerant. She is much happier.

—A Mom

To the Editor: *[1994, Vol. 8, No. 3, Page 6]*

(Our daughter is) severely retarded with autistic tendencies (including) screaming. She can go for months, then begin to scream until we can no longer control her.

Back in May we put her on B6/magnesium. She was doing fine and remained interested in activities, playing outside, continuing contact with other people. In July, we had a routine change due to a babysitter situation, and she was off the B6/magnesium for approximately 3½ weeks. At the end of that time she started screaming and we could not get her to sleep. Of course, everyone—home, babysitter, etc.—tried everything to the point of letting her scream until she decided to stop. By that time, she would be worn out, no voice left, and nerves around her frazzled. We put her back on B6/magnesium, and she soon calmed down and has not screamed now for four weeks.

—Linda Baker, Amarillo, TX

To the Editor: *[1995, Vol. 9, No. 1, Page 7]*



Although my child with Asperger syndrome is making progress (with vitamin B6/magnesium therapy), the most remarkable difference was with my daughter (who has attention deficit hyperactivity disorder)! She and I have fought like cats and dogs for eons—she has a very rebellious nature and a most difficult temperament. I immediately (the very next day) saw a change in her personality—she has been more cooperative, less argumentative, eager to help, very pleasant, more affectionate, happier, etc. It would be difficult to describe all the changes we have notice in her…

—A Georgia mother

Editor's Note: In 1979, Mary Coleman published an article in *Biological Psychiatry* on a controlled, double-blind study—using children already known to respond to Ritalin—which compared the effectiveness of Ritalin and vitamin B6 in controlling hyperactivity. Her finding: B6 was just as effective as Ritalin. (In addition, of course, B6 is much safer than Ritalin.) Yet, as far as I know, not one researcher has taken the trouble to repeat this study to see if Coleman's findings can be confirmed.

To the Editor: *[1995, Vol. 9, No. 2, Page 7]*

My son and I both have mild autism. We had our first success treating our son's autism using 8 mg of B6 per day. Some improvement was seen after only 12 hours, and his echolalia stopped after 36 hours. Eye contact, general thinking skills, language usage, and sociability improved greatly. Every single one of the 12 adults who knew him raved at his change.

I began to experiment in earnest. As the intake increased over 100 mg of B6 our son became worse. I found that he responded to between 15 and 60 mg of B6 and 250 mg of magnesium per day, with higher or lower levels of B6 causing him problems.

I think there is a different effective level of B6 and magnesium for each autistic person. I have read (and seen) that the more severely impaired autistic children—especially those who are prone to seizures—tend to need the higher levels of B6. However, for those individuals who respond adversely to the higher levels, excellent results may still be obtained at doses in the 10 to 100 mg level with a balance of B-complex vitamins and 100-250 mg of magnesium. Experiment!

—An adult with autism

Editor's Note: Good point! In our literature we emphasize that each person is very different, and that only experimentation will reveal the optimum dosage of B6 (or drugs, or anything else) for each person. Our studies, as well as those of Dr. LeLord's group in France, show 8 mg per lb. of body weight per day of B6 (and 3 mg magnesium/lb./day) to be the average amount needed, but there is wide variation around that average. —BR



To the Editor: *[1996, Vol. 10, No. 3, Page 7]*

(In April) we started our son Zach on ½ of a DMG (dimethylglycine) pill. He came home from school that day and said, "Hey you." His dad and I were shocked. He had never put two words together before. A few days later Zach said his first sentence: "I want pop please." We almost cried. I told no one at school or speech what I was doing. On his second day of DMG, his speech teacher and her boss ran him through some tests. They were amazed at how well Zach behaved, listened, and did. At school the same thing, "Zach's been trying to talk all day, just babbling." "Zach's really doing good now, he's playing so much better with the children."

Each day we saw improvement in Zach. He has a friend now at school plus all the children were excited. One little child came up to me and said, "Zachy can talk now."

At the end of the month I told everyone what I had done. They were all amazed. I have increased him to one pill in the morning and as of 6/18/96 to one pill in the afternoon. He is a little hyper sometimes but it's nothing we can't handle. We visited the doctor at Easter Seals yesterday, and she could not believe that this was the same child she saw six months ago.

—Lynn Gibbs, McKinney, TX

Editor's Note: The following letter is from the staff at the school attended by the child discussed in the letter above.

To the Editor: *[1996, Vol. 10, No. 3, Page 7]*

I am writing to you concerning Zachary Gibbs and the remarkable progress that we have seen him make over the past several months.

I am the Associate Director of the Child Development Center where Zachary attends school on a full time basis. My staff and I have worked with Zachary for a little over a year now and have seen more progress occur during the past several months than in the time previous.

We (my staff and myself) were unaware that Zachary began taking an all natural medication which has been known to help children with autism and PDD. During this time, Zachary almost instantly became potty trained. He began to use more language, sounds and gestures. His verbalization also became more clear when naming teachers, children and communicating. He also began imitating sounds and actions of other children. We have also noticed that Zachary has begun to use more pretend play than before. He will on more occasions play in the dramatic play center with the other children. He used to play more independently and now shows more of an interest in parallel play and group play.

—Cory Buie, teacher, and Dawn Worthington, Associate Director
Collin County Community College Child Development Center, McKinney, TX



To the Editor: *[1998, Vol. 12, No. 1, Page 7]*

Reading about the use of vitamin B6, magnesium, and DMG in the treatment of children with autism, we decided to give it a try; first DMG for one week, then the vitamins.

The results were amazing. Within six days our son's vocabulary began to snowball. He became more curious about the world around him and finally began to show some affection toward me. It was if a major neural circuit had been switched on.

For the first month to six weeks, we noticed an increase in activity level and our son became very "froggy." So we redirected his energy into useful channels; we took him out of public school and implemented a home-based program. He's not completely recovered yet, but he's well on his way. Medical "experts" are already doubting that he ever was autistic.

I sincerely believe that it was the combination of B6, magnesium, and

DMG that sparked our son's great leap forward.

—Evelyn Athanas-Brayton, Hope, Rhode Island

Editor's Note: Delighted! One of many such letters.

To the Editor: *[1998, Vol. 12, No. 2, Pages 6 and 7]*

I was hesitant to use the vitamin B6 and magnesium pills with my daughter (who has autism) because of a widely shared skepticism about vitamin therapy. After nothing else helped very much, I finally began to give her a moderate daily dosage, without telling anyone except my wife, and before long we started getting raves from her teachers, speech language therapist, and others who were involved in her care. Her comprehension increased, she was better behaved and achieving more at school, and she was also easier to manage at home ... If no tablets are given for more than a day, she gets irritable and has more difficulty concentrating.



It's hard to say which one of us is "hooked" on the B6, but I have no reason to believe in something that doesn't work, and, thus far, the B6 is the one thing that appears to have made a difference. Agreed, it's all confounded with ongoing development, education, etc., but the turnaround, I believe, is traceable to the B6. For all those who are dubious, I can say, with some confidence, it's worth a try.

—R. S. Ratner, Professor of Sociology
University of British Columbia, Vancouver, B.C., Canada

To the Editor: *[1998, Vol. 12, No. 3, Page 7]*

Our daughter started taking DMG about five weeks ago. She had been almost completely non-verbal, but within a week she started repeating words. (We used only) DMG for three weeks, then added B6/magnesium. She started spontaneous speech and had improved comprehension. She continues to get better every day.

P.S. She saw two therapists today. Neither one had seen her since the middle of May. They both almost fell out of their chairs. One said it was a miracle. The other couldn't believe how far she had advanced in her speech in such a short period of time.

—Lauren Underwood, Ph.D., Diamondhead, MS

To the Editor: *[1999, Vol. 13, No. 2, Page 7]*

I will always be especially thankful to you for suggesting several years ago that we try giving DMG to my grandson to help facilitate speech.

I was certain that he possessed receptive language skills and understood spoken language, but that his efforts to respond orally came out "scrambled." At the time, he was learning manual sign language used by deaf and hearing impaired children.

I remember well the evening of his third day on DMG. He was with me watching television, and had just finished drinking a cup of juice. He had handed me empty cup and I was trying to decide where to put it, when he pointed to the small table next to him and said, quite clearly, "Put it there." I was absolutely stunned—and filled with joy beyond description. I went quickly to the kitchen where I told my wife and our daughter (his mother) what had just happened. Needless to say, they were not convinced, and there was no repeat of this miracle in their presence.



A few days later, however, in my daughter's home, their doubt, too, was removed. I was not present, but they both tell how they were seated at the supper table when my grandson got up from his place and went to my wife. "I'll be right back," he said to her, then went to his mother and repeated, "I'll be right back," and then left the room.

Since then, my grandson has received (many other therapies). Today, his language skills are very well developed and he is a very bright and pleasant boy. I cannot prove scientifically that the DMG was solely responsible for unlocking his ability to speak. But for those who have not tried DMG, I can only repeat what you told me: "It can do no harm, and may prove helpful."

—Rev. Peter J. Reynierse, Bethesda, M.D,

# C. Teenagers and Adults

To the Editor: *[1995, Vol 9, No. 2, Page 7]*

I am writing to thank you for convincing me to try DMG/folic acid therapy on our 13½-year-old severely autistic daughter ... We added a DMG every other day, until she was taking twelve per day with 22 folic acid pills. The behavior changes are so dramatic; she was having several violent tantrums per day, complete with stripping off her clothes, hitting, biting, etc. That has all stopped and, when she must be disciplined, she handles it as well as our "normal" ten-year-old.

—Ken Sue Doerfel, Lawton, OK

Editor's Note: Dimethylglycine (DMG) may also be helpful in cases where there is an obsessive-compulsive component. One autistic adult developed the compulsive habit of vomiting, to the point that his weight loss was truly alarming. Drugs and behavioral treatments failed. At his mother's insistence, five tablets of DMG were given daily, with miraculously good results. I am aware of a non-autistic 15-year-old girl with severe obsessive-compulsive disorder (OCD) who had been greatly helped by Anafranil for a few weeks. When the Anafranil stopped working, DMG was tried, with excellent results. Since OCD is such a difficult problem, I would be especially interested in hearing from readers regarding their experiences with naltrexone, DMG or other treatments. –BR

To the Editor: *[1991, Vol. 5, No. 1, Page 7]*

Hurray for DMG! Our 14-year-old daughter (diagnosed as attention deficit disorder and hyperactive, with strong autistic tendencies) recently started on DMG, and within two days we were noticing some major changes in behavior. She had a greatly reduced frustration level; teenage hostility and/or oppositional behavior has diminished substantially; homework is now as pleasant as it can be; her organization skills, which were non-existent before, are definitely appearing; logic is developing; neatness is increasing; and we are seeing humor and cracking jokes about everyday problems. The bottom line: she is a much happier person. One of the most notable things was her asking for her "happy pills." She had become aware of the changes in herself, made the association, and liked the feeling.

—A California mother



To the Editor: *[1996, Vol. 10, No. 4, Page 7]*

My 18-year-old son, upon entering puberty, became an aggressive and sometimes violent autistic child. He was uncontrollable and eventually was put into a behavioral program (where) the doctors had him on strong doses of Haldol that not only didn't curb his behavior 100 percent of the time, but also left him in a drugged-like state, very sluggish and clumsy. I removed him from the facility and continued with the Haldol. I was a grown man living in fear of my own son.

Michael's teacher suggested that I try the high doses of B6, magnesium, and folic acid, along with the DMG that you recommended. I stopped the Haldol and put him on this regimen instead. That was about seven months ago, and since that time he has shown a marked improvement. I can't even remember the last time he had an outburst. He has brought home 23 awards during the last half of the school year for "most improved student," "team sports," and "positive attitude toward learning," as well as five principal's awards. He is clear-eyed and very communicative, and his comprehension has improved tenfold.

Although there are no miracle cures for autistics, this is the closest thing to a miracle for me. I love my son and want him to continue living at home with me, and with this program, I believe that it is now possible.

—Michael Lee Price, Las Vegas, NV

*[Editors' note: Read more about Michael in this book's chapter by Ed Kitt, the teacher who suggested the nutritional approach to Michael's father.]*

To the Editor: *[2001, Vol. 15, No. 1, Page 6]*

My son has autism. He is 19 years old and weighs over 200 pounds. He had been on B6/magnesium many years. Last year, I made the mistake of taking him off the vitamins.



(After I stopped the nutrients) he started yelling and laughing all day long. He started spitting, kicking, and pushing. He would have panic attacks that lasted for several minutes. I could not take him anywhere. We tried a few of the drugs that are available, but the side effects were even more frightening. The drugs made him angry and aggressive.

When I called you, you suggested that I try the B6/magnesium again. I did. Initially, I was disappointed because he was very hyperactive. Then I called Kirkman Labs, and they suggested I increase the magnesium.

In a few days he changed so much I could not believe my eyes. His yelling stopped completely, his spitting stopped, and his panic attacks stopped. He is more focused, he has started verbalizing more, he started doing well in school, and he got a job at Sears. You cannot imagine what a difference this has made in our lives.

—A mother in Glendale, CA

To the Editor: *[1993, Vol. 7, No. 1, Page 7]*

My 19-year-old autistic son, Aaron, has always loved watching videos by himself. He has always left the room, even during his favorite movies, rather than sit and watch with the whole family. Two weeks ago, Aaron started B6/magnesium therapy. Last Sunday, he watched a whole movie with the family from beginning to end. This has never happened before. Another unusual, although small, change, is his new interest in what to wear to school. Two days in the last two weeks, Aaron has dressed himself in what we would call dressier or more fashionable clothes. Aaron's changes may be small, but they are wonderful.

—Jackie Hammond, Las Vegas, NV

To the Editor: *[1992, Vol. 6, No. l, Page 7]*

My daughter Alina, who turned 22 last August, is home now and is doing meaningful work at Woolworth's. She has been on two tablets of DMG daily since August 1990, and her incidents of aggression and self-injurious behavior immediately dropped from two to three per week to two per year, and at a much milder level. She is mostly a happy person and it is a joy to have her home now. After 18 months of DMG, no ill side effects have been observed. (Editor's Note: DMG is nontoxic.)

—A Massachusetts Father

To the Editor: *[1992, Vol. 6, No. l, Page 7]*

(My daughter) Kim is a 23-year-old nonverbal adult. It is my pleasure to write that a miracle has taken place overnight in her metabolism/behavior after taking B6. She has stopped "racing." She is calm, her concentration is focused, she listens and responds to instruction. She smiles broadly and laughs. She watches for eye contact with those she chooses, has stopped the self-stimulating hitting of neck and knees, and walks instead of runs. She has always enjoyed orchestrated music, but now she enjoys listening to words of songs. Her verbal responses are logical and appropriate. I am ever so thankful and try not to think, "why wasn't B6 suggested sooner."

—Karen Carlson, Novato, CA



To the Editor: *[1992, Vol. 6, No. 2, Page 6]*

My son Brian, who is autistic (age 23), has been receiving 1,000 mg of vitamin B6 (and magnesium) since early January. After about a month we started seeing real improvement.

Brian's major problem is ritualistic behavior. This can lead to self-abusive (mostly biting his hand or arm) and aggressive behavior (hitting, etc.). After a severe episode several years ago, the tantrums were more severe than usual, and his ritualistic behavior was totally out of hand.

The B6 and magnesium have really accelerated his progress – there have been no tantrums at all since we started the B6, and the ritualistic behavior continues to improve. About one month after starting the vitamin B6 and magnesium, we started giving Brian DMG, as well as the B6. We noticed right away that he used more language, was more social, less ritualistic, and for the first time in 23 years actually watched TV. I feel that the DMG and vitamin B6 and magnesium together have helped him immensely.

Recently, during a very hectic period, I forgot the noon and evening doses of DMG three days in a row. We noticed that Brian was more withdrawn, more ritualistic, and wasn't using language very much. When his regular dose was resumed, all of that disappeared. At that time, he was on a dosage of 375 mg; now he is getting 750 mg, and we're noticing more improvement.

—Mrs. Mary Balliet, Vero Beach, FL

To the Editor: *[1994, Vol. 8, No. 4, Page 7]*

Enclosed are the results of a recent change of medication in one of our residents. This resident is an autistic individual who is 24 years old and severely mentally handicapped. He was banging his head, hollering and biting his hands to the extreme that we were at a loss in how to deal with him ... We thought we may have to give up and have him move to a better staffed facility. This is when a staff member saw your article on the use of Vitamin B6 and magnesium in *Woman's World* magazine, and I sent for more information. Graphs show that during baseline the resident had 44 bad shifts, a range of 0-2 out of 3 shifts and a mean of .94 bad shifts per day. Five months later he had 11 bad shifts, a range of 0-1 out of 3 shifts and a mean of .23 bad shifts per day ... He has shown tremendous improvement and we thank you for your assistance.

—Gary R. Stewart, M.A., Program Director
Bay Side Home ARC, Nova Scotia



To the Editor: *[1993, Vol. 7, No. 1, Page 7]*

My 41-year old brother has fragile X syndrome, mental retardation, and autism. He has been plagued with seizures for many years, often having several minor motor seizures a day. After a particularly bad run of nonstop, back-to-back seizures, he was taken to the emergency room.

(After leaving the hospital), he continued to have seizures. He was still getting phenobarbital, mysoline, and dilantin. I called the ARI and found out about DMG. I immediately bought some and sent it to his facility. They gave it to him. He has not had a single seizure since. It has been over three weeks.

Ever since (my brother) started taking the DMG (125 mg two times a day), he has been talking a blue streak. He is talking about a variety of subjects and is using more phrases and sentences. He even told a nurse, "I told you no. N-O!" He has never spelled anything before. He is better able to control himself if something upsets him. Thanks to the Autism Research Institute, we now see some light at the end of his tunnel.

—Kristin Zhivago, Menlo Park, CA

Editor's Note: Delighted! Others have also reported DMG to stop drug-resistant seizures. See *New England Journal of Medicine*, 10/21/82, pp. 1081-1082.

To the Editor: *[1991, Vol. 5, No. 4, Page 7]*

As the assistant manager of a vocational program, after hearing a lecture by Dr. Rimland, I suggested trying one of our middle aged woman clients on high dosage vitamin B6 and magnesium.

Carol was nonverbal and had many difficult fixations and problems, such as flipping up visors in parked cars as she walked by, moving office desks, and throwing items in inappropriate places. Correcting these behaviors caused screaming, biting and stamping.

On the vitamins, Carol now carries out most of her tasks independently. Staff no longer fear waiting in line with her or going to grocery stores. She accepts constructive criticism. Her speech pathologist has become very excited about her progress, both verbally and gesturally. Everyone is very impressed. Neither the speech therapist nor her employer, who says she's made remarkable progress, knew about the vitamin program.

If your readers have any doubts about pursuing the use of vitamin B6 and magnesium with adults, please make the effort. Our experience would say you have nothing to lose and everything to gain.

—Stephanie Campbell

To the Editor: *[1994, Vol. 8, No. 4, Page 7]*

I am Administrative Senior Behavior Analyst for Tacachale in Gainesville, Florida. This is a community of some 600 developmentally disabled adults. A number of the people who live here are autistic.

We have used megavitamin (B6/magnesium) therapy with two of Tacachale's autistic citizens. In both cases, staff report decreased agitation and increased attention span. These subjective reports were substantiated by these people's parents who, of course, approved the use of the procedure prior to its implementation.

—Tom Moore, Tacachale, Gainesville, FL

To the Editor: *[1991, Vol. 5, No. 1, Page 7]*

I want to pass on to you my son's successful use of DMG! He has been on it for about four months, and says it does definitely help his frustration level. He has taken a lot of different treatments over the years, and this is the very first time he has thought something has made a difference.

—An Oregon mother of a high-functioning autistic adult

To the Editor: *[1994, Vol. 8, No. 4, Page 7]*

It is a long time since we started DMG. I just wanted to let you know we are both still better for it. Paul goes less onto autopilot now and functions more "multi-track" and less mono on more levels at once. Me—big changes—much less "wobbly throwing" (especially self-directed). Also—best news—Big Black Nothing attacks are fewer and far less extreme, and I can usually seek and ask (in some form) for help to cope with the associated terror.... The terrible tremors and blood rushing in my ears and muscle flinching are mostly all gone.



—Donna and Paul Venables, England

Editor's Note: Donna Venables, formerly Donna Williams, is the author of *Nobody Nowhere* and *Somebody Somewhere*, detailing her experiences as an autistic child and adult.

To the Editor: *[1992, Vol, 6, No. 1, Page 6 and 7]*

I am extremely excited by the news about my 23-year-old autistic son, Bruce, since he has been on DMG. Today is his ninth day on DMG, and his third day on three capsules a day. As you can imagine, we have tried every conceivable remedy and method known to man for the last 23 years. Bruce has stopped yelling and screaming and biting his arm. He is quiet (not listless) and seems happy and content. He no longer performs his maddening acts of perseveration—the ritualistic and compulsive rituals that consumed hours every day and drove us crazy. On Sunday he sat and watched the Super Bowl on TV. He has never watch TV before in his life.

Because of his many compulsive rituals, it used to take him almost two hours to get dressed in the morning. Now he is getting dressed in five minutes. His eye contact has improved and he walks around with a happy smile on his face. There is something else though ... something intangible. Bruce is different. There is something in his eyes—they focus better, they have a glint in them, there is more awareness—and even more than that, there is a *je ne sais quoi* that cannot be put into words. My son is changed most remarkably.

—Alice Kutzin, M.D., Thousand Oaks, CA

Editor's Note: Several weeks after receiving this letter, Dr. Kutzin, a psychiatrist, wrote ARI again to comment on the additional progress her son made when she added vitamin B6 and magnesium to his supplementation program. "Bruce is a different person," she remarked. "He is extremely alert; he is very enthusiastic about life in general; he is interested in many things now, including his own speech," and is speaking with about 30% more frequency.

"It is now so enjoyable to talk to Bruce on the phone," she commented, "that I find myself calling him every day and looking forward to it, where before I would dread calling him once a week."

## — Chapter 41 —

# Abstracts of Studies of High-Dosage B6 (and often with Magnesium) in Autistic Children and Adults (1965-2005)

By Bernard Rimland, Ph.D.
Autism Research Institute, San Diego, California

Twenty-one of 22 studies yielded positive results, including 13 double-blind placebo-controlled trials; even minor adverse effects rarely were seen.



| AUTHOR/YEAR | SUBJECT/DOSAGE | DESIGN/OUTCOME |
|---|---|---|
| 1. Heeley and Roberts (1965) | 16 autistic children 30 mg, B6 one time (one child continued) | Tryptophan load test. 11 of 16 children normalized urine (child who continued showed "remarkable" progress). |
| 2. Bonisch (1968) | 16 autistic children 100-600 mg B6 (mostly 300-400 mg) | Open trial. 12 of 16 improved, 3 spoke for the first time. |
| 3. Rimland (1973) | 190 autistic children 4 megavitamins; 150-450 mg B6 | Compared B6 effect in computer-selected subgroups; computer "blind" to treatment effects. 45% "definite improvement" ($p<.02$). |
| 4. Rimland, Callaway, Dreyfus (1978) | 16 autistic children 75-3,000 mg B6 (mostly 300-500 mg) | Double-blind placebo crossover. 11 of 15 better on B6 ($p<.05$). |
| 5. Gualtieri, et al. (1981) | 15 autistic children 300-900 mg B6 plus other vitamins and minerals | Open trial 12 weeks, then no-treatment period. Six children showed "substantial" improvement. Basal serum prolactin levels (PRL) were lower in responders ($p<.05$). |
| 6. Ellman (1981) | 16 autistic adults and adolescents. 1 gram/day B6 500 mg/day magnesium | Double-blind placebo crossover. Four showed global improvement, five showed partial improvement. |

| | | |
|---|---|---|
| 7. Barthelemy, et al. (1981) | 52 autistic children, 11 normal controls 30 mg/kg/day B6 (up to 1 gram), 10-15 mg/kg/day magnesium | Three double-blind crossovers, comparing B6 alone, magnesium alone, and B6 + magnesium with placebo. B6 + magnesium was best. Highly significant (p<.01-p<.001). Decreases in autistic behaviors; significant (p<.02) decrease in urinary HVA. |
| 8. LeLord, et al. (1981) | *Study 1:* 44 children with autistic symptoms. *Study 2:* 21 children selected from above 44. 600-1,125 mg/day B6 400-500 mg/day magnesium | *Study 1:* open trial to identify responders. *Study 2:* double-blind placebo crossover comparing responders and non-responders. 15 of 44 improved. In 14 of 15, improvement disappeared 3 weeks after cessation of treatment. Double-blind study confirmed behavior improvement (p<.01). HVA levels (n=37) also improved (p<.01). |
| 9. Martineau, et al. (1982) | 24 autistic children 30 mg/kg/day B6, 15 mg/kg/day magnesium | Compared electrophysiological effects of magnesium given alone or with B6. In conditioning experiment, B6 + magnesium significantly improved brain response latencies and amplitudes (p<.05). |
| 10. Jonas, et al. (1984) | 60 autistic children 30 mg/kg/day B6 (up to 1 gram/day), 10-15 mg/kg/day magnesium | Four crossed-sequential double-blind trials, comparing B6 alone, magnesium alone, and B6 + magnesium with placebo. B6 + magnesium was best. Significant improvement in behavior, HVA excretion, and evoked potentials. |
| 12. Martineau, et al. (1986) | One four-year-old child 30 mg/kg/day B6, 15 mg/kg/day magnesium | Controlled study; eight weeks of treatment followed by no- treatment period. B6 group showed significant behavioral improvement, normalization of evoked potentials, drop in dopamine levels. Behaviors returned to baseline when treatment was discontinued. |

| | | |
|---|---|---|
| 14. Martineau, et al. (1989) | 6 autistic children 30 mg/kg B6, 10 mg/kg magnesium for 8 weeks, 6 autistic children given 1.5 mg/kg fenfluramine for 12 weeks. | Comparisons made in electro-physiological (AER) effects of the two treatments. B6, but not fenfluramine, "resulted in the appearance of a conditioning phenomenon and the demonstration of auditory-visual and auditory-tactile cross-modal associations during treatment." |
| 15. Rossi, et al. (1990) | Open trial on 30 autistic patients | 40% of patients improved "in the most typical behavioral features of autism." HVA, VMA and 5HIAA levels did not correlate with clinical improvement. |
| 16. Moreno, et al. (1992) | 60 families with autistic children studied with battery of clinical and biochemical tests | "Three out of eight probands who received megadoses of pyridoxine (vitamin B6), subjectively gained in language abilities, affectivity, and response to conductial modification therapy." |
| 17. Menage, et al. (1992) | 10 autistic children, 7 control children | 5 boys on megadose B6/magnesium for 8 weeks: "overall improvement of their disorders .... Particularly, improvement was observed for certain autistic symptoms (lack of interest in people, abnormal eye contact, impairment in verbal and nonverbal communication)." Improved T-cell deficits. |
| 18. Findling, et al. (1997) (See critique by Rimland, 1998) | 10 autistic children 420-1000 mg B6, 140-350 mg magnesium | Double-blind placebo crossover, four-week trials, no washout period, no test of compliance. Authors claim no benefit was seen, but were unable to produce data. |

| | | |
|---|---|---|
| 19. Hopkins (1999) | 13 autistic children 14 mg/kg/day of B6 (maximum 1 gm/day) magnesium=1/2 dosage of B6 | Double-blind placebo controlled study. One month washout period between B6-placebo phases. Eight of 13 subjects (61%) showed benefit, using behavioral and electrophysiological data (increased amplitude and decreased latency of P300 responses). |
| 20. Audhya (2002) | 184 autistic children on increasing doses of B6 and magnesium, not to exceed 20 mg/kg/day of B6 | 89 children (48%) improved significantly, 86 (47%) improved marginally, and nine (5%) showed worse behavior. (Main thrust of research was to study laboratory indices of metabolic status of the children.) |
| 21. Kuriyama (2002) | 16 "PDD" children, ages 6-16, 200 mg/day B6 (far below usual megadose range, and no magnesium was used) | Four-week randomized double blind placebo-controlled study, subjects on B6 showed 11.2 IQ point increase compared to six points for placebo group (statistically significant) |
| 22. Rimland and Edelson (2005) | 5,780 autistic children and adults, B6 and magnesium dosages decided by parents and physicians | Parents rated 85 biomedical interventions as to safety and efficacy. B6 and magnesium were rated "Helpful" in 47%, "No effect" in 49%, and "Made worse" in 4%. |



**References**

Audhya, T. (2002, October). Laboratory indices of vitamin and mineral deficiency in autism. Paper presented at the Defeat Autism Now! Conference, San Diego, California.

Barthelemy, C., Garreau, B., Leddet, I., Ernouf, D., Muh, J.P., & LeLord, G. (1981). Behavioral and biological effects of oral magnesium, vitamin B6, and combined magnesium-B6 administration in autistic children. *Magnesium Bulletin*, *3*, 150-153.

Bonisch, V.E. (1984). Erfahrungen mit pyrithioxin bei hirngeschadigten kindern mit autistischem syndrom. *Praxis der Kinderpsychologie*, *8*, 308-310.

Ellman, G. (1981, November). Pyridoxine effectiveness on autistic patients at Sonoma State Hospital. Paper presented at Research Conference on Autism, San Diego, CA.

Findling, R.L., Maxwell, K., Scotese-Wojtila, L., Huang, J., Yamashita, T., & Wiznitzer M. (1997). High-dose pyridoxine and magnesium administration in children with autistic disorder: an absence of salutary effects in a double-blind, placebo-controlled study. *Journal of Autism and Developmental Disorders, 27*, 467-478.

Gualtieri, C.T., Von Bourgondien, M.E., Hartz, C., Schopler, E., & Marcus, L. (1981, May). Pilot study of pyridoxine treatment in autistic children. Paper presented at American Psychiatric Association meeting, New Orleans, LA.

Heeley, A.G., & Roberts, G.E. (1966). A study of tryptophan metabolism in psychotic children. *Developmental Medicine and Child Neurology, 3*, 708-718.

Hopkins, J.N. (1999). *The effects of vitamin B6 supplements on the behaviour and brain activity of subjects with autism.* Unpublished master's thesis, Swinburne University of Technology, Victoria, Australia.



Jonas, C., Etienne, T., Barthelemy, C., Jouve, J., & Mariotte, N. (1984). Interet clinique et biochimique de l'association vitamine B6 + magnesium dans le traitement de l'autisme residuel a l'age adulte. *Therapie, 39*, 661-669.

Kuriyama, S., Kamiyama, M., Watanabe, M., & Tamahashi, S. (2002). Pyridoxine treatment in a subgroup of children with pervasive developmental disorders. *Developmental Medicine & Child Neurology, 44*, 284-286.

LeLord, G., Muh, J.P., Barthelemy, C., Martineau, J., Garreau, B., & Callaway, E. (1981). Effects of pyridoxine and magnesium on autistic symptoms: initial observations. *Journal of Autism and Developmental Disorder, 11*, 219-230.

Martineau, J., Garreau, B., Barthelemy, C., & LeLord, G. (1982). Comparative effects of oral B6, B6-Mg, and Mg administration on evoked potentials conditioning in autistic children. In A. Rothenberger (Ed.), *Proceedings: Symposium on Event-Related Potentials in Children* (pp.411-416). Essen, F.R.G. 11-13 June, 1982. Elsevier Biomedical Press, Amsterdam.

Martineau, J., Barthelemy, C., Garreau, B., & LeLord, G. (1985). Vitamin B6, magnesium and combined B6-Mg: therapeutic effects in childhood autism. *Biological Psychiatry, 20*, 467-468.

Martineau, J., Bathelemy, C., & LeLord, G. (1986). Long-term effects of combined vitamin B6-magnesium administration in an autistic child. *Biological Psychiatry, 21*, 511-518.

Martineau, J., Barthelemy, C., Cheliakine, C., & LeLord, G. (1988). Brief report: an open middle-term study of combined vitamin B6-magnesium in a subgroup of autistic children selected on their sensitivity to this treatment. *Journal of Autism and Developmental Disorders, 18*, 435-447.

Martineau, J., Barthelemy, C., Roux, S., Garreau, B., & LeLord, G. (1989). Electrophysiological effects of fenfluramine or combined vitamin B6 and magnesium on children with autistic behavior. *Developmental Medicine and Child Neurology, 31*, 728-736.

Menage, P., Thibault, G., Barthelemy, C., LeLord, G., & Bardos, P. (1992). CD4+ CD45RA+ T lymphocyte deficiency in autistic children: effect of a pyridoxine-magnesium treatment. *Brain Dysfunct., 5*, 326-333.

Moreno, H., Borjas, L., Arriela, A., Saez, L., Prassad, A., Estevez, J., & Bonilla, E. (1992). Heterogeneidad clinica del syndrome autista: un estudio en sesenta familias. *Invest Clin, 33*, 13-31.

Rimland, B. (1973). High dosage levels of certain vitamins in the treatment of children with severe mental disorders. In D. Hawkins & L. Pauling (Eds.), *Orthomolecular Psychiatry* (pp. 513-538). New York: W.H. Freeman.

Rimland, B. (1988). Controversies in the treatment of autistic children: vitamin and drug therapy. *Journal of Child Neurology, 3* (suppl.), S68-S72. (The data reported in this paper are augmented by a greatly increased number of cases in: Rimland, B. and Edelson, S.M., 2005, cited in present review).

Rimland, B. (1998). High dose vitamin B6 and magnesium in treating autism: Response to study by Findling et al. *Journal of Autism and Developmental Disorders, 28*, 581-582.

Rimland, B., Callaway, E., & Dreyfus, P. (1978). The effects of high doses of vitamin B6 on autistic children: a double-blind crossover study. *American Journal of Psychiatry, 135*, 472-475.

Rimland, B., & Edelson, S.M. (2005). *Parent ratings of behavior effects of biomedical interventions* (Pub. 34, Rev. March 2005). San Diego: Autism Research Institute.

Rossi, P., Visconti, P., Bergossi, A., & Balcatra, V. (1990, November). Effects of vitamin B6 and magnesium therapy in autism. Paper presented at the Neurobiology of Infantile Autism Conference, Tokyo, Japan.

# Part IV

# How to Help Your Child: Other Treatment Modalities



Part IV consists of the results from ARI's treatment effectiveness surveys and articles from the *Autism Research Review International* on a large variety of interventions that have been reported to be useful in the treatment of autism. Each autistic child is different, so it is important to have access to a wide variety of treatment options in the quest for those that may be effective.

# Parent Ratings of Behavioral Effects of Biomedical Interventions

The following two tables, based on ratings provided to the Autism Research Institute by well over 24,500 parents since 1967, have been described as the most valuable documents available to those responsible for the care and treatment of children and adults with autism.

Take a few minutes to study and understand these tables, and you will agree that they provide invaluable information.

The Autism Research Institute continues to solicit parent ratings of the efficacy and safety of biomedical interventions as the number of available interventions increases. Please contribute your own ratings at www.AutismTreatmentRating.com.

ARI Publ. 34/Feb. 2006

# PARENT RATINGS OF BEHAVIORAL EFFECTS OF BIOMEDICAL INTERVENTIONS

**Autism Research Institute 4182 Adams Avenue San Diego, CA 92116**

The parents of autistic children represent a vast and important reservoir of information on the benefits—and adverse effects—of the large variety of drugs and other interventions that have been tried with their children. Since 1967 the Autism Research Institute has been collecting parent ratings of the usefulness of the many interventions tried on their autistic children.

The following data have been collected from the more than 24,578 parents who have completed our questionnaires designed to collect such information. For the purposes of the present table, the parents responses on a six-point scale have been combined into three categories: "made worse" (ratings 1 and 2), "no effect" (ratings 3 and 4), and "made better" (ratings 5 and 6). The "Better:Worse" column gives the number of children who "Got Better" for each one who "Got Worse."

| DRUGS | Parent Ratings: Got Worse[A] | No Effect | Got Better | Better: Worse | No. of Cases[B] |
|---|---|---|---|---|---|
| Aderall | 41% | 26% | 34% | 0.8:1 | 589 |
| Amphetamine | 47% | 28% | 25% | 0.5:1 | 1248 |
| Anafranil | 32% | 38% | 31% | 1.0:1 | 386 |
| Antibiotics | 32% | 55% | 13% | 0.4:1 | 1915 |
| Antifungals[C] | | | | | |
| Diflucan | 5% | 42% | 52% | 9.7:1 | 409 |
| Nystatin | 5% | 46% | 49% | 9.2:1 | 1095 |
| Atarax | 26% | 53% | 22% | 0.8:1 | 489 |
| Benadryl | 24% | 51% | 25% | 1.1:1 | 2809 |
| Beta Blocker | 17% | 51% | 32% | 1.8:1 | 265 |
| Buspar | 26% | 44% | 30% | 1.1:1 | 350 |
| Chloral Hydrate | 42% | 38% | 20% | 0.5:1 | 431 |
| Clonidine | 21% | 31% | 48% | 2.2:1 | 1363 |
| Clozapine | 38% | 43% | 19% | 0.5:1 | 129 |
| Cogentin | 19% | 54% | 27% | 1.4:1 | 167 |
| Cylert | 45% | 35% | 20% | 0.4:1 | 608 |
| Deanol | 15% | 56% | 29% | 2.0:1 | 202 |
| Depakene[D] | | | | | |
| Behavior | 26% | 43% | 31% | 1.2:1 | 992 |
| Seizures | 12% | 33% | 56% | 4.7:1 | 651 |
| Desipramine | 36% | 31% | 33% | 0.9:1 | 72 |
| Dilantin[D] | | | | | |
| Behavior | 28% | 49% | 23% | 0.8:1 | 1087 |
| Seizures | 14% | 36% | 50% | 3.4:1 | 408 |
| Felbatol | 22% | 52% | 26% | 1.2:1 | 46 |
| Fenfluramine | 20% | 52% | 28% | 1.4:1 | 465 |
| Halcion | 39% | 37% | 24% | 0.6:1 | 59 |
| Haldol | 38% | 27% | 34% | 0.9:1 | 1169 |
| IVIG | 8% | 46% | 46% | 5.4:1 | 59 |
| Klonapin[D] | | | | | |
| Behavior | 28% | 38% | 34% | 1.2:1 | 207 |
| Seizures | 30% | 54% | 16% | 0.5:1 | 50 |
| Lithium | 25% | 44% | 31% | 1.2:1 | 424 |
| Luvox | 30% | 36% | 34% | 1.1:1 | 181 |
| Mellaril | 29% | 38% | 33% | 1.2:1 | 2070 |
| Mysoline[D] | | | | | |
| Behavior | 42% | 44% | 14% | 0.3:1 | 140 |
| Seizures | 21% | 57% | 22% | 1.1:1 | 68 |
| Naltrexone | 20% | 46% | 34% | 1.7:1 | 234 |
| Paxil | 30% | 32% | 38% | 1.3:1 | 336 |
| Phenergan | 30% | 46% | 24% | 0.8:1 | 278 |
| Phenobarb.[D] | | | | | |
| Behavior | 47% | 37% | 16% | 0.3:1 | 1090 |
| Seizures | 18% | 43% | 39% | 2.2:1 | 495 |
| Prolixin | 31% | 40% | 29% | 0.9:1 | 93 |
| Prozac | 31% | 33% | 37% | 1.2:1 | 1181 |
| Risperidal | 18% | 27% | 55% | 3.0:1 | 780 |
| Ritalin | 44% | 26% | 29% | 0.7:1 | 3921 |
| Secretin | | | | | |
| Intravenous | 7% | 46% | 47% | 6.5:1 | 376 |
| Transderm. | 11% | 50% | 39% | 3.6:1 | 157 |
| Stelazine | 29% | 45% | 27% | 0.9:1 | 424 |
| Tegretol[D] | | | | | |
| Behavior | 25% | 45% | 31% | 1.2:1 | 1456 |
| Seizures | 13% | 33% | 55% | 4.3:1 | 794 |
| Thorazine | 36% | 40% | 24% | 0.7:1 | 922 |
| Tofranil | 30% | 38% | 32% | 1.1:1 | 726 |
| Valium | 35% | 41% | 24% | 0.7:1 | 834 |
| Zarontin[D] | | | | | |
| Behavior | 36% | 43% | 20% | 0.6:1 | 143 |
| Seizures | 20% | 53% | 27% | 1.3:1 | 98 |
| Zoloft | 32% | 34% | 34% | 1.1:1 | 368 |

| BIOMEDICAL/ NON-DRUG/ SUPPLEMENTS | Parent Ratings: Got Worse[A] | No Effect | Got Better | Better: Worse | No. of Cases[B] |
|---|---|---|---|---|---|
| Vitamin A | 2% | 59% | 40% | 23:1 | 803 |
| Calcium[E] | 3% | 62% | 36% | 14:1 | 1636 |
| Cod Liver Oil | 4% | 47% | 49% | 12:1 | 1093 |
| Cod Liver Oil with Bethanecol | 11% | 50% | 39% | 3.4:1 | 80 |
| Colostrum | 6% | 58% | 36% | 6.5:1 | 428 |
| Detox. (Chelation)[C] | 3% | 22% | 75% | 27:1 | 470 |
| Digestive Enzymes | 3% | 39% | 58% | 18:1 | 979 |
| DMG | 8% | 51% | 42% | 5.5:1 | 5367 |
| Fatty Acids | 2% | 43% | 54% | 23:1 | 804 |
| 5 HTP | 13% | 52% | 36% | 2.7:1 | 200 |
| Folic Acid | 4% | 54% | 42% | 11:1 | 1613 |
| Food Allergy Trtmnt | 3% | 35% | 62% | 22:1 | 684 |
| Magnesium | 6% | 65% | 29% | 4.6:1 | 301 |
| Melatonin | 9% | 29% | 62% | 7.0:1 | 720 |
| P5P (Vit. B6) | 13% | 37% | 51% | 4.0:1 | 318 |
| Pepcid | 10% | 62% | 28% | 2.8:1 | 120 |
| SAMe | 17% | 65% | 18% | 1.1:1 | 93 |
| St. Johns Wort | 17% | 65% | 18% | 1.1:1 | 107 |
| TMG | 14% | 44% | 42% | 3.0:1 | 571 |
| Transfer Factor | 10% | 50% | 40% | 4.0:1 | 119 |

| BIOMEDICAL/ NON-DRUG/ SUPPLEMENTS | Parent Ratings: Got Worse[A] | No Effect | Got Better | Better: Worse | No. of Cases[B] |
|---|---|---|---|---|---|
| Vitamin B3 | 4% | 54% | 41% | 9.3:1 | 746 |
| Vit. B6 alone | 8% | 63% | 30% | 3.9:1 | 620 |
| Vit. B6/Mag. | 4% | 48% | 47% | 11:1 | 6079 |
| Vitamin B12 | 4% | 33% | 62% | 14:1 | 445 |
| Vitamin C | 2% | 56% | 41% | 17:1 | 1938 |
| Zinc | 3% | 49% | 48% | 18:1 | 1486 |
| **SPECIAL DIETS** | | | | | |
| Candida Diet | 3% | 43% | 54% | 18:1 | 811 |
| Feingold Diet | 2% | 44% | 54% | 24:1 | 797 |
| Gluten- /Casein-Free Diet | 3% | 32% | 65% | 20:1 | 1818 |
| Removed Chocolate | 2% | 49% | 49% | 28:1 | 1846 |
| Removed Eggs | 2% | 57% | 40% | 17:1 | 1199 |
| Removed Milk Products/Dairy | 2% | 48% | 50% | 32:1 | 5847 |
| Removed Sugar | 2% | 50% | 48% | 24:1 | 3862 |
| Removed Wheat | 2% | 49% | 49% | 27:1 | 3367 |
| Rotation Diet | 2% | 48% | 49% | 20:1 | 831 |

A. "Worse" refers only to worse behavior. Drugs, but not nutrients, typically also cause physical problems if used long-term.
B. No. of cases is cumulative over several decades, so does not reflect current usage levels (e.g., Haldol is now seldom used).
C. Antifungal drugs and chelation are used selectively, where evidence indicates they are needed.
D. Seizure drugs: top line behavior effects, bottom line effects on seizures
E. Calcium effects are not due to dairy-free diet; statistics are similar for milk drinkers and non-milk drinkers.

ARI Publ. 34 Asp/Feb. 2006

## Note: The data below are based on cases identified as "Asperger Syndrome" N=1,124

# PARENT RATINGS OF BEHAVIORAL EFFECTS OF BIOMEDICAL INTERVENTIONS

**Autism Research Institute 4182 Adams Avenue San Diego, CA 92116**

The parents of autistic children represent a vast and important reservoir of information on the benefits—and adverse effects—of the large variety of drugs and other interventions that have been tried with their children. Since 1967 the Autism Research Institute has been collecting parent ratings of the usefulness of the many interventions tried on their autistic children.

The following data have been collected from 1,124 parents who have completed our questionnaires designed to collect such information. For the purposes of the present table, the parents responses on a six-point scale have been combined into three categories: "made worse" (ratings 1 and 2), "no effect" (ratings 3 and 4), and "made better" (ratings 5 and 6). The "Better:Worse" column gives the number of children who "Got Better" for each one who "Got Worse."

| DRUGS | Parent Ratings: Got Worse[A] | No Effect | Got Better | Better: Worse | No. of Cases[B] |
|---|---|---|---|---|---|
| Aderall | 37% | 24% | 39% | 1.0:1 | 127 |
| Amphetamine | 28% | 29% | 44% | 1.6:1 | 94 |
| Anafranil | 23% | 38% | 38% | 1.6:1 | 47 |
| Antibiotics | 34% | 41% | 25% | 0.7:1 | 64 |
| Antifungals[C] | | | | | |
| Diflucan | 5% | 32% | 62% | 12:1 | 37 |
| Nystatin | 11% | 35% | 55% | 5.0:1 | 55 |
| Atarax | 40% | 37% | 23% | 0.6:1 | 35 |
| Benadryl | 28% | 51% | 22% | 0.8:1 | 152 |
| Beta Blocker | 13% | 50% | 38% | 3.0:1 | 24 |
| Buspar | 18% | 55% | 27% | 1.4:1 | 49 |
| Chloral Hydrate | 32% | 53% | 16% | 0.5:1 | 19 |
| Clonidine | 21% | 38% | 42% | 2.0:1 | 168 |
| Clozapine | 32% | 45% | 23% | 0.7:1 | 22 |
| Cogentin | 30% | 50% | 20% | 0.7:1 | 10 |
| Cylert | 32% | 51% | 17% | 0.5:1 | 59 |
| Deanol | 0% | 50% | 50% | | 2 |
| Depakene[D] | | | | | |
| Behavior | 25% | 39% | 36% | 1.4:1 | 56 |
| Seizures | 11% | 61% | 28% | 2.5:1 | 18 |
| Desipramine | 29% | 71% | 0% | | 7 |
| Dilantin[D] | | | | | |
| Behavior | 25% | 69% | 6% | 0.2:1 | 16 |
| Seizures | 14% | 29% | 57% | 4.0:1 | 7 |
| Felbatol | 0% | 100% | 0% | | 2 |
| Fenfluramine | 0% | 80% | 20% | | 5 |
| Halcion | 50% | 50% | 0% | | 2 |
| Haldol | 34% | 41% | 25% | 0.7:1 | 32 |
| IVIG | 33% | 33% | 33% | 1.0:1 | 3 |
| Klonapin[D] | | | | | |
| Behavior | 7% | 64% | 29% | 4.0:1 | 14 |
| Seizures | 0% | 75% | 25% | | 4 |
| Lithium | 20% | 40% | 40% | 2.0:1 | 40 |
| Luvox | 29% | 48% | 23% | 0.8:1 | 31 |
| Mellaril | 34% | 28% | 38% | 1.1:1 | 32 |
| Mysoline[D] | | | | | |
| Behavior | 50% | 50% | 0% | | 2 |
| Seizures | 0% | 100% | 0% | | 1 |
| Naltrexone | 20% | 10% | 70% | 3.5:1 | 10 |
| Paxil | 42% | 23% | 34% | 0.8:1 | 64 |
| Phenergan | 37% | 41% | 22% | 0.6:1 | 27 |
| Phenobarb.[D] | | | | | |
| Behavior | 44% | 44% | 11% | 0.2:1 | 18 |
| Seizures | 25% | 25% | 50% | 2.0:1 | 12 |
| Prolixin | 0% | 83% | 17% | | 6 |
| Prozac | 26% | 32% | 42% | 1.6:1 | 149 |
| Risperidal | 20% | 21% | 58% | 2.9:1 | 118 |
| Ritalin | 34% | 30% | 36% | 1.0:1 | 349 |
| Secretin | | | | | |
| Intravenous | 7% | 43% | 50% | 7.0:1 | 14 |
| Transderm. | 0% | 33% | 67% | | 6 |
| Stelazine | 38% | 63% | 0% | | 8 |
| Tegretol[D] | | | | | |
| Behavior | 33% | 49% | 18% | 0.6:1 | 55 |
| Seizures | 27% | 31% | 42% | 1.6:1 | 26 |
| Thorazine | 50% | 33% | 17% | 0.3:1 | 18 |
| Tofranil | 22% | 42% | 36% | 1.6:1 | 67 |
| Valium | 42% | 42% | 16% | 0.4:1 | 31 |
| Zarontin[D] | | | | | |
| Behavior | 50% | 50% | 0% | | 6 |
| Seizures | 0% | 100% | 0% | | 3 |
| Zoloft | 27% | 31% | 42% | 1.5:1 | 62 |

| BIOMEDICAL/ NON-DRUG/ SUPPLEMENTS | Parent Ratings: Got Worse[A] | No Effect | Got Better | Better: Worse | No. of Cases[B] |
|---|---|---|---|---|---|
| Vitamin A | 4% | 65% | 31% | 7.3:1 | 72 |
| Calcium[E] | 2% | 63% | 35% | 16:1 | 139 |
| Cod Liver Oil | 5% | 45% | 50% | 11:1 | 106 |
| Cod Liver Oil with Bethanecol | 0% | 75% | 25% | | 8 |
| Colostrum | 3% | 60% | 37% | 11:1 | 30 |
| Detox. (Chelation)[C] | 8% | 15% | 77% | 10:1 | 53 |
| Digestive Enzymes | 3% | 36% | 62% | 21:1 | 104 |
| DMG | 10% | 50% | 40% | 3.8:1 | 193 |
| Fatty Acids | 2% | 34% | 64% | 28:1 | 86 |
| 5 HTP | 5% | 55% | 41% | 9.0:1 | 22 |
| Folic Acid | 6% | 44% | 50% | 8.0:1 | 96 |
| Food Allergy Trtmnt | 4% | 38% | 58% | 16:1 | 81 |
| Magnesium | 11% | 74% | 16% | 1.5:1 | 19 |
| Melatonin | 5% | 23% | 73% | 15:1 | 62 |
| P5P (Vit. B6) | 12% | 26% | 62% | 5.2:1 | 34 |
| Pepcid | 0% | 54% | 46% | | 13 |
| SAMe | 0% | 100% | 0% | | 5 |
| St. Johns Wort | 13% | 73% | 13% | 1.0:1 | 15 |
| TMG | 11% | 39% | 50% | 4.5:1 | 36 |
| Transfer Factor | 0% | 78% | 22% | | 9 |

| BIOMEDICAL/ NON-DRUG/ SUPPLEMENTS | Parent Ratings: Got Worse[A] | No Effect | Got Better | Better: Worse | No. of Cases[B] |
|---|---|---|---|---|---|
| Vitamin B3 | 5% | 45% | 50% | 9.7:1 | 58 |
| Vit. B6 alone | 10% | 67% | 23% | 2.3:1 | 30 |
| Vit. B6/Mag. | 5% | 47% | 49% | 11:1 | 266 |
| Vitamin B12 | 6% | 30% | 63% | 10:1 | 63 |
| Vitamin C | 3% | 50% | 47% | 15:1 | 157 |
| Zinc | 3% | 39% | 57% | 17:1 | 117 |
| **SPECIAL DIETS** | | | | | |
| Candida Diet | 2% | 38% | 60% | 33:1 | 55 |
| Feingold Diet | 0% | 49% | 51% | | 80 |
| Gluten- /Casein-Free Diet | 2% | 29% | 69% | 30:1 | 171 |
| Removed Chocolate | 2% | 52% | 46% | 28:1 | 124 |
| Removed Eggs | 3% | 61% | 36% | 13:1 | 106 |
| Removed Milk Products/Dairy | 2% | 45% | 53% | 30:1 | 279 |
| Removed Sugar | 4% | 52% | 44% | 11:1 | 175 |
| Removed Wheat | 1% | 46% | 53% | 48:1 | 182 |
| Rotation Diet | 2% | 40% | 58% | 30:1 | 52 |

A. “Worse” refers only to worse behavior. Drugs, but not nutrients, typically also cause physical problems if used long-term.
B. No. of cases is cumulative over several decades, so does not reflect current usage levels (e.g., Haldol is now seldom used).
C. Antifungal drugs and chelation are used selectively, where evidence indicates they are needed.
D. Seizure drugs: top line behavior effects, bottom line effects on seizures
E. Calcium effects are not due to dairy-free diet; statistics are similar for milk drinkers and non-milk drinkers.

## — Chapter 42 —

# Vitamin C in the Prevention and Treatment of Autism

By Bernard Rimland, Ph.D.
Autism Research Institute, San Diego, California

*Autism Research Review International*, 1998, Vol. 12, No. 2, page 3

Vitamin C is an extremely safe substance that is immensely beneficial to the brain and body in a multitude of ways. Its potential for preventing and treating autism has barely been touched.

Vitamin C is heavily concentrated in the brain, but its exact role in brain function is not understood. A recent Medline search turned up 400 references referring to vitamin C and the brain, but the mystery remains.



We don't need to understand its biochemistry to know that vitamin C is crucial to brain function. The earliest signs of vitamin C deficiency are confusion and depression. Vitamin C also improves cognition, as shown by increased IQ scores in normal and Down's children. Other studies have shown improved EEGs and alertness, as measured in a variety of ways. Hoffer and Osmond, in a series of brilliant studies, showed vitamin C's effectiveness in treating schizophrenia.

Most of what we hear of vitamin C relates to its role in destroying viruses and bacteria. A 1995 review by Hemilä and Herman cited 21 placebo-controlled studies in which giving 1 or more grams of C daily significantly reduced the severity and duration of colds. (It doesn't *prevent* colds, it *mitigates* colds.) In *ARRI* 12-1, I discussed the work of Australian physician Archie Kalokarinos, who used vitamin C to reduce the vaccine caused death rate of aborigine infants from 50 percent to zero.

But vitamin C's anti-germ defense is only one of its many roles in the body. Irwin Stone's superb book *The Healing Factor: Vitamin C Against Disease* discusses many other ways in which vitamin C protects the body against substances implicated as causative of some cases of autism. A few examples:

- **Toxins.** Stone reviews a number of studies, starting in the 1930s, showing that industrial workers suffering from lead poisoning as a result of their exposure to lead in smelters, storage battery plants, and the like experienced quick relief from their mental and physical symptoms when given vitamin C supplements. He discusses a 1940 case of a 27-month-old child who had eaten materials containing lead who improved greatly when given vitamin C supplements. He discusses a Chinese study in which 100 tadpoles were put in water with high lead content, then removed and put into either plain water or water containing vitamin C. Six days later, all the tadpoles in the ascorbic acid-treated water were still alive, while 88% in the plain water had died. He also discusses the protective effect of vitamin C against mercury, arsenic, benzene, and other chemicals, as well as such organic poisons as botulism, snake bites, spider and scorpion bites, and bacterial toxins.

- **Vitamin C in autism?** Has vitamin C been used in the treatment of autism? I am aware of only two studies in which vitamin C was specifically evaluated as an intervention in autism. The first was the study I initiated in 1967 to evaluate the effects of four vitamins: B3, B5, B6, and C. We used a dose range of only 1 to 3 grams per day of vitamin C (about 20 mg/lb.), and the C at that dosage level was easily outshone by the vitamin B6. (Eighteen consecutive positive studies confirm the value of the vitamin B6.)

  The second study of vitamin C in autism was conducted by Dolske et al. (1993). The study consisted of a 30-week double-blind, placebo-controlled trial of 52 mg/lb. per day as a treatment for 18 autistic children (ages six to 19) in a residential setting. Statistically significant improvement on various outcome measures was reported. Clearly, Dolske's higher dosage produced better results than our earlier study of vitamin C. But what is the right dose for autism? Nobody knows. But vitamin C is extremely safe, even in massive doses, so it would be well to find out what the optimal dose for autism might be.



What is the safe dose of vitamin C? *A lot.* Vitamin C expert Robert Cathcart proposes the "bowel tolerance" method of determining one's own vitamin C requirement. You simply take increasingly large amounts of vitamin C each day until your body reaches the vitamin C saturation point. Going beyond that level, the vitamin C becomes a laxative. For most people in good health, the well-tolerated level tends to be about 10 to 15 grams of vitamin C per day. If you start to get sick, your body requires more vitamin

C, and your "bowel tolerance" may rise to 30 or 100 or more grams per day. But, according to Cathcart and other experts on vitamin C, increasing your input when you are sick will dramatically abbreviate your illness. Cathcart's patients with mononucleosis were functioning normally after a few days of 200 grams per day of vitamin C, given orally and IV, while the patients of the other doctors in the same community were hospitalized for several weeks during a mononucleosis outbreak (Dr. Cathcart's website is www.orthomed.com).

When my teenage daughter Helen was hospitalized with "terminal" (stage 4B) Hodgkin's disease in 1974, I put her on 40 grams of vitamin C per day (526 mg/lb.). Her doctors were aghast: "You'll kill her!" "Nonsense!" I replied. She recovered quickly, and 24 years later is in vibrant good health.

In 1966 VanderKamp published a seldom-cited but significant paper showing that adult schizophrenic men required 36 to 48 grams of vitamin C a day to reach the vitamin C saturation level that control group men reached by taking 4 grams of vitamin C per day. Saturation level was measured by a simple test in which one drop of urine is added to a test tube containing a reagent.



I found fascinating not only the fact that schizophrenics needed 10 times as much as the normal controls, but that the high doses of vitamin C brought about marked improvement in the *socialization* of the patients. While the patients were by no means cured, they "expressed a feeling of well-being. The anxious, tense facial expression was replaced with a smile and friendliness. They stated that they didn't feel so 'hemmed in.' 'People didn't seem to be against me.' 'I can now think more clearly.' Those who were shy, seclusive, and withdrawn began to participate in ward activities, in conversation with other patients and ward personnel."

Obviously, autism and schizophrenia are very different disorders (as I emphasized in my 1964 book *Infantile Autism*), but the enhanced socialization that VanderKamp reported in his schizophrenic patients would certainly be welcome among autistic patients, particularly those with Asperger syndrome. I hope that there are a few readers out there who are as curious as I am about what the outcome might be if the VanderKamp studies were repeated on Asperger's or autistic patients.

Other researchers have also reported improvement in the personalities of psychiatric patients on high doses of vitamin C. Milner (1963), for example, reported "statistically significant improvement in the depressive, manic and paranoid symptom complexes, together with an improvement in overall personality functioning…."

Research also has shown vitamin C to bring about improvement in patients with depression and manic depressive illness, which, as I pointed out in *Infantile Autism, do* appear to be genetically related to autism.

If vitamin C is used in large amounts, most experts suggest that buffered vitamin C (sodium ascorbate) should be used rather than ascorbic acid, since the acid form may be too acidic in multi-gram doses. Sodium ascorbate powder (1 level tsp. equals 4 grams) may be purchased inexpensively by the pound or the kilogram from the Wholesale Nutrition Company (800-325-2664) or from Bronson (800-610-4848).

## — Chapter 43 —

# Controlling Self-Injurious and Assaultive Behavior in Autism

By Bernard Rimland, Ph.D.
Autism Research Institute, San Diego, California

*Autism Research Review International,* 2001, Vol. 15, No. 4, page 3



Nothing is more difficult for the parents of autistic children to tolerate than self-injurious and assaultive behavior (SIB/A). SIB/A behaviors are unpleasant to observe, to think about, or to discuss, but they do exist, and must be dealt with. Some autistic children hit their heads against walls or floors so hard that they have fractured their skulls, detached their retinas, or caused deafness. Others hit themselves with their fists or their knees so hard that they have broken noses, deformed ears, and even blinded themselves. Some children bite themselves and others, and hit other children and their parents with such violence they have broken bones.

The first approach, when one is confronted with SIB/A, is to try to determine why the child is engaging in those activities. Is it pain or frustration that is causing the child to strike out at himself or at others? One nonverbal child was severely self-injurious from age two to 18, when it was discovered that he had been suffering from a very painful mastoid infection. Many medical examinations had failed to disclose this source of severe pain. Try to find a physician who is the parent of an autistic or other handicapped child to do an extremely careful medical exam to determine if there is a cause of pain underlying the intolerable behavior. Tim Buie, M.D., has found that undetected stomach pain has caused SIB in his autistic patients.

A good deal of time and attention have been devoted to methods of dealing with these terrible problems, including:

1. **Behavior modification** using positive enforcement only. This approach is certainly to be recommended if and when it works, but there are many instances when it does not work. A review of the literature by the Association for Persons With Severe Handicaps (TASH) found that positive reinforcement is effective approximately 60% of the time. We are concerned with the other 40%.

2. **Aversives.** While many people are ideologically opposed to aversives, a blue-ribbon government panel investigated this problem and concluded that there were many instances where aversives were the preferred approach, in those many cases where positive reinforcement does not work.

3. **Drugs.** Many drugs, including most recently Naltrexone, have been partially effective in some cases. However, most drugs bring about their own problems, which are by no means trivial.

4. **Correcting body chemistry,** through the use of nutritional supplements, or by detoxifying the body of toxic elements such as mercury, is an under-utilized alternative.

**Detoxification:** Amy Holmes, M.D., who has treated many hundreds of autistic children for mercury poisoning, reports that while the best improvement in terms of speech, sociability, cognitive gain, etc., is seen in the younger children, teenagers often show a marked and very welcome reduction in SIB/A when the mercury is removed.



**Vitamin B6 and magnesium, and DMG (dimethylglycine):** Over the past 40 years I have encountered a great many cases of severely SIB/A individuals who have responded wonderfully well to nutritional supplementation, particularly high dose B6 and magnesium, and DMG. Surprisingly, these improvements have been seen not only in autistic individuals, but in girls with Rett syndrome and boys with fragile X syndrome, as well as children with Angelman syndrome. A few sample cases:

*Case 1:* Anthony, an 18-year-old autistic man in England, was so violent that he had to be institutionalized. At the institution he broke seven windows in three minutes, and tried to attack women sexually, requiring severe restraints. Drugs did not work, and his mother, who runs an organization to support research in autism in the U.K., contacted me for help. I suggested high-dose vitamin B6 and magnesium. The result was miraculous. When Anthony was taken on a train trip, his parents forgot to bring along the vitamins. The next day, he again became "a raging beast." I was invited to speak at the institution where Anthony resided, and took the opportunity to meet him and discuss his case with the staff. All agreed that Anthony had shown remarkable improvement when given the high-dose vitamin B6/magnesium.

*Case 2:* Some years ago I was asked to speak in Caracas, Venezuela, by Dr. Lilia Negrón. Dr. Negrón introduced me by telling the audience, and me, about an autistic young man whose mother had come crying to Lilia's office trying to get help for her son. He was about to be evicted from the third mental hospital, since even massive amounts of drugs did not control him, and he was too violent to be kept in the hospital. Dr. Negrón tried the B6 and magnesium as a last resort. The young man calmed down quickly. Dr. Negrón reported at the meeting that she had recently visited the family, and had found him to now be a pleasant and easy-going fellow who sang and played his guitar for her.

*Case 3:* The boy's mother told me that he was considered to be the most severely self-injurious and assaultive autistic person in her state—a very large state. Nothing would stop his self-injurious behavior. The drugs he was given had such an adverse effect on his heart that increasing the dosage would probably kill him, yet his self-injurious behavior continued. The mother was so distraught that she had seriously considered killing both her son and herself because she could no longer tolerate the situation. She tried the B6 and magnesium, with incredibly good results in a short time. She was elated. However, she called me back a year or so later to tell me that he had started hitting himself again. I suggested she switch to P-5-P, a different type of vitamin B6, rather than pyridoxine hydrochloride, since that might make the difference. I have not heard from her whether that change helped. Research is needed.



*Case 4:* Michael was a 180-pound, 18-year-old autistic young man who had broken his mother's jaw and beaten his father so badly that he had missed work for several days. The police had been called on a number of occasions, when he flew into one of his rages. Ed Kitt, the principal of the school in Las Vegas that he attended, told the family to contact me for advice. I suggested the B6 and magnesium, as well as DMG, and the results were nothing short of miraculous. Michael's very good and pleasant behavior has continued now for a number of years. He continues to take massive amounts of B6 and magnesium (1500 mg of B6, 700 mg of magnesium) and 18 DMG tablets per day. The father told me that these nutrients are expensive, but he is glad to pay for them. They are less expensive than the drugs he had been buying, and certainly much more effective, safer, and more helpful for his son *[Editors' note: Ed Kitt's story about Michael is included in this book]*.

**Rett syndrome:** Several years ago I received a phone call from a mother telling me that her teenage Rett syndrome daughter was gouging her eyes, and hitting herself very severely, with great likelihood of bodily damage. I suggested the B6 and magnesium, and DMG. Several months later I got an excited phone call from Kathy Hunter, president of the Rett Syndrome Association, who told me about a Rett syndrome girl who had been severely self-injurious, and had been helped enormously with nutritional supplements. She gave me the mother's phone number. When I called, it turned out to be the mother whom I had spoken with earlier.

**Angelman syndrome:** A number of mothers who had attended a convention of the Angelman Syndrome Association called to tell me that they had been told of an Angelman's child who had been hitting himself, scratching and biting his mother, and generally being quite aggressive. DMG brought about excellent results, so other mothers also tried DMG and got the same results. I asked them the name of the national authority on Angelman's and wrote to that physician, asking if he would be willing to collaborate on a study of DMG's effects on self-injurious behavior in Angelman syndrome. I have never received a reply.

## — Chapter 44 —

# Puberty, Aggression, and Seizures

By Bernard Rimland, Ph.D.
Autism Research Institute, San Diego, California

*Autism Research Review International*, 2005, Vol. 19, No. 1

Puberty in autistic children is often accompanied by the onset of seizures or an increase in seizures and/or aggressive behavior. These problems have been addressed in many previous issues of the *Autism Research Review International.* The back issues of the ARRI, volumes 1-18, 1987 through 2004, may now be accessed, along with an extensive index, free of charge at www.ARInewsletter.com or may be purchased from ARI. Readers are urged to refer to our previously published articles on puberty, seizures and aggression, as well as on self-injurious behavior (SIB) for much more comprehensive discussions than can be provided here.



Our immediate purpose in this article is to provide an overview of the issues, as well as to discuss several previously undiscussed, or underdiscussed, ideas that merit your attention.

A great many cases of aggression or self-injurious behavior have been found to be the child's response to physical pain. In one case a child's decades-long severe SIB was found to be caused by a chronic painful mastoid infection. In recent years, late-onset autism, which comprises the autism epidemic, has often been characterized by severe abdominal pain, frequently accompanied by constipation, diarrhea or both. Gastroenterologists Andrew Wakefield, Tim Buie, Arthur Krigsman and other speakers at our Defeat Autism Now! (DAN!) Conferences have addressed these issues in considerable detail.

A pediatric gastroenterologist may perform a colonoscopy to determine if a patient needs treatment. A highly effective treatment protocol has been developed by Tim Buie, M.D., and colleagues at the Massachusetts General Hospital and Harvard Medical School. A consortium of other medical schools in various parts of the U.S., known as the Autism Treatment Network, has been formed to implement this treatment approach for the GI issues of autism.

Migraine headaches and the pain of hypersensitive hearing have also been found to cause aggression or self-injurious behavior in many individuals. Food allergies are a frequent cause of migraines and seizures. Keeping a food diary may be helpful in identifying foods which cause migraines and seizures. Avoiding common allergenic foods has been found to be helpful.

Joseph Egger et al., in a 1989 study, found that 40 of 45 patients with migraines and epilepsy reported improvement on what Egger referred to as an "oligoantigenic" (few foods) diet. The foods found to be most troublesome (most important to eliminate from the patient's diet) were cow's milk and cheese, citrus fruits, wheat, artificial food colorings and flavorings, eggs, tomato, pork and chocolate.

Hypersensitive hearing can be painful and often is exacerbated in puberty. Covering the ears when certain sounds are heard is an obvious clue. Since hypersensitive hearing is a common sign of magnesium deficiency, simply supplementing the diet with magnesium should be the first priority. Irritability may also be a sign of magnesium deficiency. I suggest giving 4 mg of magnesium per pound of body weight (e.g. 400 mg of magnesium for a 100-pound person) per day. Magnesium citrate and magnesium glycinate are the two best absorbed forms of magnesium. In purchasing magnesium supplements, be sure you read the label correctly. Look for the number of milligrams of *elemental* magnesium in the tablet or capsule. The magnesium should be given with a B-vitamin supplement to help the body absorb the magnesium properly.



If magnesium supplements do not correct the hypersensitive hearing in a few days, ear plugs, purchased at drug stores or hardware stores, may be helpful. Berard-type auditory integration training (AIT) is often helpful for hypersensitive hearing, and many other problems common in autistic children and adolescents. (I do not recommend the Tomatis type of auditory training. The Tomatis approach does not have the extensive research validation which provides support for the Berard method. For a review on the research on Berard auditory integration training go to www.SAIT.org.)

The increase in seizures that accompanies puberty is well known, but not at all understood. Puberty has been found to increase the need for vitamin B6 in both in boys and girls. In my opinion the top priority in responding to aggression, self-injurious behavior, and seizures in adolescence should be to increase the dosage of B6 and magnesium in those already on B6 and magnesium, and to initiate B6 and magnesium treatment in those not already on it. The same is true for dimethylglycine (DMG), another very safe and effective nutritional supplement. In a number of cases, patients with multiple severe seizures while on four or five anticonvulsant drugs have experienced complete relief from seizures upon being given B6 and magnesium and/or DMG.

In his book *Nerves in Collision*, Walter Alvarez, M.D., "the Sherlock Holmes of medicine," reports that "nonconvulsive epilepsy" (seen only on an EEG) may cause fits of sudden explosive aggression. He observed that remorse was common in such cases, while rare in violently aggressive persons with normal EEGs. Small maintenance doses of the anticonvulsant drug Dilantin were found to be helpful in such cases.

Although there are many newer anticonvulsant drugs (see Parent Ratings of the Effectiveness of Biomedical Interventions in Autism, at www.AutismResearchInstitute.com *[Editors' note: See also pages 382-385 of this book]*), Dilantin may nevertheless be especially useful in autism. In our first study on B6 in autism, the six children who responded best to vitamin B6 had, as it turned out, also been taking Dilantin.

High-dose vitamin B6 and magnesium, which has been reported as helpful in autism in 21 of 22 studies to date, is even more likely to be helpful in adolescents and adults than in children. B6 and magnesium are immeasurably safer than any of the drugs used to treat autism, including the anticonvulsant drugs. See "Vitamin B6 in autism: The safety issue" (ARRI 10/3/3). See also "What is the right 'dosage' for B6, DMG, and other nutrients useful in autism?" (ARRI 11/4/3). To summarize our findings on the dosage of B6 and of DMG: every individual is unique, and the "right dose" varies enormously from person to person. Since these nutrients are very safe, trial and error is a valid approach. On average, 8 mg of vitamin B6 per pound of body weight per day seems to work well for many, but some individuals need much more, and some need much less. Read the article! DMG is classified by the FDA as a food. No toxicity has ever been reported. Read the article!



A 2004 study at Emory University reported that patients with uncontrolled epilepsy had low blood levels of DHA, an essential fatty acid. Studies of autistic children also frequently find essential fatty acid (EFA) deficiencies. The moral is clear: if the kids won't eat salmon, give them EFA supplements!

If other approaches fail, consider medical marijuana, which has proven to be a lifesaver, literally, for many desperate families. See ARRI 12/2/7, 16/2/7, 16/3/7, and 17/1/2,3,4 for discussions. Also see the new book *Jeffrey's Journey*.

In this brief overview I could only touch on various topics which have been covered in depth in previous issues of the ARRI, which are now readily available.

# — Chapter 45 —
# *Candida*-Caused Autism?

By Bernard Rimland, Ph.D.
Autism Research Institute, San Diego, California

*Autism Research Review International,* 1988, Vol. 2, No. 2, page 3

*Candida* albicans is a yeast-like fungus that inhabits almost all humans. It lives on the moist dark mucous membranes that line the mouth, vagina and intestinal tract. Ordinarily it exists only in small colonies, prevented from growing too rapidly by the human host's immune system, and by competition from other microorganisms in and on the body's mucous membranes. When something happens to upset this delicate natural balance, *Candida* can grow rapidly and aggressively, causing many unpleasant symptoms to the host. Some of the symptoms are widely known and acknowledged. Vaginal yeast infections, primarily caused by *Candida*, present the most common case in point. Thrush, the white yeast infection of the mouth and tongue that is common in infants, is another well-known example of *Candida* overgrowth.



In recent years a minority of physicians have begun to try to persuade their colleagues, and the public, that *Candida* may present consequences far more devastating to human well-being than vaginitis and thrush. They cite Japanese studies showing that *Candida* is able to produce toxins that cause severe long-term disruption of the immune system and may also attack the brain. In extreme cases, they claim, severe disorders, totally resistant to conventional treatment, can occur as a result of candidiasis. These include depression, schizophrenia, and, in some cases, autism.

It is much too early to reach a firm conclusion, but, based on the weight of the information gathered to date, it seems to me highly probable that a small, but significant, proportion of children diagnosed as autistic are in fact victims of a severe *Candida* infection. I further believe that if the *Candida* infection were successfully treated in these few cases—much easier said than done—the symptoms of autism would show dramatic improvement.

In a typical case of this kind, the child appears to be a normal, reasonably healthy infant for the first 18 to 24 months. Speech has started, and the child displays the usual level of interest in his family and his surroundings. A series of ear infections occur that are routinely treated by antibiotics. Soon thereafter, ominous changes begin to occur. Speech development stops, then regresses, often to the point of muteness. Within a few weeks or months the child becomes unresponsive and loses interest in his parents and his surroundings. The concerned parents take the child to various specialists, and finally come up with a diagnosis of "late-onset autism." The story is familiar. We all know of such cases.

In 1981, this happened to Duffy Mayo, the then three-and-a-half-year-old son of Gianna and Gus Mayo of San Francisco. Duffy had been a bright and active youngster, learning to speaking both English and Italian before regression set in. After the diagnosis of autism had been applied by two specialists, the Mayos were lucky enough to take Duffy to allergist Alan Levin in their search for help. Levin found that Duffy's immune system was severely impaired. Of special interest was the fact that Duffy had been given a number of treatments with antibiotics, which were intended to control his ear infections. Levin knew that such antibiotics often kill the microorganisms that compete with *Candida* in the human body and thus allow *Candida* to grow to overwhelming proportions.



Aware of the mounting evidence that *Candida* might be less benign than commonly believed, Levin tried nystatin, an antifungal drug that is toxic to *Candida* but not to humans. Duffy at first got worse (a common reaction, caused by the toxins released by the dying *Candida* cells). Then he began to improve. Since Duffy was sensitive to molds, the Mayos moved inland to a dryer climate. Since *Candida* thrives on certain foods (especially sugars and refined carbohydrates) Duffy's diet required extensive modification. Today Duffy is an active, greatly improved 10½-year-old child with few remaining signs of autism. His immune system is still impaired, however, and he still requires treatment.

Most physicians are skeptical.

When *The Los Angeles Times* published a long, syndicated article about Duffy in 1983, the Mayos, and the Autism Research Institute (ARI), which was mentioned in the article, began receiving letters and phone calls from parents of autistic children throughout the country. It seems that there are many autistic children whose problems started soon after long-term antibiotic therapy, or whose mothers had chronic yeast infections that they had passed along to the infants. How many of these might in fact be caused by candidiasis? No one knows.

William G. Crook, the well-known pediatric allergist of Knoxville, Tennessee, has mentioned several similar cases in his book *The Yeast Connection* and in his lectures. Cecil Bradley (one of Duffy Mayo's physicians) recently told me that he has seen eight "autistic" children who respond favorably to anti-*Candida* drugs and diet treatment.

ARI has been gathering information on the possible link between autism and *Candida* since 1966, when our first research assistant, Dale Meyer, noticed that thrush seemed to be mentioned unusually often in the letters and questionnaires sent to us by parents. I am fairly well convinced that there is a connection and that perhaps 5% to 10% of autistic children—those given many courses of antibiotics, or born with thrush or afflicted with thrush soon after birth—will improve when properly treated for *Candida*. However, there is no consensus among physicians on the *Candida*/autism linkage.

Judging from contacts with several hundred parents over the past few years, only about one physician in 20 or 30 will give serious consideration to the possibility that treating *Candida* may alleviate the symptoms of autism. Most physicians regard concern with *Candida* as just another fad, soon to be forgotten. I wish they were right, but I don't think they are.

Even if the parent is lucky enough to find a knowledgeable physician, the battle is a long way from won. There are 30 or 40 strains of *Candida*, and some are very resistant to treatment. Nystatin, quite possibly the safest prescription drug on the market, will work on the weakest *Candida* strains. Ketoconazole (Nizoral) is a stronger drug, but much more likely to have adverse side effects. Diet is said to be at least as important as drugs in treating *Candida*. There are also non-prescription substances said to have anti-*Candida* effects, such as acidophilus, caprylic acid, and other readily available substances, some of which have been used to treat *Candida* for hundreds of years. All of these approaches have been tried, with varying degrees of success.

Although we have learned a good deal about the possible link between autism and *Candida* in the past few years, there is a great deal more that we need to know.

# — Chapter 46 —
# Our Children: Victims of Both Autism and Dogma

By Bernard Rimland, Ph.D.
Autism Research Institute, San Diego, California

*Autism Research Review International,* 1997, Vol. 11, No. 3, page 3

In the morning's mail was a letter from my keen-eyed friend Ted Melnechuk, who, it seems, reads everything, and often sends me clippings of special interest. This clipping was a four-page article from the August 10 *New York Times Magazine,* and Ted had penned across the top: "Bernie: Stick to your guns!" I was delighted to see that the article was about Kilmer McCully.



I've never met Kilmer McCully, but I've known about him since the 1970s, and had been thinking about him a lot during the past year. In fact, I'd mentioned him in a recent *ARRI* editorial (*ARRI* 10/3).

Why was a four-page article about Kilmer McCully in the *New York Times Magazine*? McCully had been a highly regarded pathologist at the Harvard Medical School and Massachusetts General Hospital until he was "let go" in the late '70s. He wasn't just let go—he had become an object of great hostility. "McCully would hear of a job opening, go for interviews, and the process would grind to a stop. Finally, he heard rumors of what he calls 'poison phone calls' from Harvard." It took legal intervention to stop the campaign of vilification against him.

What was his crime? How had he generated such animosity? He had committed the cardinal sin—especially for a medical school professor—of suggesting that increasing the intake of certain vitamins could save people's lives. He was right, but that didn't matter. People, including "scientists," tend to hate those who challenge their beliefs.

In our *ARRI* editorial last year, I briefly mentioned a study by Ellis and McCully which found that elderly patients given 100-300 mg of vitamin B6 over a period of years who died of a heart attack had an average age at death of 84.5 years—eight years more of life than heart attack victims from the same county who did not take vitamin B6.

The truth sometimes emerges despite the best efforts of the authorities to protect us from it. The media, including the cover story of *Newsweek* (August 11, 1997), tell us, as McCully tried to decades ago, that vitamin

B6, folic acid, and B12 play an important role in protecting against heart attacks.

McCully is but the most recent of a long list of pioneers who suffered outrageous injustices at the hands of dogmatic authorities who are so sure that they are right that they never trouble themselves to consider the evidence. How many millions of lives would have been saved if the authorities had been less smug?

It has been estimated that over 100,000 British sailors died a horrible death from scurvy in the 60 years between the time Dr. Lind discovered that lime juice (a source of vitamin C) would prevent—and cure—scurvy and the time his discovery was implemented. Lives that could have been saved by vitamin B6, and vitamin C, were sacrificed to dogma. "Don't bother me with the facts."

Autistic children have been, and still are, very much the victims of dogma. Every day I hear from mothers that their children's pediatricians, neurologists, or psychiatrists proclaimed that vitamin B6 will not help their children, and in fact may very well cause harm. Never mind that 18 consecutive studies have shown B6 to be helpful in autism, and no study has reported detrimental effects to any autistic child. Never mind that all of the drugs used for autism (except nystatin, an antifungal) can and do cause harm.



Autistic children have been the victims of dogma from the very beginning, when autism was declared an emotional disorder, brought on by covert maternal rejection. This dogma was universally believed and caused immense harm to the children and their families, in the total absence of substantiating evidence.

The next damaging dogma was the belief that behavior modification was futile in autism. It was a good way to teach a dog to roll over, or a seal to balance a ball on his nose, the parents were told, but a treatment for autism—absurd! A major reason for my having founded the Autism Society of America in 1965 was to spread the word to parents across the U.S. that behavior modification could make a big difference.

It is now very well established that, contrary to prevailing dogma:

- Yeast infections, usually brought on by antibiotic overuse, can cause or exacerbate autism.

- Intolerances to certain foods, particularly cow's milk and certain cereals including wheat, can cause autism.

- Vaccinations, whatever their value to some children, can cause autism in others.

- Auditory integration therapy (AIT), however counterintuitive it may be, can and does often produce significant improvement.

Each of the foregoing causes/treatments is well documented and quite plausible from a purely scientific standpoint, but each is politically incorrect in terms of currently accepted dogma. And the children are worse off as a result.

The topics listed above by no means exhaust the list of topics on which data and dogma collide. The underlying conflict is between conventional medicine ("try this or that drug") and alternative medicine, which seeks means of helping the body heal itself.

Biological therapy: To me the most exciting frontier is an area of great interest and great ferment at the moment. For want of a better term, I'll call it biological therapy, at least tentatively. It entails the injection, infusion, or implantation of complex biological products, of human or animal origin, into the autistic child to stimulate a therapeutic response. Examples are IVIg infusion (*ARRI* l0/3, 11/1) and transfer factor therapy (*ARRI* 11/2). IVIg is being studied as a treatment in a series of multi-center trials. Transfer factor therapy is far more controversial (*ARRI* 3/4).



Cell therapy, involving the injection of cells from certain organs taken from fetal farm animals (usually sheep), has been practiced in Europe for fifty years, and has been used on millions of patients, including many Down syndrome patients and some autistic children, with reported good results and no significant adverse effects. (Dr. Hans Kugler told me some years ago about a Down syndrome child born in a large West Coast medical center. "Hopeless," the parents were told. They took the child to Dr. Franz Schmid in Germany for cell therapy, which brought such great improvement that the delighted parents brought the child back to the prestigious medical center in the U.S. "This couldn't be the same child," they were told, "or we made a wrong diagnosis." Dogma dies hard.)

FGF therapy: Dr. Luis Aguilar of Mexico has used a different approach, injections of FGF (fibroblast growth factor), with what so far appear to be promising results.

A compilation of recent papers on biological therapies is available on request from ARI to those donating $10 or more.

The Autism Research Institute's Defeat Autism Now! (DAN!) project has as a major goal the bringing together of pioneers and advocates in these various controversial fields so they may share their knowledge and expertise. They will be doing so at our DAN! Conference in San Diego on September 19-21, 1997. Persuade your child's doctors to come and to learn.

# — Chapter 47 —
# Specific Carbohydrate Diet Reduces Autistic Symptoms

By Bernard Rimland, Ph.D.
Autism Research Institute, San Diego, California

*Autism Research Review International*, 2004, Vol. 18, No. 4

A small pilot study supports the many parent reports (see ARRI 18/3) indicating that the Specific Carbohydrate Diet (SCD) benefits some autistic children who do not respond fully to the gluten-free/casein-free (GFCF) diet.



Jeffrey Trelka and Brian Hooker placed two young autistic girls first on the GFCF diet, and then on the SCD. The researchers report that while the children improved on both diets, they exhibited "significantly less behavioral and physiological problems" during SCD treatment than during the GFCF intervention. Behavioral changes seen in the children following the SCD diet included better sleep, better eye contact, fewer tantrums, better speech, greater awareness, improved imitation skills, less self-injury and aggression, and improved sociability. Physiological benefits included elimination of food-induced eczema, reduced abdominal distension, solid stools, elimination of "panda eyes" (dark circles under the eyes), and improved body odor. No adverse physical or behavioral changes were seen in either child during the SCD diet.

Trelka says, "In no way are we suggesting that a GF/CF diet is unhelpful. Our study clearly shows the opposite is true. We are claiming, though, that in contrasting each diet's contribution to change in these girls, i.e., improved behavior and improved physiology, the SCD is clearly more effective."

The SCD eliminates nearly all starches and most sugars, allowing only monosaccharides (carbohydrates that have a molecular structure small enough for them to be readily transported from the intestine into the blood stream without requiring extensive breakdown). The diet, originally developed by pediatrician Sidney Haas, has recently received a large amount of publicity due to the work of biochemist Elaine Gottschall, whose daughter's severe digestive problems responded dramatically to the diet.

According to Gottschall, when the intestines are not functioning correctly, large carbohydrate molecules cannot be broken down and transported out of the digestive system. The result, she says, is that these molecules, rather than entering the bloodstream, remain in the intestines and serve as a source of food for bacteria and fungi. The resulting overgrowth of these bacteria and fungi causes increased acidity, which further damages the intestines; increases production of bacterial toxins and metabolic by-products of fermentation; and may cause some normally harmless bacteria to mutate into pathological forms. In addition, Gottschall says, excess mucus production triggered by damage to the intestines further inhibits the proper digestion and absorption of nutrients.

The purpose of the SCD is to "starve" undesirable intestinal bacteria and fungi by removing the large carbohydrate molecules that provide food for them. The diet consists primarily of meat, fish, eggs, fruits and vegetables, certain dairy products (including goat's milk yogurt), and nuts and seeds.

---

"Specific Carbohydrate Dietary Trial: Understanding the effectiveness of a specific carbohydrate dietary intervention in autistic children," Jeffrey Allen Trelka and Brian S. Hooker, in press.

—and—

"The gut, brain, diet connection—The Specific Carbohydrate Diet," presentation at the DAN! Conference, Los Angeles, October 2004.

—and—

*Breaking the Vicious Cycle*, Elaine Gottschall, Kirkton Press, Baltimore, Ontario, 2004.

## — Chapter 48 —

# Methylation: The Link Between Thimerosal and Autism?

By Bernard Rimland, Ph.D.
Autism Research Institute, San Diego, California

*Autism Research Review International*, 2004, Vol. 18, No. 1



Rates of autism have climbed dramatically over the past three decades, a trend paralleled by the escalating numbers of thimerosal-laden vaccines given to children since the 1970s. A possible explanation for this link comes from new research by Richard Deth and colleagues, who report that exposure to even low levels of thimerosal, a vaccine preservative that is nearly 50 percent mercury, can drastically alter a critical process called methylation.

Methylation occurs when methyl groups (molecules consisting of one carbon atom and three hydrogen atoms) are added to or subtracted from other molecules. Because this process regulates DNA function and gene expression, proper methylation is critical to normal neurological development.

Deth et al. found that methylation is stimulated by insulin-like growth factor-1 (IGF-1) and the neurotransmitter dopamine. The researchers discovered that thimerosal inhibits these pathways, even at concentrations typically found following vaccination. They also found that ethanol and lead inhibit methylation, but Deth says that thimerosal "was by far the most potent" inhibitor. Thimerosal, he says, disrupted the methylation process at doses 100 times lower than a child would receive after a single dose of a thimerosal-containing vaccine.

"Scientists certainly acknowledge that exposure to neurotoxins like ethanol and heavy metals can cause developmental disorders, but until now, the precise mechanisms underlying their toxicity have not been known," Deth says. "The recent increase in the incidence of autism led us to speculate that environmental exposures, including vaccine additives, might contribute to the triggering of this disorder."

The researchers say thimerosal appears to interfere with methylation by inhibiting the biosynthesis of methylcobalamin, the active form of vitamin B12. *(Editor's note: this finding is of particular interest because doctors using the Defeat Autism Now! [DAN!] approach are reporting dramatic improvements in many autistic children receiving injected methylcobalamin.)*

Deth says thimerosal may also play a role in attention deficit hyperactivity disorder (ADHD), another behavioral problem that is on the rise. "During the first years of life, networks of neurons that represent the matrix for learning are being developed in the brain," he says. "Methylation and the development of neuronal cells to create these networks are critical during this time. If the process is interrupted, the ability to learn and pay attention would naturally be impaired."

Reports that autism rates have not dropped since drug companies started phasing out thimerosal from some vaccines do not disprove the thimerosal-autism link, Deth says. "The epidemiological studies are looking at whole populations," he comments, "and we are trying to determine what it is about an individual kid that might make him more susceptible to this exposure."

Deth cautions that his research group's findings are preliminary, but calls for more research into the possible link between autism and thimerosal. "Up to now, people have said the cause or causes of autism are unknown," Deth says. "Our work isn't final in any sense at all, but it seems to point to this biochemistry as a potential, or even primary, cause of autism."



In 1999, the FDA requested that manufacturers eventually reduce or eliminate the mercury in vaccines, but thimerosal-containing vaccines are still being used.

---

"Activation of methionine synthase by insulin-like growth factor-1 and dopamine: a target for neurodevelopmental toxins and thimerosal," M. Waly, H. Olteanu, R. Banerjee, S. W. Choi, J. B. Mason, B. S. Parker, S. Sukumar, S. Shim, A. Sharma, J. M. Benzecry, V. A. Power-Charnitsky, and R. C. Deth, *Molecular Psychiatry*, January 27, 2004 (epub). Address: Richard C. Deth, Dept. of Pharmaceutical Sciences, Northeastern University, Boston, MA 02115.

—and—

"New research suggests link between vaccine ingredients and autism, ADHD," news release, Northeastern University, February 5, 2004.

—and—

"Study suggests vaccine, autism link," Salynn Boyles, WebMD, February 5, 2004.

—and—

"Vaccine additive linked to brain damage in children," Sharon Kirkey, Canadian Press, February 5, 2004.

## — Chapter 49 —

# The 14th DAN! Conference: An Historical Event

By Bernard Rimland, Ph.D.
Autism Research Institute, San Diego, California

*Autism Research Review International*, 2004, Vol. 18, No. 3

No doubt about it! The 14th Defeat Autism Now (DAN!) Conference held in Los Angeles October 1-3 was the best ever. The large enthusiastic crowds, the many standing ovations, and the superlatives on the attendee evaluation forms all told the same story—a truly great conference—the best yet!



The highlight of the conference was the eagerly anticipated, standing-room-only Sunday morning session at which stage and screen star Lou Diamond Phillips did a superb job of introducing, to the audience and to the media, for the first time ever, a group of recovered autistic children. There were many heartwarming and humorous moments. ("Hunter, what is the name of your soccer team?" "Gannon Plumbing.")

Although the public announcement listed October 1-3 as the Conference days, the scheduled events actually covered September 29 through October 4. A think tank of scientists and physicians involved in mercury detoxification—an extremely important treatment modality—took place on September 29 and 30. Thursday evening, September 30, was devoted to three pre-conference workshops: "Healthier Babies" (Nancy O'Hara, M.D., and Stuart Freedenfeld, M.D.); "Bioscience Behind DAN!" (Lauren Underwood, Ph.D.); and "Mercury and Autism" (Lyn Redwood, R.N.). Monday, October 4 was devoted to DAN! training sessions for MDs and RNs. Both classes were sold out.

As ARI readers are well aware, mercury toxicity, especially the mercury in vaccines, is a major issue in autism. Of the 77 biomedical interventions rated for efficacy by parents (see www.TreatmentRatings.com *[Editor's note: See also pages 382-385 of this book]*), mercury detoxification received a higher rating than any drug, supplement, or special diet. Mercury detoxification was rated helpful by 73% of parents, with the gluten/casein-free diet coming in second at 63%.

The pre-conference think tank was focused largely at updating ARI's

May 2001 Mercury Detoxification Consensus Report, posted on the ARI website. The 2004 think-tankers agreed, as had the 2001 group, that DMPS is a more effective detoxifying (chelating) agent than DMSA, but DMPS lacks FDA approval, so physicians using it risk penalties and sanctions. The group agreed it would be desirable to initiate the lengthy and expensive task of obtaining FDA approval for DMPS use in autism. ARI will do what it can to help fund and facilitate this project. An updated Mercury Detoxification Report should be completed and posted on our website by December 2004.

A number of conference speakers addressed various other aspects of the mercury/autism problem. The evidence is overwhelming, and continues to grow, that thimerosal-containing vaccines are a major cause of the worldwide autism epidemic. Father-and-son team Mark and David Geier provided compelling evidence for the role of thimerosal (mercury)-containing vaccines in causing autism and other neurodevelopmental disorders in children. The Geiers have used the Freedom of Information Act to discover major evidence of serious cover-up attempts by government agencies.



Although the toxicity of mercury has been recognized for centuries, the specific biochemistry of mercury toxicity has been unclear until very recently. The research of Richard Deth, Boyd Haley, Jill James and several other presenters at our conference has pinpointed the biochemical pathways in which mercury damage is implicated, and thus clarified the measures required for remediation. Much of this breakthrough-level research has been funded by the Autism Research Institute.

Another major topic addressed by several conference speakers is the role of special diets in the treatment of autism. Digestive problems, many of which are the result of heavy-metal toxicity, are very common in autistic children. Lisa Lewis, Ph.D., provided a very informative update on the gluten-free, casein-free (GFCF) diet, about which she has written extensively.

A major development in the treatment of autism is the Specific Carbohydrate Diet (SCD) which was discussed by the SCD's major pioneer and advocate, Elaine Gottschall. The SCD is designed to provide the patient with adequate nourishment while carefully avoiding foods which foster the growth of intestinal microbes which produce toxins that cause or aggravate the symptoms of autism. Pediatrician Sid Baker, who along with Jon Pangborn and me founded the DAN! Project in 1995, has become a strong advocate of the SCD diet. His talk included presentations by three very savvy and experienced mothers whose children had remained severely autistic despite the best efforts of the best doctors. Only the SCD diet made a difference, and in each case the difference was huge. Elaine Gottschall's book *Breaking the Vicious Cycle* is now available from ARI. See publication list on www.AutismResearchInstitute.com. SCD information may be found at www.pecanbread.com.

The remarkable effectiveness of injected methylcobalamin, a form of vitamin B12, was discussed by Jim Neubrander, M.D.

Gastroenterologists Andrew Wakefield, M.D., Arthur Krigsman, M.D., and Sophie Rosseneu, M.D., provided interesting and informative lectures on the nature and treatment of the gastrointestinal problems which are a very common feature of the regressive form of autism. Regressive, or late onset, autism constitutes the majority of cases in the worldwide autism epidemic.

Jane El-Dahr, M.D., and Aristo Vojdani, Ph.D., discussed new findings and new treatments, addressing the role of the immune system in autism.

A number of speakers provided valuable insights on the specific measures needed to bring about significant improvement in autistic children, using the DAN! approach. These included Sid Baker, M.D., Anju Usman, M.D., Andrew Levinson, M.D., Lynn Hamilton, Jerry Kartzinel, M.D., Jacquelyn McCandless, M.D., Ken Bock, M.D., Jeff Bradstreet, M.D., and a parent panel titled "Successfully Treating Autism" moderated by Stephen M. Edelson, Ph.D, and me.



Paul Hardy, M.D., addressed the emerging field of nutraceuticals—the use of plants and nutrients extracted from plants—in the treatment of autism.

Martha Herbert, M.D., Ph.D., spoke about recent developments in brain research as it pertains to autism, and Marvin Boris, M.D., and Alan Goldblatt, P.A.C., presented their findings on newly emerging information about the role of genetics in the causation of autism.

Doreen Granpeesheh, Ph.D., discussed her work at the Center for Autism and Related Disorders (CARD) and offered valuable advice for the parents of newly diagnosed children. CARD is the only ABA organization that endorses and practices the biomedical interventions associated with autism. She provided a number of case study demonstrations of the efficacy of the combined DAN! and ABA approaches.

Those who were unable to attend the conference may still benefit from the vast amount of information presented. The conference was videotaped and audiotaped, and copies of the conference syllabus are available. For the first time, we will be broadcasting highlights of the conference on the Internet. See www.ARIWebConference.com for further information.

## — Chapter 50 —

# Two Letters to the Editor: Physician, Mom, Offer Success Stories

By Bernard Rimland, Ph.D.
Autism Research Institute, San Diego, California

*Autism Research Review International,* 2004, Vol. 18, No. 1

To the Editor:

With my years of experience dealing with hundreds of children suffering from autism in the Gulf and the Middle East area, there is no doubt in my mind concerning the importance of using supplements (high doses of B6 and magnesium, DMG, essential fatty acids, etc.) as well as a gluten- and casein-free (GFCF) diet. My patients are the greatest proof of this.



One of my patients, a ten-year-old boy diagnosed with autism, was put on the dietary treatments and nutritional supplements. He exhibited great improvement, as he became much calmer, followed directions, became more alert, had better eye contact, and progressed considerably at school. He remained on the protocol for the last three years, continually improving. A month ago, however, access to the supplements became a problem and he was forced to continue without them for 20 days, while at the same time not completely following the GFCF diet. As a result, he became hyperactive and aggressive, and exhibited all of his former symptoms. The diet, as well as the supplements, were resumed directly after, resulting in dramatic improvement in his behavior and communication.

Another child was diagnosed much earlier, at the age of four. He was put on the same regimen for four years and improved to the point where he was placed in a high-functioning student class at his school for special needs. For personal reasons, the parents decided to take him off the protocol, leading to a complete relapse. His school even began to feel his behavior was so extreme they could not keep him. This pushed his parents to return to the protocol, after which he improved radically, both at home and at school.

These are only two of the many cases I encountered where supplements and a GFCF diet have made a remarkable difference in the lives of these children and their families. I hope people begin to recognize how important and necessary these supplements are for children with autism, as well as other developmental disorders. Although some children may not benefit from the supplements, it would be a serious shame to deprive the majority that would.

—Abeer Awadh, M.D., Ph.D., Consultant Developmental Pediatrician

To the Editor:

Thank you for the wonderful improvements in my seven-year-old daughter. She was diagnosed in 1999 with severe autism. I stumbled upon your website shortly afterward. I learned about ABA therapy and ran out to buy the Lovaas book and begin therapy with her.... I also got occupational and speech therapy. She responded some to therapy, but the behaviors were still out of control.

Later, I read about the GFCF diet and supplements and implemented that with good results. Then, in 2001, I attended a DAN! Conference and decided to try the DAN! approach. I took our daughter to see DAN! doctors who prescribed compounded nutrients for her chemical imbalances. I also read Dr. Bradstreet's website and had her IgG and IgA subclasses checked only to find a severe immune deficiency, [so] IVIg was started. Our daughter made remarkable progress and was being mainstreamed in school.



At her last appointment, the DAN! doctors found that her copper was still very elevated.... I found that the juice boxes that I purchased contained added copper. I immediately stopped giving her those and added B12 (methylcobalamin) per their recommendation. Everyone who knows her can't believe the difference they saw in her within a three-day period [as a result].

Our daughter is now going to a typical school without any therapy or assistance. Her teachers told me they have never seen anyone make progress like this before. Even though our daughter is completely back she still has some autistic traits. Sometimes she doesn't look us in the eye or she starts acting a little goofy, but that's okay because she tells us she loves us and she means it with her whole heart. She is no longer aloof. She responds to our questions, jokes with us and even blames her little brother for messes she makes.

Our daughter was tested this week by the school district, and is testing at the average to above-average mark academically. She has lost her diagnosis for autism. When she was first diagnosed at three-and-a-half, she was testing in the range of nine months to two years old.... Every day I watch her thrive, and every day I have to pinch myself to make sure this is real.

—A Mom in San Clemente

— Chapter 51 —

# Hyperbaric Oxygen Therapy: Dramatic Results Reported in Treating "Untreatable" Long-Term Neurological Damage

By Bernard Rimland, Ph.D.
Autism Research Institute, San Diego, California

*Autism Research Review International,* 2005, Vol. 19, No. 3

Two recent studies offer support for the use of hyperbaric oxygen therapy (HBOT) as a treatment for neurological disorders. The first, by Kenneth Stoller and colleagues, indicates that HBOT—an intervention being used increasingly for autistic children—can cause improvement even in children with long-standing structural brain damage. The second, by Stephen Thom and colleagues, indicates that HBOT mobilizes stem cells which can repair damage to the brain.



**Stoller et al.: HBOT reverses some FAS symptoms**

Kenneth Stoller used low-pressure HBOT to treat a 15-year-old boy with Fetal Alcohol Syndrome, a condition causing brain abnormalities leading to mental impairment and learning and behavioral problems. The boy underwent 40 HBOT sessions, followed seven months later by an additional 33 sessions, each lasting 60 minutes.

Stoller reports that following the first round of treatments, the boy showed improvement in all six categories on a neuropsychological test battery. He maintained his gains in verbal memory, and continued to exhibit lower levels of impulsive behavior, at a six-month follow-up after treatment. After 33 additional treatments, Stoller says, "[the subject's] verbal memory was 95 percent (pretreatment 55 percent), visual memory was 57 percent (pretreatment 38 percent), reaction time was 0.64 second (pretreatment 1.03 second), visual motor speed score was 20.1 (pretreatment 18.6 [higher score is better]) and all previously reported symptoms resolved."

Stoller says that his findings indicate that "it is time to revise the old concept that brain injury is a condition for which there is no treatment other than supportive measures." He cites research showing that stem cells in the adult brain can cause neural regeneration, a process that is oxygen-dependent. Stoller also says that the retinal damage that sometimes results from hyperbaric oxygen therapy should not be an issue in treating neurological disorders that do not stem directly from hypoxia, as it appears to be the hypoxia—rather than the HBOT itself—that sets the stage for this complication. He concludes, "Low-pressure hyperbaric oxygen therapy is a therapy with an extremely low-risk profile and relatively low cost, with potential benefits that seem to be significant and measurable for a condition considered incurable."

Stoller's findings are consistent with the anecdotal reports of a number of physicians using HBOT, sometimes in conjunction with chelation, to treat autistic children. One of these physicians, Paul Harch, testified before the U.S. House of Representatives in 2004 that HBOT causes marked improvement in brain blood flow pattern, often leading to significant improvement. For instance, Harch testified, one child he treated with HBOT "was able to be weaned from the powerful psychoactive drugs Ritalin and Prozac, and improve his emotional outbursts, autistic behavior, ability to play sports and attend school." Harch testified that the combination of HBOT and chelation appears to be more successful than the use of either therapy alone.



### Thom et al.: HBOT mobilizes stem cells

In a study to be published in April, Stephen Thom et al. report that positive effects of HBOT may arise from its ability to mobilize stem cells. When mobilized, stem cells can move from the marrow and differentiate into different types of cells that can aid in repairing damage to the brain or other organs.

Thom et al. studied 26 patients undergoing HBOT, and found that a standard course of HBOT therapy increased by eightfold the number of stem cells circulating in the human body. An analysis of mice exposed to HBOT revealed that the treatment increases synthesis of nitric oxide, which in turn triggers enzymes that mediate stem cell release.

"This is the safest way clinically to increase stem cell circulation," Thom says, "far safer than any of the pharmaceutical options."

Editor's Note: ARI, and its Defeat Autism Now! (DAN!) Project, have hosted several think tanks and HBOT research planning meetings. Plans for conducting carefully designed HBOT evaluation studies are underway.

---

"Quantification of neurocognitive changes before, during, and after hyperbaric oxygen therapy in a case of fetal alcohol syndrome," Kenneth P. Stoller, *Pediatrics*, Vol. 116, No. 4, October 2005, e586-e591. Address: Kenneth P. Stoller, 404 Brunn School Road #D, Santa Fe, NM 87505, hbotnm@netzero.net.

—and—

"Announcement of a new treatment protocol for autism spectrum disorders and other neurological impairments," Paul Harch, testimony on behalf of the International Hyperbaric Medical Association Foundation, presented at the May 6, 2004 United States House of Representatives Hearing on "Autism spectrum disorders: An update of federal government initiatives and revolutionary new treatments of neurodevelopmental diseases."

—and—

"Stem cell mobilization by hyperbaric oxygen," Stephen R. Thom, Veena M. Bhopale, Omaida C. Velazquez, Lee J. Goldstein, Lynne H. Thom, and Donald G. Buerk, *American Journal of Physiology-Heart and Circulation Physiology*, November 18, 2005 (epub in advance of publication). Address: Stephen R. Thom, Institute for Environmental Medicine, University of Pennsylvania, 1 John Morgan Building, 3620 Hamilton Walk, Philadelphia, PA 19104, sthom@mail.med.upenn.edu.

—and—

"Hyperbaric oxygen treatments mobilize stem cells," review article by Priya Saxena, *RxPG News*, January 1, 2006.

## — Chapter 52 —

# Medical Marijuana: A Valuable Treatment for Autism?

By Bernard Rimland, Ph.D.
Autism Research Institute, San Diego, California

*Autism Research Review International,* 2003, Vol. 17, No. 1

I am certainly not an advocate for drugs—either legal or illicit. I have never smoked and I don't care at all for alcohol. And I agree with Oliver Wendell Holmes when he said, "I firmly believe that if the whole *materia medica* could be sunk to the bottom of the sea it would all the better for mankind and all the worse for the fishes."



Having said that:

In ARRI 16-2 we published a letter from a mother in Florida whose very large autistic son changed from a sweet, loving boy to a teenager who flew into unpredictable rages which "were usually associated with self injury, aggression and property damage." She went on, "At times I had to lock myself in the bathroom; otherwise he would attack me. We gave him many medications, but nothing worked."

A friend suggested a solution: a brownie with marijuana baked into it. "Soon after he ate the brownie," she said, "my son's anxiety disappeared, and his sweet, loving behavior returned. He shows no signs of being under the influence of a drug. He now receives one marijuana brownie and several doses of Marinol, which contains the active ingredient in marijuana, each day. This has clearly saved my child's life and my family's life."

In a letter to the editor published in the ARRI, Ray Gallup, a well-known autism activist in New Jersey, describes his teenage son who has become extremely assaultive, sending members of his family to the hospital and requiring police intervention on a number of occasions. Like Ray, thousands of parents are dealing with children who are so out of control, and so violent to themselves and others, that they can make their own lives and that of their families hellish.

In ARRI 16-1 we published an editorial on various means of dealing with such severely self-injurious and assaultive behavior, but marijuana use was not an approach that we mentioned. Many drugs are used to control these kinds of behaviors in autistic individuals, including risperidone (Risperdal), which has a large range of highly toxic effects (ARRI 16-4). It seems to me if one is going to need to use drugs, one ought to consider a relatively safe drug, like marijuana, if research bears out the good results that a number of parents have reported.

I use the term "relatively safe" because marijuana and Marinol, the prescription drug that contains the active marijuana ingredient tetrahydrocannabinol (THC), do cause adverse effects—but these effects, evidence suggests, are generally much less harmful than those caused by psychotropic drugs. Marijuana may cause subtle long-term memory and cognitive decrements, although evidence is equivocal. The drug can cause cardiovascular problems including abnormally high or low blood pressure, fainting, or abnormal heartbeat, can exacerbate depression or other mental changes in vulnerable individuals, and can cause nausea, vomiting, weakness, or sedation. The word is still out as to whether orally ingested marijuana is carcinogenic (although there is some evidence suggesting that it is *anti*-carcinogenic), and there is some concern that it can precipitate schizophrenic symptoms in some individuals. Also, the drug can cause dependency and possibly birth defects.



Clearly, medical marijuana is not a drug to be administered lightly. But compare its side effects to the known effects of Risperdal, which include massive weight gain, a dramatically increased risk of diabetes, and an elevated risk of deadly heart problems, as well as a host of other major and minor problems. Other psychotropic drugs are no safer, causing symptoms ranging from debilitating tardive dyskinesia to life-threatening malignant hyperthermia or sudden cardiac arrest. Of all drugs, the psychotropic drugs are among the least useful and most dangerous, and the benefit/risk profile of medical marijuana seems fairly benign in comparison.

Moreover, the reports we are seeing from parents indicate that medical marijuana often works when no other treatments, drug or non-drug, have helped. Among the comments received by a parent soliciting feedback from other parents who are using this treatment for autistic individuals:

• "I know it's not the end-all answer, but it's been the best answer for the longest time for us in [comparison] to ALL the other medications. I cannot tell you how many months we would go on a medication wondering if it was doing anything, anything at all. Here we can see the difference in 30 to 60 minutes."

• "My son (who is almost nine years old) has been on medications to address his severe autistic behaviors.... None of the medications has ever made a difference, except for making his behaviors worse.... A few months ago we tried the prescription drug Marinol and noticed a drop in the severe episodes, no fits and little to no aggression toward his teacher and family members on a daily basis. A few weeks ago we started him on cannabis and stopped the Marinol. He has been in a much better mood and is much easier to keep on task in the classroom now.... He still has days when he gets angry and moody, but we can adjust the dose to help him through those days.... I feel much more comfortable administering cannabis than something like Risperdal."

According to information ARRI has received, medical marijuana is not legal in many states. Information on whether or not medical marijuana can be legally prescribed in your state is available on the Internet, at www.mpp.org. Additional information can be found at www.maps.org/mmj, www.NORML.org, and www.druglibrary.org.

It is important to keep in mind the distinction between legalizing marijuana for medical uses, which has been done in some states, and "recreational" drug use which is illegal throughout the U.S. Judging from the evidence in hand, I believe legalization of medical use is justified. Legalizing marijuana for nonmedical use (as has been done for alcohol) is quite another issue.



Even if medical marijuana can be legally prescribed in your state, doctors are likely to be very reluctant to help you obtain the drug. You may be able to obtain information or help from local AIDS awareness and advocacy groups, which have been in the forefront of making medical marijuana available to the public.

If you decide to try this approach, the Autism Research Institute would very much like to learn about the results—positive or negative. We are also interested in hearing from physicians with expert knowledge about the benefits and adverse effects of either short-term or long-term use of medical marijuana.

Again, I stress that I am strongly opposed to drugs in general, and consider them a last resort to be employed only when safer and more efficacious treatments fail. But while I am not "pro-drug," I am very much "pro-safe and effective treatment," especially in cases where an autistic individual's behaviors are dangerous or destructive. Early evidence suggests that in such cases, medical marijuana may be a beneficial treatment, as well as being less harmful than the drugs that doctors routinely prescribe.

---

A two-page letter provided to ARI by a parent, providing additional information about medical marijuana and a list of more than 20 websites on the topic, is available upon request. Fax ARI (619-563-6840) or send a self-addressed, stamped envelope and specify that you would like Marinol information.

---

*"Medical Marijuana"*

To the Editor: *[Vol. 17, No. 2, 2003]*

I deeply respect you and your work and I would hate to see your views on the possible role of THC in the amelioration of some destructive or dangerous behaviors in some autistic persons (which I agree with) "hijacked" by advocates for the legalization of marijuana for recreational use to support their position.

In my view, unless you make a clear distinction between the use of Marinol (dronabinol—delta-9-THC), which is now a legitimately available, by prescription, Schedule II controlled substance, and the use of smoked marijuana—"smoked dope"—you will be unwittingly drawn into the sham of using the "medical marijuana" debate as a front to make marijuana more generally available for recreational use. The mantra goes, "If marijuana is good for cancer patients (and now autistic patients) it can't be all that bad for the rest of us." In my practice and drug treatment programs I have established, I have seen too much damage to too many children and adolescents for that to occur.



As my 1991 article (see Ref. 1) explains, Marinol is presently available as a Schedule II drug for prescription in all states. While treatment of some autistic behaviors is an "off-label" use according to the PDR, it is a presently available, standardized dose of a pure substance in a conventional delivery method (capsule). If smoked marijuana were to be cleared by the FDA for medical purposes, it would be the only drug using smoking as a delivery system (and a very poor one) at the time when, I thought, we were discouraging smoking. The reasons why advocates for legalizing marijuana for recreational use are so disinterested in Marinol are also outlined in my article: the onset of action is slow and gradual, it is only weakly reinforcing, it has no street value, and it produces dysphoria rather than euphoria. What is needed is some careful study of Marinol's effectiveness in treating the kind of behaviors you list, followed by an effort to get those behaviors listed as "on label" if Marinol proves to be effective in reducing these behaviors.

My 1983 article (Ref. 2) notes that TCH relieved symptoms in some cancer chemotherapy patients, but that adverse side effects were prevalent and that questions about the drug's safety and effectiveness needed to be resolved. Since that time Marinol has become available, and later studies echo our earlier results. The third reference is an article I did on the detrimental effects of marijuana on some cases of otherwise well-controlled schizophrenia.

I support the study of THC and its use in autism by prescription if it proves to be effective, but that is not "medical marijuana" use as advocates for legalized recreational marijuana refer to it, and should not be used to do the wrong thing for the wrong reasons.

—Darold A. Treffert, M.D.

1. "Medical marijuana: It's déjà vu all over again," Darold A. Treffert, *Wisconsin Psychiatrist*, Spring 1999.
2. Delta-9-Tetrahydrocannabinol and therapeutic research legislation for cancer patients," Darold A. Treffert and David E. Joranson, *Journal of the American Medical Association*, Vol. 249, No. 11, March 18, 1983, 1469-72.
3. "Marijuana use in schizophrenia: A clear hazard," Darold A. Treffert, *American Journal of Psychiatry*, Vol. 135, No. 10, October 1978, 1213-5.



Editor's Note: Dr. Treffert is a longtime researcher on autism and the author of the excellent book on autistic and other savants, *Extraordinary People.*

---

Editor's note: We have received several letters in response to Dr. Darold Treffert's comments on our editorial on marijuana use in autism. Below are two of these responses, as well as a reply from Dr. Treffert.

To the Editor: *[Vol. 17, No. 3, 2003]*

I read with great dismay Dr. Treffert's letter to you re medical marijuana. Without ingesting the pure plant in various ways that their loving parents have to devise, [some children currently using marijuana] are so agitated that they cannot stop themselves from hitting those they love, hitting themselves, biting themselves. Their parents have tried every drug on the market, every single one. Shall they think about their children's future in an institution, being locked up, injured or tied down and drugged into a stupor so that they will not hurt themselves or others?

We have tried Marinol. For whatever the reason, as with so many of the other drugs that have been prescribed, it has caused our children to become only more agitated. [On marijuana] these children do not become stoned… they become calm, they return to their sweet beings, and they are grateful.

—East Coast Mother

To the Editor: *[Vol. 17, No. 3, 2003]*

Marinol was effective for my son for a very few months. I now believe that this medication was effective only because he was also receiving the full cannabinoid profile through other means. Marinol has been of no value to other boys and of limited value to one young woman. I consider it a total waste of time.

My son and other boys use [marijuana] cookies, candies and Happy Caps. Cooking oils and tincture are used by some other children. The race to find effective and simple methods of delivery never stops.

Cannabis is a safe and effective alternative to the potential liver- and brain-damaging psychiatric drugs. We also need to understand that the drug companies are the major beneficiaries of this use and not our children. Cannabis use puts no money into the major drug companies' pockets, so it will always be attacked by the establishment. This is NOT a pro/anti drug issue. This is a medical and scientific issue and patients' welfare and indeed lives depend upon rational and compassionate decisions versus the drug war farce that has warped the debate.

Yes, parents who have experienced cannabis helping their children when nothing else did, want to use it legally, of course! MS patients feel the same way. So do patients with chronic arthritis, hepatitis C, diabetes, Crohn's, irritable bowel syndrome, Parkinson's, and so many other illnesses for which there is little relief or the medicines are terribly toxic.

—Joe's Mom

Dr. Treffert replies: *[Vol. 17, No. 3, 2003]*

The plea by families for a rapid and unencumbered search for treatment modalities that help with very difficult behaviors in some autistic persons is certainly understandable, as is the frustration they feel when those treatments are not readily available. But proceeding more deliberately should not be confused with callousness, distance or insensitivity to those families, because the readily available, legal use of marijuana and cannabis compounds in autism treatment, given all the conflict and various agendas surrounding marijuana, will occur only when clinical trials have determined appropriateness, effectiveness, a simple and reliable delivery system, and safety of these compounds.

Marinol is a beginning effort in that regard, albeit an imperfect one. The search for more effective compounds should continue. Centers have been established now, such as the University of California Center for Medicinal Cannabis Research, and hopefully from these and other centers will come, quickly, reliable answers as to the safety and efficacy of cannabis and cannabis compounds for the treatment of a number of medical conditions, and information as to how this might apply to autistic disorders.

Meanwhile the search should continue as well for other medications or compounds that are helpful, without some of the side effects and other problems those medications have presented to date. The good news is that some of these more recent compounds do show such promise. That such a search will continue to be helpful is my hope and the direction in which I feel we ought to proceed in a considered, and considerate, manner.

—Darold A. Treffert, M.D.

## — Chapter 53 —

# Clinical Use of Methyl-B12 in Autism

By Jaquelyn McCandless, M.D.

*Autism Research Review International*, 2006, Vol. 19, No. 3

*The Autism Research Institute has received many positive reports from clinicians and parents on the use of methyl-B12 on autistic children. We would like to thank Jaquelyn McCandless, author of* Children with Starving Brains, *for writing this article.*

---

One of the most important treatment modalities to come out of the strong focus on biomedical and metabolic aspects in autism in recent years is the use of injectable methylcobalamin, or methyl-B12. The evidence for transmethylation defects in autism disorders was already starting to accrue thanks to talented researchers helping us to understand the basic science behind our clinical observation that certain nutrients help these children.



In May 2002 my DAN! colleague and friend Dr. James Neubrander made the "accidental" discovery that showed him methyl-B12's profound effect on autism. Experimenting with different members of the cobalamin family, Dr. Neubrander was able to ascertain that the benefits of methylcobalamin far surpassed the cyanocobalamin and hydroxycobalmin forms used for autism prior to 2002. Since every cell in the body expresses the folate/methionine cycle, defects in transmethylation can affect vital biochemical reactions at many places in intermediary metabolism. At the 2003 Fall DAN! conference we heard researcher Jill James, Ph.D., from University of Arkansas for Medical Sciences discuss impairment in transulfuration and the resulting oxidative stress that occurs in ASD from depletion of glutathione, the major intracellular antioxidant essential for detoxification in the body. Her studies using certain nutrients showed a highly significant increase in plasma methionine, cysteine, and glutathione after only three weeks.

Because of Dr. Neubrander's work, methyl-B12 was provided for eight of the 20 children in Dr. James' group. These eight children continued on their dietary schedule for 3-4 months with the added injectable methyl-B12 and results were even more positive, suggesting that methylation capacity and antioxidant potential can be increased with obvious clinical benefits in ASD children. The dietary nutrients Dr. James showed as supportive of methionine synthesis were: zinc, folinic acid, methyl-B12, choline, and betaine (TMG), later seen as part of an alternate pathway and only helpful for a small percentage of children. This exciting presentation at the DAN! was followed by that of Richard Deth, Ph.D., from Northeast University, where he described his research showing the effects of thimerosal on methionine synthase and emphasized the devastating role this neurotoxin can have in the disordered methylation in our afflicted children. We had been finding more every day about how sulfhydryl (SH) reactive metals such as mercury, lead, arsenic, and cadmium appeared to be "triggers" for multiple disease symptoms in ASD. Dr. Deth's studies showed how thimerosal alters methionine synthesis activity with the potential to disrupt normal development via its neurotoxic effect on DNA methylation and gene expression. His studies lent tremendous credence to the importance of methylation disorders and their treatment in autism. Prior to my DAN! presentation in Spring 2005 I queried three of the more popular compounding pharmacies for the number of autistic children for whom they were providing the methyl-B12 injectables, and the total was 4,500 children being given injections two or three times per week at that time. By now it is being used all over the United States and in many other countries all over the world.



Methyl-B12 is estimated to be active and effective to some degree in 80-90% of ASD children. Dr. Neubrander has an elegant Parent Designed Report Form which helps parents assess whether their child is a responder, downloadable for free from his website www.drneubrander.com. He advises parents to make no changes in their child's nutrient program when adding the methyl-B12 for a period of five weeks to see how responses show its effect. Then he adds folinic acid and any other nutrients that testing has shown the child needs, as he agrees with the DAN! principle that these children need a broad-spectrum treatment approach. Though the parent form looks for many possible responses, the primary ones for methyl-B12 are executive function, speech, language, socialization, and emotion. However, Dr. Neubrander fears that if parents only look for these signs, they may give up before adequately utilizing this treatment, and feels that if given in the right dosage, timing, and form that up to 94% will show benefit.

Besides the myths that methyl-B12 only works in 30-40% of ASD children, other myths Dr. Neubrander would like to dispel is:

1) That this nutrient works better for younger children.

2) That oral, sublingual, transdermal, or intramuscular routes are just

as effective as the subcutaneous injections. (At the present time, a nasal spray has been introduced that has become popular with parents who do not want to give their children injections; many of us are testing to compare this with the tried and true subcutaneous route, and the jury is still out at this time).

3) That the concentration of the methyl-B12 solution does not matter as long as the total dose remains the same. (Many tests have shown that the 25 mg/ml injections at 64.5 mcg/kg every three days is the optimal dose, volume, and frequency.)

4) That the fat in the arm, abdomen, or thigh produce the same results as from the fatty part of the buttocks.

Lowering the dose until side effects disappear is a mistake—the children with the most side effects who stay with the course are the ones who make the most recovery. However, side effects must be dealt with—the most common are hyperactivity with or without increased "stimming," changes in sleep patterns, and increased mouthing (not pica, or eating of nonfood item) of objects.



Dr. Neubrander agrees that certain side effects are an indication to stop this nutrient, such as an older child becoming uncontrollable and potentially dangerous to others or side effects that are so disruptive that a child can no longer function or learn. However, he encourages parents to continue as long as a child can learn, attend to tasks, and stay focused in a controlled situation no matter how much increased activity there may be at home when the child can just let loose. Mouthing objects is a sign that previously inactivated peripheral nerves are waking up and this represents a "positive negative" and a sign that the methyl-B12 is working. Within two to six months the majority of side effects diminish or disappear completely while the child continues to improve.

Other caveats: Use a good compounding pharmacy that knows how to make the proper dose as recommended by Dr. Neubrander. Do not pinch the fat for the injection. Inject as narrow an angle as possible to avoid hitting any muscle; pink urine means you injected too deeply. The shots if given correctly are seldom painful. There is no way if proper needles (BD 3/10 cc insulin syringe with an 8 mm, 31-gauge needle, item #328438 only) and injection technique are used that the sciatic nerve could possibly be injured, even in the smallest baby. There is no way to test who will or will not be a responder to methyl-B12. Blood B12 levels are high-normal in almost all children documented to be responders. Though there may be a high level in the blood, it is in an oxidized form that cannot be reduced and recycled. Genomic testing is not yet advanced enough to reliably predict response, as these tests may miss the majority of children that clinically respond and should be treated. The only way to know if your child is one of the majority of autistic children that will benefit from this important treatment with methyl-B12 is to use it. This is one of the important DAN! biomedical interventions along with dietary restriction, nutrients, attaining gut health, detoxification, and immune enhancing strategies that are improving and even recovering more and more autistic children every day now.

# — Chapter 54 —
# New Therapy: Low-Dose Naltrexone for Immunomodulation

By Jaquelyn McCandless, M.D

*Autism Research Review International*, 2006, Vol. 20, No. 2

*Thanks to DAN! doctor Jaquelyn McCandless, author of* Children with Starving Brains, *for providing this report on a very promising new treatment.*

---



Naltrexone is an FDA-approved drug used as an opiate antagonist for treating opiate drug and alcohol addiction since the 1970s, available in generic form as well as under the brand name ReVia, in 50 mg tablets. At regular dosing, usually 50 mg a day, it blocks the euphoric response to opiate drugs such as heroin or morphine.

Opioids are known to operate as cytokines, the principal communication signalers of the immune system, creating immunomodulatory effects through opioid receptors on immune cells. A popular immune classification method is referred to as the Th1/Th2 balance: Th1 cells promote cell-mediated immunity, while Th2 cells induce humoral immunity. The inability to respond adequately with a Th1 response can result in chronic infection and cancer; an overactive Th2 response can contribute to allergies and various syndromes and play a role in autoimmune disease, which most autism spectrum children show on immune testing. The November 13, 2003 issue of the *New England Journal of Medicine* notes: "Preclinical evidence indicates overwhelmingly that opioids alter the development, differentiation, and function of immune cells, and that both innate and adaptive systems are affected."

Bernard Bihari, M.D., a New York physician studying the immune responses in AIDS patients, discovered that a very low dose of naltrexone, approximately one-tenth the usual dosage, boosts the immune system and helps fight diseases characterized by inadequate immune function. Low-dose naltrexone (LDN) tends to normalize the immune system by elevating the body's endorphin levels, and accomplishes its results with virtually no side effects or toxicity; naltrexone is considered very safe and has never been reported as being addicting. When this tiny dose of naltrexone is given between 9 p.m. and midnight, the body attempts to overcome the opioid block and the endorphins rise, to stay elevated throughout the next 18 hours. Studies in human cancer patients show that LDN acts to increase natural killer cells and other healthy immune defenses against cancer. Restoration of the body's normal production of endorphins in those with cancer or autoimmune diseases is the major therapeutic action of LDN.

The use of LDN for children with autism spectrum disorders was previously studied in the 1990s, with researchers using from 5 to 50 mg daily or every other day. In these trials, researchers were looking for opioid antagonism. Panksepp and other researchers noted better results with low doses; studies on higher doses were more equivocal in children, with noncompliance due to the bitterness of the drug. For my study, Dr. Tyrus Smith at Coastal Compounding agreed to create a transdermal cream. This allowed us to adjust the dose easily (some of the smaller kids did better with only 1-1/2 mg), the bitter taste was no problem, and the cream could be put on the patients' bodies while they slept. The cream is put into syringes, with 1/2 cc providing 3 mg for children or 4.5 mg for adults; most adults prefer capsules; both are equally effective.



I recently completed an eight-week informal clinical study on 15 of my autism spectrum disorder patients using 3 mg of LDN transdermally between 9:00 and 12:00 p.m. Several adults participated also, one with Crohn's Disease and one with Chronic Fatigue Syndrome using 4.5 mg nightly. Parents reported weekly on the results of the treatment.

Eight of the 15 children in this study had positive responses, with five of these eight having results considered quite phenomenal according to their parents. The primary positive responses have been in the area of mood, cognition, language, and socialization. Five of the children had equivocal results and three children dropped out, one because of no response after four weeks and the others for non-drug related issues. Two small children responded better when changed to 1-1/2 mg dosing. No allergic reactions were noted, and the primary negative side effect was insomnia and earlier awakening when the cream was first administered. The two adults in the study had very positive responses, and the Crohn's participant says she has been in remission since starting LDN (almost three months now).

All of the children in my study were on well-controlled dietary restriction. I am receiving reports from the e-lists I monitor of about five percent of other children having side effects such as irritability, agitation, and restlessness, subsiding as soon as the drug is withdrawn. I am querying these parents about gluten/casein/soy in the children's diets, as this response is very likely indicative of withdrawal symptoms of opioid block. I suspect that children on a strict GF/CF/SF diet are less apt to show this response.

I do not know the cause of the immediate positive mood/cognitive/relating effects seen in the children in my study; it is unlikely the immune benefits are showing this quickly. For other autoimmune groups, the evidence is that the optimum immune response can take four to six months.

I am hoping LDN will be another weapon in our ever-expanding arsenal to help children with autism spectrum disorders become as immune-efficient as possible. Clinical responses must be what we go on for now, as it will take time to get a research study done. Evaluative lab tests show that the majority of our children have autoimmune issues. In my opinion an intervention that is effective, nontoxic, non-invasive, and inexpensive is worth a try.

I want to thank my trusting patients who participated in the study, as well as Dr. Tyrus Smith at Coastal Compounding for helping devise a successful form of LDN to use for our children. (Dr. Smith has offered to share his formula with any compounding pharmacist who wishes to call him; his number is 912-354-5188.) I have started a Yahoo e-list for reporting and discussion of this intervention at Autism_LDN@yahoogroups.com.

## — Chapter 55 —

# Chelation: The Story Behind the Headlines

By Bernard Rimland, Ph.D.
Autism Research Institute, San Diego, California

*Autism Research Review International*, 2005, Vol. 19, No. 3

"Death of boy linked to controversial chelation therapy," the headlines shouted. The tragic story of a young autistic boy who died after suffering cardiac arrest following a round of chelation therapy provided mainstream physicians with a golden opportunity to crow about "quackery," foolish and impressionable parents "grasping for straws," and the dangers of "unproven" alternative treatments for autism.



To my knowledge, none of these doctors retracted their comments following the recent report issued by Mary Jean Brown of the Centers for Disease Control and Prevention. According to Brown, the boy's death resulted, quite simply, from a drug error. The problem, according to Brown: a "look-alike" drug, Disodium EDTA, was mistakenly used instead of Calcium Disodium EDTA. Brown stated that "without a doubt" the mix-up caused the boy's cardiac arrest, and she noted moreover that the correct treatment is virtually harmless.

So we have one tragic death, resulting *not* from proper chelation procedures as used by hundreds of doctors, but apparently from a medical mistake. Weighed against this, we have tens of thousands of children and hundreds of thousands of adults who have been treated safely with chelation therapy for decades. According to physician Ralph Miranda, former president of the American College for Advancement in Medicine, there have been no deaths associated with correctly performed chelation in the past 50 years.

Since 1967 The Autism Research Institute has collected "Parent Ratings of Behavioral Effects of Biomedical Interventions." To date, almost 25,000 parent responses have been collected. Chelation is a recent addition to our list of interventions. So far, of the first 470 parents who reported on the efficacy of chelation, 75% report "good" results, which is by far the highest "good" percentage reported for any of the 88 biomedical interventions (including 53 drugs) the parents have rated (see www.TreatmentRatings.com). *[Editors' note: See also pages 382-385 of this book.]*

Nevertheless, mainstream medical authorities would have us believe that chelation therapy—which now has a proven track record of thousands of children helped, and *no deaths due to properly performed treatment*—is a radical, dangerous, and improper treatment. Similarly, they say, nutritional approaches to autism treatment, such as megavitamin therapy, are unproven and possibly harmful. The only proper medical treatments for autism, these "experts" say, are drugs such as Risperdal, Ritalin, antidepressants, and other psychotropic medications.

Really? Let's look at just how safe those drugs are.

—Risperdal is one of the favorite drugs of doctors treating autism. It is linked to dangerous and potentially fatal alterations in blood sugar levels, and to a life-threatening condition called malignant neuroleptic syndrome. It is implicated as a cause of cholestatic hepatitis, causes massive weight gain in many users, and is also a suspected cause of benign pituitary tumors).

—Olanzapine is another popular psychotropic drug. In 2004, doctors in the U.K. reported on the deaths of three patients who developed hyperglycemic ketoacidosis as a result of olanzapine treatment.

—According to psychologist John Breeding, "One hundred and sixty Ritalin-related deaths were reported to the FDA between 1990 and 1997, mostly cardiovascular in nature."



—The Canadian government recently suspended the use of the ADHD drug Strattera, after the ADHD drug was linked to 20 deaths. The response of the U.S. Food and Drug Administration? "As with any drug, FDA will continue to carefully assess any new data that emerges which significantly affects the safety profile of this drug and will take immediate, appropriate action to promote the public health and make the public aware of its findings." (In other words, "Twenty deaths aren't enough to worry us.")

—The antipsychotic drug Clozaril substantially increases the risk of diabetes.

—Other adverse effects reported for psychotropic drugs include osteoporosis, heart arrhythmias, tardive dyskinesia, life-threatening "serotonin syndrome," drastic hormonal alterations, deaths due to falls or aspiration of food, and serious increases in aggressive or suicidal behavior.

—The American Medical Association itself admits that about 100,000 people die each year as a result of prescription drugs—and psychiatric medications are one of the most dangerous categories of these drugs.

What is the response of doctors to this frightening list of dangerous or deadly side effects? They prescribe more drugs. A study conducted by Brandeis University and published in January 2006 reports that psychotropic drug prescriptions for teenagers rose 250 percent between 1994 and 2001, even as scientists uncovered the deleterious effects of these drugs on patients' hearts, livers, brains, bones, and brains. Millions of younger children are taking antidepressants, ADHD drugs, and antipsychotics, and the number rises each year.

Worse yet, when a single drug doesn't work, doctors typically prescribe a "cocktail" of drugs. Of children taking psychiatric drugs, 40% are taking two or more drugs together. Autistic children often are prescribed three, four, or even more psychotropic and anticonvulsant drugs, with each new drug adding to the toxic "soup" and increasing the risk of fatal interactions. Three children, for example, died after being given a combination of Ritalin and clonidine.

"This is a critical issue," says Joseph Penn, who conducted a study on polypharmacy. "It's not uncommon to find a child on an antidepressant, a mood stabilizer and a sleep agent all at the same time, but there's no research to see how these drugs interact with each other."



I am not arguing that there is never a place for psychiatric drugs. In some cases, *when all else fails*, psychotropic drugs may be necessary evils—particularly when autistic children exhibit life-threatening aggression or self-injury. I certainly do not fault parents who turn to these drugs after all other avenues have been exhausted. But in the overwhelming majority of cases, psychiatric drugs do far more harm than good. They never correct the innate problems of autistic children. They never "cure." They only suppress symptoms, while causing a host of horrific and sometimes lethal side effects.

In contrast, chelation and the other therapies advocated by DAN! doctors *do* treat the underlying causes of autism. These treatments are very safe, and highly effective. They make our children healthier, not sicker. And they can lead to dramatic improvement and even to recovery—to see proof, go to www.Autism-RecoveredChildren.com.

The bottom line: do not let the medical establishment's campaign of misinformation deter you from pursuing chelation therapy or the other DAN! treatments being used successfully by knowledgeable parents and professionals. Rely on the truth, as evidenced by thousands of children who are becoming healthier, happier, more loving, and more capable of living a normal life as a result of chelation therapy and other safe and natural therapies—not on propaganda disseminated by mainstream doctors who have never helped autistic children, and possibly never will.

# — Chapter 56 —
# Overview: Detoxification through Chelation Therapy

By John Green, M.D.
The EverGreen Center, Oregon City, Oregon

*Autism Research Review International*, 2006, Vol. 20, No. 1

*Dr. Green is a specialist in clinical ecology and nutritional medicine. A DAN! physician, he committed his full attention to the treatment of autistic children in 1999.*

———



What is chelation therapy? How does it work? How is it performed? Why does chelation therapy in autism have such avid proponents and opponents? What are the risks and benefits of chelation therapy? Why does it receive the highest effectiveness rating from parents of all the current treatments being used for autism?

Chelation works like the body's natural sulfur defense system, wherein sticky molecules bind toxic metals to sequester and eliminate them. The commonly used chelators in autism treatment are DMSA, DMPS, and EDTA. All three of these are effective for removing lead and cadmium, while DMPS and DMSA are also effective for mercury, tin and arsenic. EDTA is also somewhat effective for aluminum. EDTA and DMSA are available over the counter in the U.S., as is DMPS in several western European countries. These three agents can be given orally or rectally, and DMPS and Calcium EDTA can be given intravenously. DMPS is also effective by intramuscular injection. Transdermal forms of all three are available, with proven efficacy for DMPS and DMSA, and uncertain efficacy for EDTA.

The best diagnostic test for toxic metal overload is the chelation challenge test. The chelation drug is administered, followed by a timed urine test to help assess the body's burden of toxic elements. This test is repeated periodically to evaluate treatment progress. In our office we use DMPS, the most potent mercury chelator (which must be prepared by a compounding pharmacy), as it can be injected with glutathione enhancement and avoids the problem of poor oral absorption. Others prefer DMSA, as it does not cross the blood-brain barrier, and is FDA approved for lead. Transdermal challenge tests are not reliable.

The choice of a chelating agent and route of administration should be individualized to the child. After implementing treatment, it is important to evaluate both effectiveness and tolerance. It is not necessary to push the therapy too vigorously; the best rule is to "go low and go slow." Transdermal methods of delivering either DMPS or DMSA are often preferred, as this helps to minimize the exposure of the bowel to the chelator/toxin complex. If there are problems with one method, it is reasonable to change to another method. After the levels of mercury drop to a low level, transdermal alpha lipoic acid is often given along with DMPS or DMSA, to provide additional benefits.

There is strong evidence that autistic children have impairments in their body detoxification systems, causing increased vulnerability to toxic injury. In addition to heavy metals (particularly mercury, lead, arsenic, antimony, and aluminum), we have found elevated blood levels of PCBs and volatile organic solvents in every autistic child tested in our office. These toxins further weaken their detoxification systems, by causing oxidative injury, immune dysfunction, impairment of enzyme and energy functions, disruption of cellular communications, and initiation and aggravation of chronic inflammation. The result of these disturbances is a complex set of self-perpetuating cycles of tissue injury. Detoxification by chelation and attendant supportive treatments helps break these cycles and restore healthy physiology.



Intravenous EDTA chelation has been used safely for decades in thousands of elderly patients and in lead-poisoned children. However, questions about safety have arisen in the past year because two children have died from the improper use of a version of EDTA (disodium—instead of calcium—EDTA). They received the wrong drug (a mistake stemming from the drugs' similar names) by an improper intravenous technique, and died from severe depletion of blood calcium levels. If a child is treated with EDTA, it must be with the calcium EDTA drug, which has been proven safe.

The risks of chelation therapy, properly done, are few. The most common problems seen are yeast or bacterial disturbances in the gut and depletion of trace minerals, especially zinc. These tend to cause behavioral upsets, generally preventable by intestinal supports, mineral supplements, and/or change of chelation system. Rashes may necessitate change in the drug or in the method of delivery. Serious allergic reactions are very rare. Concerns have been expressed about chelation effects on the liver, kidney, and bone marrow, but there has been no evidence of irreversible problems with these organs in children receiving chelation treatment. To the contrary, thorough safety testing and experience with thousands of autistic children have demonstrated the extraordinary safety of these drugs.

In our office, we prefer using DMPS by the transdermal route (with intermittent oral dosing to help clear the gut). We also may vary the chelator and the route of administration to optimize the effects of each and ascertain which is most helpful. For instance, we may use TD DMPS for three days one week, TD DMSA for three days the next week, and oral DMPS for two days the next week. If the child shows more benefit with one, we will continue with that agent. While some doctors use an alternate-day treatment regimen, we find it most effective to use these medications intermittently, such as three days on and four to 11 days off, and a washout of three or more days between different medications is necessary.

Why are there such avid proponents and opponents? The proponents are professionals who use chelation regularly and have seen excellent results in their patients. The opponents are individuals who have not used chelation therapy in practice, and raise theoretical reasons against its use.



Why does chelation therapy have the highest effectiveness rating from parents of all the therapies evaluated by the Autism Research Institute? The simple answer is that chelation therapy is extremely helpful for autistic spectrum children, with very few side effects. Chelation helps break many of the self-perpetuating cycles contributing to the tissue damage and symptom complex of autism and opens the way for repair and recovery to take place.

If your child has been diagnosed with autism, and particularly if he/she has regressed or lost skills from an earlier stage in life, it is extremely likely that environmental factors have caused injury. In the DAN! Group, we believe that genetic and probably epigenetic (gene switching due to environmental influences) predispositions, interacting with toxic exposures, cause the syndrome of autism. Detoxification treatment commences when you optimize diet and nutrition, reduce exposure to known environmental toxins, and provide support for optimal digestive and immune function as described in the DAN! diagnostic and therapeutic guidelines. Upon this supportive foundation, chelation therapy will enhance your child's healing. May the day come when your child thanks you for all your efforts in bringing the best of biomedical treatments to facilitate his or her recovery!

---

For more in-depth information regarding chelation therapy for autistic children, see "Treatment options for mercury/metal toxicity in autism and related developmental disabilities: Consensus position paper," at www.AutismMercuryDetox.com.

# PART V

# APPENDICES

*Appendix A* Resources

*Appendix B* ARI Internet Sites

*Appendix C* Autism Treatment Evaluation Checklist (ATEC)

*Appendix D* Abbreviations and Acronyms

## Appendix A
# Resources

Autism Research Institute (ARI)
4182 Adams Avenue
San Diego, CA 92116
Fax: 619-563-6840
Website: *Please see pages 442-443 for a listing of ARI sites*

Autism Society of America (ASA)
7910 Woodmont Avenue, Suite 300
Bethesda, MD 20814-3015
Telephone: 800-3-AUTISM
Website: www.Autism-Society.org

Autism Network for Dietary Intervention (ANDI)
P.O. Box 335
Pennington, NJ 08534-0335
Email: AutismNDI@aol.com
Website: www.AutismNDI.com

Schafer Autism Report (Daily Internet newsletter)
9629 Old Placerville Road
Sacramento, California 95827
Email: schafer@sprynet.com
Website: http://home.sprynet.com/~schafer/

Developmental Delay Resources
5801 Beacon St.
Pittsburgh, PA 15217
Email: devdelay@mindspring.com
Telephone: 800-497-0944
Fax: 412-422-1374
Website: www.DevDelay.org

The Autism Autoimmunity Project
P.O. Box 293144
Davie, FL 33329
Telephone: 800-939-8227; 954-583-4860
Fax: 954-587-6509
Email: Autism@AutismAutoimmuntyProject.org
Website: www.AutismAutoimmunityProject.org



Unlocking Autism
P.O. Box 237
Walker, LA 70785
Telephone: 225-665-7270
Fax: 225-665-7547
Website: www.UnlockingAutism.org

**Additional Informative Websites**

Center for the Study of Autism
(An affiliate of the Autism Research Institute)
Website: www.Autism.org

AutismInfo: www.AutismInfo.com
Autism Resources: www.Autism-Resources.com
Autism Today: www.AutismToday.com
The Autism Research Unit:
http://osiris.sunderland.ac.uk/autism/durham95.html
Generation Rescue: www.GenerationRescue.org
Safe Minds: www.SafeMinds.org

## Appendix B

# ARI Internet Sites

** Indicates the site includes information in Spanish and other languages*

1. www.AutismResearchInstitute.com: This is our primary website, containing a great deal of information on many topics in the field of autism.

2. www.DanWebcast.com: Presents the lectures given by the leading physicians and researchers who spoke at the most recent major Defeat Autism Now! (DAN!) conference (Spring—East Coast; Fall—West Coast). This is the most up-to-date information available on the effective biomedical approaches to the treatment of autism.

3. *www.Autism-RecoveredChildren.com: UPDATED—Now includes a video of our second event featuring recovered autistic children, held at the October 2005 Defeat Autism Now (DAN!) conference in Long Beach, California. Also includes our original video featuring stage and screen star Lou Diamond Phillips introducing a group of recovered autistic children to an audience of 1,200 parents and professionals at the DAN! conference in Los Angeles in October, 2004. This video shows not only interviews with the children (the first 15 minutes), but also interviews with the parents of the children and with some of the leading doctors, who discuss the treatments that have proven so helpful in bringing about recovery in autistic children. (October 2004 video segments available in Spanish, Italian, and six other languages.)

4. www.AutismMercuryDetox.com: Treatment Options for Mercury/ Metal Toxicity in Autism and Related Developmental Disabilities: Consensus

Position Paper: The most current version of this evolving document (February 2005).

5. www.AutismNewsletter.com: Easy access to all of the back issues of the ARI newsletter, the *Autism Research Review International (ARRI)*, Volumes 1-19 (1987-2005). A comprehensive index provides instant access to the approximately 1,500 articles that have been published in the *ARRI* during the past several decades. A wide range of topics is covered.

6. www.Autism.tv: This website provides links to websites containing audio and video files. ARI's website, channel 2, includes videos on the use of vitamin B6 and magnesium; vaccines and autism; impaired metal excretion; and the Defeat Autism Now! (DAN!) approach. Additional autism-related videos are in production.

7. www.DANConference.com: Offers information on program and registration for upcoming DAN! conferences.



8. *www.ARI-ATEC.com: The Autism Treatment Evaluation Checklist (ATEC) was designed to assist parents, physicians, and researchers in evaluating virtually any treatment for autism. ARI has developed a convenient no-cost Internet scoring procedure that will immediately provide five ATEC scores: Speech/Language/Communication, Sociability, Sensory/Cognitive Awareness, Health/Physical/Behavior, and Total.

9. *www.Autism.org: Sponsored by the Center for the Study of Autism, an affiliate of ARI. Website contains information about understanding and treating autistic children, interviews with professionals in their field, papers written by Temple Grandin, and information about sibling issues.

10. *www.AutismTranslations.com: Many of ARI's most important articles on autism, as well as videos, have been translated into Spanish, French, Italian, and other languages, and others are being translated. *NEW: Spanish translation of the first edition of "Treating Autism". An Index of available translations is currently being prepared.

11. www.AutismTreatmentRating.com. Ratings by more than 24,500 parents of the efficacy of various biomedical interventions (45 drugs; 35 non-drug interventions).

## Appendix C
# Autism Treatment Evaluation Checklist (ATEC)



A major obstacle in autism research has been the lack of a valid means of measuring the effectiveness of various treatments. The Autism Treatment Evaluation Checklist (ATEC) was developed by Bernard Rimland and Stephen M. Edelson of the Autism Research Institute to fill this need. The ATEC is a one-page form designed to be completed by parents, teachers, or caretakers. It consists of four subtests: I. Speech/Language Communication (14 items); II. Sociability (20 items); III. Sensory Cognitive Awareness (18 items); and IV. Health/Physical/Behavior (25 items).

The ATEC is not copyrighted and may be used—and scored—free of charge.

Users of the ATEC may have it scored (four subscores and a total score) by entering the responses to the ATEC form on www.ARI-ATEC.com for immediate and free-of-cost scoring.

**Norms.** The purpose of the ATEC is to measure change in an individual as a result of various interventions; that is, the difference between the initial (baseline) ATEC scores and later ATEC scores. (The lower the scores, the better.) Nevertheless, we are often asked for normative data, which permit comparison of one individual with others. Here are the score distributions based on the first 1,000 ATECs entered at www.ARI-ATEC.com. These norms must be considered only preliminary estimates, because they include subjects covering a wide range of ages. At a later date, we will publish norms for specific age groups.

| Centile | **Scale I** Speech **Range: 0-28** | **Scale II** Sociability **Range: 0-40** | **Scale III** Sensory/ Cognitive Awareness **Range: 0-36** | **Scale IV** Health/ Physical/ Behavior **Range: 0-75** | Total **Range: 0-180** |
|---|---|---|---|---|---|
| *Mild* | | | | | |
| 0-9 | 0-2 | 0-4 | 0-5 | 0-8 | 0-30 |
| 10-19 | 3-5 | 5-7 | 6-8 | 9-12 | 31-41 |
| 20-29 | 6-7 | 8-10 | 9-11 | 13-15 | 42-50 |
| 30-39 | 8-10 | 11 | 12-13 | 16-18 | 51-57 |
| 40-49 | 11-12 | 12-13 | 14-15 | 19-21 | 58-64 |
| 50-59 | 13-15 | 14-15 | 16-17 | 22-24 | 65-71 |
| 60-69 | 16-19 | 16-18 | 18-19 | 25-28 | 72-79 |
| 70-79 | 20-21 | 19-21 | 20-21 | 29-32 | 80-89 |
| 80-89 | 22-24 | 22-25 | 22-25 | 33-39 | 90-103 |
| 90-99 | 25-28 | 26-40 | 26-36 | 40-75 | 104-179 |
| *Severe* | | | | | |



The ATEC is being employed as a criterion of treatment efficacy in a variety of studies, including chelation therapy, hyperbaric oxygen treatment (HBOT), neurotherapy, and dietary change. For more information on the ATEC, its reliability, validity and uses, visit www.ARI-ATEC.com

## References

1. Betty Jasusiewicz (2002). Efficacy of neurofeedback for children in the autism spectrum: A pilot study. *Journal of Neurotherapy, 6 (4),* 39-49

2. Jørgen Klaveness and Jay Bigam (August, 2002). The GFCFKids Diet Survey. Paper published on the Internet. www.gfcfdiet.com/dietsurveysept2.htm

3. Derrick Lonsdale, Raymond J. Shamberger, Tapan Audhya (2002). Treatment of autism spectrum children with thiamine tetrahydrofurfuryl disulfide: A pilot study. *Neuroendocrinology Letters, 23 (4),* 303-308

4. Daniel A. Rossignol and Lanier W. Rossignol (2006, In press). Hyperbaric oxygen therapy may improve symptoms in autistic children. *Medical Hypotheses.*

ARI/Form
ATEC-1/11-99

# Autism Treatment Evaluation Checklist (ATEC)

Bernard Rimland, Ph.D. and Stephen M. Edelson, Ph.D.
**Autism Research Institute**
4182 Adams Avenue, San Diego, CA 92116
fax: (619) 563-6840; www.ARI-ATEC.com

| Project/Purpose: | | | | |
|---|---|---|---|---|
| | | | | |
| | | | | |
| | | | | |
| Scores: I | II | III | IV | Total |

This form is intended to measure the effects of treatment. Free scoring of this form is available on the Internet at: www.autism.com/atec

Name of Child ____________ ____________ ☐ Male Age ________
Last First ☐ Female Date of Birth ________
Form completed by: ____________ Relationship: ____________ Today's Date ________

## *Please circle the letters to indicate how true each phrase is:*

### I. Speech/Language/Communication: *[N] Not true [S] Somewhat true [V] Very true*

N S V 1. Knows own name
N S V 2. Responds to 'No' or 'Stop'
N S V 3. Can follow some commands
N S V 4. Can use one word at a time (No!, Eat, Water, etc.)
N S V 5. Can use 2 words at a time (Don't want, Go home)
N S V 6. Can use 3 words at a time (Want more milk)
N S V 7. Knows 10 or more words
N S V 8. Can use sentences with 4 or more words
N S V 9. Explains what he/she wants
N S V 10. Asks meaningful questions
N S V 11. Speech tends to be meaningful/ relevant
N S V 12. Often uses several successive sentences
N S V 13. Carries on fairly good conversation
N S V 14. Has normal ability to communicate for his/her age

### II. Sociability: *[N] Not descriptive [S] Somewhat descriptive [V] Very descriptive*

N S V 1. Seems to be in a shell – you cannot reach him/her
N S V 2. Ignores other people
N S V 7. Shows no affection
N S V 8. Fails to greet parents
N S V 14. Disagreeable/not compliant
N S V 15. Temper tantrums

N S V 3. Pays little or no attention when addressed
N S V 4. Uncooperative and resistant
N S V 5. No eye contact
N S V 6. Prefers to be left alone
N S V 9. Avoids contact with others
N S V 10. Does not imitate
N S V 11. Dislikes being held/cuddled
N S V 12. Does not share or show
N S V 13. Does not wave 'bye bye'
N S V 16. Lacks friends/companions
N S V 17. Rarely smiles
N S V 18. Insensitive to other's feelings
N S V 19. Indifferent to being liked
N S V 20. Indifferent if parent(s) leave

## III. Sensory/Cognitive Awareness: *[N] Not descriptive [S] Somewhat descriptive [V] Very descriptive*

N S V 1. Responds to own name
N S V 2. Responds to praise
N S V 3. Looks at people and animals
N S V 4. Looks at pictures (and T.V.)
N S V 5. Does drawing, coloring, art
N S V 6. Plays with toys appropriately
N S V 7. Appropriate facial expression
N S V 8. Understands stories on T.V.
N S V 9. Understands explanations
N S V 10. Aware of environment
N S V 11. Aware of danger
N S V 12. Shows imagination
N S V 13. Initiates activities
N S V 14. Dresses self
N S V 15. Curious, interested
N S V 16. Venturesome - explores
N S V 17. "Tuned in" — Not spacey
N S V 18. Looks where others are looking

## IV. Health/Physical/Behavior:

***Use this code:*** ***[N] Not a Problem [MI] Minor Problem [MO] Moderate Problem [S] Serious Problem***

N MI MO S 1. Bed-wetting
N MI MO S 2. Wets pants/diapers
N MI MO S 3. Soils pants/diapers
N MI MO S 4. Diarrhea
N MI MO S 5. Constipation
N MI MO S 6. Sleep problems
N MI MO S 7. Eats too much/too little
N MI MO S 8. Extremely limited diet
N MI MO S 9. Hyperactive
N MI MO S 10. Lethargic
N MI MO S 11. Hits or injures self
N MI MO S 12. Hits or injures others
N MI MO S 13. Destructive
N MI MO S 14. Sound-sensitive
N MI MO S 15. Anxious/fearful
N MI MO S 16. Unhappy/crying
N MI MO S 17. Seizures
N MI MO S 18. Obsessive speech
N MI MO S 19. Rigid routines
N MI MO S 20. Shouts or screams
N MI MO S 21. Demands sameness
N MI MO S 22. Often agitated
N MI MO S 23. Not sensitive to pain
N MI MO S 24. "Hooked" or fixated on certain objects/topics
N MI MO S 25. Repetitive movements (stimming, rocking, etc.)

## APPENDIX D
# ABBREVIATIONS AND ACRONYMS

ABA – Applied behavior analysis: A popular behavioral method of teaching

ADD – Attention deficit disorder

ADHD – Attention deficit/hyperactivity disorder

AIT – Auditory integration training: A sound-based intervention using specially modulated music, developed by Guy Berard

ANDI – Autism Network for Dietary Intervention: a source for information on special diets

Apgar Score – An index used to evaluate the physical condition of a newborn infant

ARI – Autism Research Institute

ASA – Autism Society of America

ASD – Autism spectrum disorder

DAN! – Defeat Autism Now!: A biomedical treatment program that emphasizes finding and treating the underlying causes of autism and related disorders, using natural substances, such as vitamins and minerals, rather than drugs

DMG – Dimethylglycine: A nutritional supplement, formerly called vitamin B15

DMPS - Dimercaptopropane sulfonate or 2,3-dimercaptopropane sulfonic acid: A sulfur-based, water-soluble detoxifying agent used to chelate heavy metals, such as lead and mercury, from the body

DMSA - Meso-2,3-dimercaptosuccinic acid; also Chemet and Succimer: A sulfur-based, water-soluble detoxifying agent used to chelate heavy metals, such as lead and mercury, from the body

DPT (also DTP and DTaP) – Diphtheria/pertussis/tetanus vaccine

GFCF or GF/CF – Gluten-free, casein-free: A diet without gluten (a protein found in barley, rye, oats, and wheat—or "BROW") and without casein (a protein found in dairy products)



IVIg – Intravenous immunoglobulin: A treatment involving an infusion of antibodies to help the immune system battle infection in the body

MMR – Measles/mumps/rubella vaccine

PDD – Pervasive developmental disorder

SCD – Specific Carbohydrate Diet: Foods containing complex sugars and starches should be avoided. Food allowed in SCD include meats, fish, eggs, nuts, honey, fruit, and vegetables, as well as foods consisting of simple sugars.

# INDEX

ABA. *See* Applied behavior analysis
Abdominal colic, 79, 144, 263, 273
Abdominal pain, 394
ABR test. *See* Auditory brain response (ABR) test
Absolute pitch, 275
*Acidophilus* supplements, 235, 399
"Acquired autism," 225
Activated charcoal, 56
Actos, 230, 298
Acyclovir, 72
ADD. *See* Attention deficit disorder
Additive-free food, 218, 317
Aderall, parent ratings of behavioral effects of, 383, 384
ADHD. *See* Attention deficit hyperactivity disorder
Age of diagnosis, 50, 54, 60, 90, 95, 108, 125, 129, 173, 211, 221, 232, 245, 285
Aggressiveness
  Dilantin and, 396
  pain and, 394
  parent accounts of, 47, 136, 138, 179, 365, 367, 393
Agitation, 357
Aguilar, Luis, 402
Air filters, 235
AIT. *See* Auditory integration training
ALA. *See* Alpha lipoic acid
Albuterol, 300
Alertness, 346
Allergies, 55, 64, 99, 120, 286
Allithiamine (TTFD), 132, 227
Aloe Immune, 119
Aloe vera supplement, 119
Alpha lipoic acid (ALA), parent accounts of use of, 52, 58, 84, 85, 157, 163, 247-248
Aluminum level, elevated, 52, 56, 112, 113, 156, 242, 304
Alvarez, Walter, 396
Ambrotose, 84, 119, 268, 272, 320
American Academy of Environmental Medicine, 26
American Enzyme Potentiated Desensitization Society (EPD Society), 26
American Holistic Medical Association, 26
Amino acids, 84, 140, 254, 255
Amino Support, 56
Amphetamines, parent ratings of behavioral effects of, 383, 384
Amylase, 237
Anafranil
  for obsessive-compulsive disorder, 365
  parent ratings of behavioral effects of, 383, 384
ANDI. *See* Autism Network for Dietary Intervention
Angelman syndrome, 393
Anger issues, 54, 70, 136
Antibiotic-free food, 235, 317
Antibiotics
  parent ratings of behavioral effects of,

383, 384
repeated courses of, 46, 123, 263, 264, 302, 397-398
Anticonvulsant drugs, 383, 384, 396
Antifungal drugs. *See also* Flagyl; Nystatin
die-off reaction, 51, 56-57, 242, 308
parent accounts of use of, 224, 242, 282, 299, 302, 310, 398
parent ratings of behavioral effects of, 383, 384
Antigen-specific transfer factors, 140
Antimony level, elevated, 52, 126, 304
Antipsychotic drugs
safety of, 431
use for autism, 19, 40, 179, 220
Antiviral drugs, 72, 224
Anxiety, 47
Appetite, 306, 307, 310
Applied behavior analysis (ABA), parent accounts of, 40, 82, 86, 90, 98, 101, 114-115, 127, 135, 140, 155, 157, 168, 211, 213, 221, 235, 239, 241, 248, 259, 281, 282, 287, 293, 317, 319, 320
ARI. *See* Autism Research Institute
Arithmetic, 57
Arm, biting of, 371, 390
*ARRI. See Autism Research Review International*
Arsenic level, elevated, 126, 156, 304
Artesiminin, 75
ASA. *See* Autism Society of America
ASD. *See* Autism spectrum disorder
Aspartame, 85, 214
Asperger syndrome, 71, 384
Association for Persons with Severe Handicaps (TASH), 390
Asthma, 300
Atarax, parent ratings of behavioral effects of, 383, 384
ATEC. *See* Autism Treatment Effectiveness Checklist
Athanas-Brayton, Evelyn, 363
Attention deficit disorder (ADD), 65, 162, 248
Attention deficit hyperactivity disorder (ADHD), 261, 407
Attention span, 345, 350, 351, 352
Audhya, T., 375
Auditory brain response (ABR) test, 145
Auditory integration training (AIT), 402
hypersensitive hearing and, 395
parent accounts of, 63, 109, 117, 120, 140, 167, 168, 216, 274, 275
Auditory sensitivity, 46-47, 63, 111, 158, 273, 274, 354, 395
Auditory training tapes, 224
Autism. *See also* Autism Research Institute (ARI); Defeat Autism Now! (DAN!)
abbreviations and acronyms, 448-449
age of diagnosis, 50, 54, 60, 90, 95, 108, 125, 129, 173, 211, 221, 232, 245, 285
biomedical approach, 20, 39, 223, 269, 282, 294, 320, 383-384
conventional medicine and, 28, 29, 35
evaluation of, 41-43
family issues, 43
holistic treatment approach, 30-31, 32, 34-35
homeopathic treatment of, 185, 190-195, 203, 204, 205
impairments of, 31-32
interventions outlined, 39-41, 42
prevalence of, 15, 18, 36, 200, 286
symptoms of, 46-47
Autism Autoimmunity Project, 441
*Autism: Effective Biomedical Treatments*, 20, 21, 40
Autism Network for Dietary Intervention (ANDI), 111, 148, 285, 289, 440
Autism Research Institute (ARI), 6, 7, 19, 22, 24, 219, 268, 292, 440. *See also* Defeat Autism Now! (DAN!)
address of, 21, 41-42, 440
history of, 17
Internet resources, 442-443
Mercury Detoxification Consensus Report, 23
parent packet, 39
parent ratings of behavioral effects of biomedical interventions, 383, 384, 430
publication list, 10

Treatment Effectiveness Survey, 9
Treatment Evaluation Checklist (ATEC), 10, 24, 41, 443, 444-447
*Autism Research Review International (ARRI)*, 7, 9, 39, 137
Autism Society of America (ASA), 16, 21-22, 39, 147, 440
Autism spectrum disorder (ASD), 27, 50, 110
Autism Treatment Effectiveness Checklist (ATEC), 10, 24, 41, 443, 444-447
Aversives, 391
Awadh, Abeer, 411
Awareness, 353, 359, 404

Babbling, 128, 142, 351
*Babesia* infection, 74
Baker, Linda, 360
Baker, Sidney M., 19, 20-21, 32, 409
Balance problems, 155, 288, 294
Balliet, Mary, 368
Banging head, parent accounts of, 46-47, 125, 166, 187, 264, 305, 307, 308, 310, 368, 390-393
Barley, 112, 289
Barnhart, Kristin, 49
Barthelemy, C., 373
Bauman, Margaret, 38
Bayliss, Debbie, 54
Behavioral therapy, 62, 98, 118
Behavior/education approach, 40
Behavior modification, 351, 390, 401
Belk, Judith, 120
Belyakova, T.L., 337
Benadryl, parent ratings of behavioral effects of, 383, 384
Bentonite clay, 56-57
Berard, Guy, 38, 274, 395
Berliner, Deborah, 359
Berliner, Steven H., 359
Bernard, Sallie, 163
Berries, 158
Beta blockers, parent ratings of behavioral effects of, 383, 384
Beta Glucan, 56
Beta-glucose, 84
Betaine, 237, 424
Bethanecol
parent accounts of use of, 56, 242
parent ratings of behavioral effects of, 383, 384
Bezalel, Cheryl and Ike, 60
Bihari, Bernard, 427
Binge eating, 232
Binstock, Teresa, 226
Bio-Botanical Research Institute, 83
Biocare, 83
Biocidin, 56, 83, 84
Bio-Kult, 83, 84
Biological therapy, 402
Biomedical approach, 20, 40, 223, 269, 282, 294, 320, 383-384
Bio-neurofeedback, 230
Biaxin, 72
Bismuth level, elevated, 304
Biting, parent accounts of, 166, 353, 367, 368, 369, 371, 390, 393
Black circles under eyes, 50, 80, 212
Blanco, Kathy, 67
Bloating, 232
Bloodshot eyes, 212
Bloody lesions, 232
Blue color around mouth and hands/feet, 305
Blumena, M.G., 337
Bolles, Mary, 117
Bonisch, V.E., 325, 372
Borage oil, 212
Borna, 74
Boronat, Lorretta, 357
Bowel problems
colic, 79, 144, 263, 404
constipation, 47, 254, 293, 315, 318
diarrhea, 47, 70, 90, 114, 154, 157-158, 221, 224, 274, 285, 289, 292, 293, 294, 307, 310, 312, 315
parent accounts of, 51, 54, 55, 79, 83, 84, 158, 233, 237, 243, 300, 305, 307, 308
Bradley, Cecil, 398-399
Bradstreet, Jeffrey, 112, 113, 282, 297
Bread, 55, 57
*Breaking the Vicious Cycle* (Gottschall), 410
Breast milk, 126

Breecher, Maury, 226
Breeding, John, 431
Brester, Tami, 255
Bronson, 389
Brown, Mary Jean, 430
Buckwheat bread, 57
Buie, Cory, 362
Buie, Tim, 311, 390, 394
Burrell-Stella, Claire, 45, 77
Buspar, parent ratings of behavioral effects of, 383, 384
Buttars protocol, 132

Cadmium level, elevated, 126, 304
Calcium EDTA, 430, 433, 434
Calcium supplements
  parent accounts of use of, 56, 127, 243, 321
  parent ratings of behavioral effects of, 383, 384
Callaway, Enoch, 326, 327, 329, 372
Calmness, 63, 151, 356, 367
Calouri, Kathy, 259
Cambridge Probiotics, 83
Campbell-McBride, Natasha, 45, 89
Campbell, Stephanie, 369
Cancer, DMG and, 347-348
*Candida*, 70, 72, 83. *See also* Yeast infection
  autism and, 397-399
*Candida* diet, parent ratings of behavioral effects of, 383, 384
Cannabis, 418, 421. *See also* Marijuana use
Caprylic acid, 399
Carbo, 310
Carbone method, 241
Carcinosin, 192, 199
CARD. *See* Center for Autism and Related Disorders
Carlson, Karen, 367
Carpeting, 235
Casein, 112, 136, 268, 315. *See also* Gluten-free casein-free diet (GFCF)
Cathcart, Robert, 387-388
Cave, Stephanie, 161, 162, 163, 225, 264
Cell therapy, 402
Center for Autism and Related Disorders (CARD), 410
Center for Complex Infectious Diseases (CCID), 71
Center for the Study of Autism, 317, 440
Cerebral palsy, DMG and, 355
Change, intolerance of, 46-47
Chelation challenge test, 433
Chelation therapy, 430-435
  method of action of, 433-435
  parent accounts of, 51, 52, 56, 58, 73, 100, 104, 113, 121, 127, 129, 131, 132, 140, 156, 157, 158, 161, 225, 230, 242, 247-248, 253, 296, 312
  parent ratings of behavioral effects of, 383, 384
Chemet, 225
Chemical-free diet, 274
Chewing on non-food items, 121
Child Essence, 121
Child Protective Services, 28
Children, harm to, 28
Children's Biomedical Center of Utah, 175
*Children with Starving Brains: A Medical Treatment Guide for Autism Spectrum Disorder* (McCandless), 22, 45, 226
Childscreen, 73
Chiropractic care, 152
*Chlamydia pneumoniae*, 74
Chloral hydrate, parent ratings of behavioral effects of, 383, 384
Chocolate, removal from diet, 383, 384, 395
Choice Prime, 130
Choline, function of, 424
Cipro, 74
Circles under eyes, 50, 80, 212, 315, 404
Claritin, 120
Clonidine
  parent accounts of use of, 58, 119, 120
  parent ratings of behavioral effects of, 383, 384
*Clostridium* infection, 227, 234, 235, 305
Clozapine, parent ratings of behavioral effects of, 383, 384
Clozaril, safety of, 431
Coastal Compounding, 429
Cod liver oil

parent accounts of use of, 51, 56, 84, 85, 113, 114, 138, 140, 212, 218, 235, 242
parent ratings of behavioral effects of, 383, 384
CoEnzyme Q10, 56, 84, 152
Cogentin, parent ratings of behavioral effects of, 383, 384
Colic, 79, 144, 263, 273
Colitis, 314
Colloidal silver, 158, 302
Colostrum
parent accounts of use of, 51, 56, 261, 310
parent ratings of behavioral effects of, 383, 384
Colostrum Gold, 56
Communication. *See* Language use; Speech issues
Compulsive rituals, 367, 370
Concentration, parent accounts of changes in, 155, 253, 269, 273, 275, 345, 346, 356, 359, 367
Congestion, 300, 302
Constipation, 47, 254, 293, 315, 318
Conventional medicine, 28, 29, 35
Convulsions, 69
Cooperation, 345
Coordination, 289
Copper level, 242, 412
CoQ10, 56, 84, 152
Corcoran, Londa, 94
Co-regulation, 239
Corn allergy, 212, 301
Cott, Allan, 337-338
Counting, 142, 316
Covering the ears, 395. *See also* Hypersensitive hearing
Cranberry capsules, 56
Cranial osteopathy, 87
Creon5, 275
Crook, William G., 398
Croup attacks, 232
Crying, parent accounts of, 60, 106, 120, 124, 134, 136, 139, 143, 199, 357
*Cryptosporidium*, 114
Cuddling, 95
Culturelle, 56, 74, 83, 84
Curtin, Jean, 308, 350, 357
Curtin, Michael, 308, 309, 350
Cylert, parent ratings of behavioral effects of, 383, 384

Dagenais, Donna, 188
Dairy products. *See also* Gluten-free casein-free diet (GFCF); Milk
allergy to, 64
autism and, 287
refusal to accept, 79
removal from diet, 136, 302, 383, 384, 395
DAN!. *See* Defeat Autism Now!
Dance therapy, 167
Dark circles under eyes, 50, 80, 212, 315, 404
Deanol, parent ratings of behavioral effects of, 383, 384
Defeat Autism Now! (DAN!), 219, 268
*Autism: Effective Biomedical Treatments* (DAN! Manual/Protocol), 20, 21, 40, 52, 97, 137, 162, 163, 215, 226, 274, 320
conference, 6, 20, 137, 227, 234, 408-410
doctors, 97-98
group, 26
program, 7, 20, 39-40
Deficiencies to immune defenses, 31
Dental amalgam, 225
Depakene
parent ratings of behavioral effects of on behavior, 383, 384
for seizures, 268, 383, 384
Depakote, 253, 254
Depression
*Candida* as cause of, 397
vitamin C and, 389
Deshane, Nikki, 243-244
Desipramine, parent ratings of behavioral effects of, 383, 384
Destructiveness, 47
Deth, Richard, 406, 407, 409, 424
Detoxification, 22-23, 31, 75, 227, 433-435. *See also* Chelation therapy

Developmental Delay Resources, 441
Developmental milestones, in autistic children, 49, 60, 79, 134, 143, 165, 220, 240, 285, 315
Dexedrine, 253
DHA, 396
Diagnosis, age of. *See* Age of diagnosis
Diaper rash, 166, 263, 294, 299
Diarrhea, parent accounts of, 47, 70, 90, 114, 154, 157-158, 221, 224, 274, 285, 289, 292, 293, 294, 307, 312, 315
Die-off reaction, 51, 56-57, 242, 308
Diet. *See also* Feeding/eating problems; Gluten-free casein-free diet (GFCF)
  *Candida* diet, 383, 384
  chemical free-diet, 274
  dye-free diet, 274
  Feingold diet, 116, 142, 148, 188, 383, 384
  Internet resources for, 217, 218
  ketogenic diet, 70
  oligoantigenic diet, 395
  organic foods, 235, 274, 317
  parent accounts of changes to, 53, 55, 57, 82-83, 83, 91, 97, 111-112, 214, 216, 274, 294, 317, 359, 399
  picky eating habits, 52, 53, 55, 87, 91, 135, 253, 301
  rotation diet, 383, 384
  specific carbohydrate diet (SCD), 152, 158, 239, 404-405, 409-410
Diflucan
  parent ratings of behavioral effects of, 383, 384
  parent report of use of, 299
Digestive enzymes
  deficiencies of, 31
  parent accounts of use of, 57, 79, 103, 149, 237, 243, 255, 275
  parent ratings of behavioral effects of, 383, 384
Digestive system, 90, 237. *See also* Bowel problems
  colic, 79, 144, 263, 273, 310
  colitis, 314
  "leaky gut," 136, 261, 274, 301, 303
  rectal abscess, 315
  reflux, 263
  yeast overgrowth, 51, 55, 70, 83, 99, 110, 112, 140, 162, 166, 227, 234, 235, 253
Dilantin
  explosive aggression and, 396
  parent ratings of behavioral effects of, 383, 384
2,3-Dimercaptosuccinic acid. *See* DMSA
Dimethylglycine (DMG)
  carcinogenicity of, 347-348
  dosage of, 342-343
  Letters to the Editor, 344-371
  parent accounts of use of, 22, 24, 40, 63, 66, 84, 88, 140, 167, 182, 183, 222, 272, 295
  parent ratings of behavioral effects of, 383, 384
  safety of, 323
  self-injurious and assaultive behavior and, 391, 395
  studies of, 336-340, 372-375
Dipentum, 307
Dipeptidyl peptidase IV (DPP-IV), 243, 272
Diphtheria/pertussis/tetanus (DPT) vaccine, 18, 46-47, 68-69, 293-294, 305, 316-317
Discrete trial therapy, 260
Disodium EDTA, 430, 434
Distraction, 273
DMG. *See* Dimethylglycine
DMPS
  method of use of, 433-435
  parent accounts of use of, 100, 104, 157, 158, 239
DMSA
  method of use of, 433-435
  parent accounts of use of, 52, 100, 113, 121, 156, 157, 161, 162, 163, 225, 247-248, 312
Doctors, 28, 97-98, 172, 225, 289, 335, 400-402
Doerfel, Ken Sue, 364
Doggett, Dianne, 105
Dooley, Robin, 349

Dorfman, Kelly, 306-307
DPP-IV. *See* Dipeptidyl peptidase IV
DPT vaccine, 18, 46-47, 68-69, 293-294, 305
Dragging head on floor, 285, 286, 305, 307, 308, 310
Dreyfus, Pierre, 326, 329, 372
Drug-resistant seizures, 368-369
Drugs. *See* Psychotropic drugs
Druker, Brian, 75
DTaP vaccine, 247
DTP vaccination, 18, 46-47, 68-69, 293-294, 305
Duffield, Julie, 123
Dunn, Karl L., 356
Durie, Brian, 71
Dye-free diet, 274
Dysbiosis, 100, 103
Dyspraxia, 102

Ear infections
  parent accounts of repeated infections, 46-47, 54, 99, 106, 123, 124, 126, 210, 220, 263, 264, 286, 292, 300, 397-398
  response to pain of, 394
Eating problems. *See* Feeding/eating problems
Echolalia, parent accounts of, 189, 265, 269, 273, 316, 352, 360
Eczema, 300, 305, 315, 404
Edelson, Stephen M., 8, 13, 38, 62, 63, 163, 167, 170, 268, 375
Eden Institute, 255
EDTA
  method of use of, 433-435
  parent accounts of use of, 158, 298, 430
Education. *See* Schools
EFA. *See* Essential fatty acids
*The Effectiveness of Early Intervention* (Guralnick), 259
Egan, William M., 249
Egger, Joseph, 395
Eggs, removal from diet, 383, 384, 395
El-Dahr, Jane, 410
Electroencephalogram (EEG), 40, 54, 129
Ellman, George, 327, 372
Emerson Ecologics, 56
Engerix-B, 248
Environmental sensitivities, 36-37, 302-303, 304, 307
EnzymAid, 56
EnZym-Complete, 56, 149, 272
Enzymedica, 310
EPD Society. *See* American Enzyme Potentiated Desensitization Society
Epilepsy, 67, 74, 75, 395, 396
Epsom salt, 56, 296, 349
Erenberg, Gerald, 142
Essential fatty acids (EFA)
  parent accounts of use of, 51, 140, 183, 212, 396
  parent ratings of behavioral effects of, 383, 384
Essiac tea, 307, 308, 310
Evening primrose oil, 51, 84, 212
Excitotoxins, 214
Eye contact, parent accounts of changes in, 46-47, 51, 81, 95, 107, 113-114, 126, 128, 160, 168, 187, 212, 216, 220, 232, 233, 241, 259, 269, 275, 285, 287, 306, 307, 315, 318, 345, 346, 348, 349, 353, 359, 360, 367, 404
Eyes
  bloodshot, 212
  dark circles under, 50, 80, 212, 315, 404
  gouging, 392
Eyesight problems, 155, 236

Face, dragging on floor, 285, 286, 305, 307, 308, 310
*Facing Autism: Giving Parents Reason for Hope and Guidance for Help* (Hamilton), 45, 114, 137, 293
Family issues, 43, 91
Fat digestion, 310
Fatty acids. *See* Essential fatty acids
Fearfulness, 47
Feeding/eating problems, 47, 357
  binge eating, 232
  picky eating habits, 52, 53, 55, 87, 91, 135, 253, 301, 307

pushing feet against something while eating, 209
Feet, ash color around, 300
Feingold diet
parent accounts of use of, 116, 142, 148, 188
parent ratings of behavioral effects of, 383, 384
Felbatol, parent ratings of behavioral effects of, 383, 384
Fenfluramine, parent ratings of behavioral effects of, 383, 384
Fibroblast growth factor (FGF), 227, 402
Findling, R.L., 374
Fine motor skills, 306
Finger pointing, 47, 81
Finger poking, 187
Finicky eating. *See also* Feeding/eating problems
parent accounts of, 52, 53, 54, 55, 87, 91, 135, 301
Fish oils, 127, 182
Flagyl, 56, 235, 242, 305
Flax oil, 56
Flax seed powder, 55
*Flesh and Spirit, The Mystery of Intimate Relationship* (McCandless and Zimmerman), 223
"Floor Time" seminar, 147
Fluoride, 128
Focusing. *See* Concentration
Folic acid
dosage of, 343
parent accounts of use of, 182, 183, 272, 364
parent ratings of behavioral effects of, 383, 384
Folinic acid
function of, 424
parent accounts of use of, 119, 121, 239
Food. *See* Diet; Feeding/eating problems; Food allergies
Food additives, 64, 218, 395
Food allergies, 401
migraines and, 394-395
parent accounts of, 64, 99, 120, 212, 237, 275, 286, 290, 300, 310
seizures and, 394-395
Food allergy treatment, parent ratings of behavioral effects of, 383, 384
Food coloring, 64, 395
Food intolerances, 210
Food preservatives, 218
Forehead
dragging on floor, 285, 286, 305, 307, 308, 310
sweaty, 315
Foubister, D.M., 192
Fragile X syndrome, 391
Free-form amino acids, 255
Friends Club, 158
Fructolite, 83
Fructooligosaccharide liquid, 83
Fruit allergies, 301, 395
Fuller-Nordberg, Kathy, 345
Fussing, 145, 273

Gaby, Alan, 335
Galantamine, 230
Gallup, Ray, 416
Ganciclovir, 72
Gastrointestinal problems. *See* Bowel problems; Digestive system
Geier, David, 409
Geier, Mark, 409
Genetics, 37, 72
Gerdes, Crystal, 267
GFCF. *See* Gluten-free casein-free diet
Giangiabbe, Rose, 346
"Giant cells," 72
Gibbs, Lynn, 361
Glutathione, parent accounts of use of, 31, 73, 75, 116, 120, 121, 131, 132, 242, 296
Gluten, 111-112, 136, 268, 288, 301, 315
Gluten-free casein-free diet (GFCF)
parent accounts of, 18, 23, 24, 25, 40, 51, 70, 82, 83, 88, 97, 110, 111, 126, 131, 136, 137, 140, 142, 148, 155, 157, 212, 224, 233, 241, 252, 274-275, 278, 282, 288, 294, 317, 320
parent ratings of behavioral effects of, 383, 384
Glycomannans, 70

Glyconutrients, 321
Glycoproteins, 235
Gottschall, Elaine, 404, 409, 410
Grains, 18, 57, 112, 136, 286, 289, 383, 384, 395. *See also* Gluten-free casein-free diet (GFCF)
Grandin, Temple, 38, 241, 267
Green, John, 8, 13, 26, 98, 115, 158, 268, 433
Greenspan's Floor Time, 98, 101
Greenspan, Stanley, 101
Growth, 124
Gualtieri, Thomas, 327, 372
*Guide to Intestinal Health in Autism Spectrum Disorder* (Kirkman Labs), 57
Gupta, Sudhir, 115
Guralnick, Paul, 259
Gurgling sounds, 285
*Gut and Psychology Syndrome: Natural treatment for autism, ADHD, ADD, dyslexia, dyspraxia, depression and schizophrenia* (Campbell-McBride), 45, 92
Gutstein, Steven, 103, 118, 261

Haas, Sidney, 404
Hair analysis, 161-162
Hair-pulling, 83
Hair testing, 242, 304
Halcion, parent ratings of behavioral effects of, 383, 384
Haldol
  parent ratings of behavioral effects of, 383, 384
  use of, 365
Haley, Boyd, 163, 409
Hamilton, Lynn, 45, 114, 134, 293
Hammond, Jackie, 367
Hands
  ash color around, 300
  biting, 367, 368, 390
  flapping, 46-47, 61, 155, 158
Hands-on healing, 196
Hannaford, Carla, 118
Harch, Paul, 414
Hardy, Paul, 410
Harrington, Nancy, 359
Hart, Darlene, 354
Harvard-Mass General study, 236
HBOT. *See* Hyperbaric oxygen therapy
Head
  banging, 46-47, 125, 166, 187, 264, 305, 307, 308, 310, 368, 390-393
  dragging on floor, 285, 286, 305, 307, 308, 310
  sweating, 85, 315
*The Healing Factor: Vitamin C Against Disease* (Stone), 386
Health from the Sun, 310
Health insurance, 27, 36, 39, 280
"Healthy home," 235
Hearing
  hypersensitivity, 46-47, 63, 111, 158, 273, 274, 354, 395
  lack of response to environment, 145, 166, 173, 174, 221, 233, 245
Hearing testing, 145, 166, 174, 221, 233
Heavy metal poisoning, parent accounts of, 51, 57, 112-113, 114, 126, 129, 162, 242, 247, 304
Heeley, A.F., 325, 372
HEG, 230
Helmick, Marian, 142
Hemogenics, 243
Hendler, Sheldon, 347
Hepatitis B vaccine, 46-47, 106, 127, 202, 225, 247, 248, 314
Herbert, Martha, 410
Herbs, 307-308
HIB vaccine, 247
High-dosage vitamins, 131
High-dose phosphatidyl choline, 230
High pain threshold, 46-47, 220
High-pitched voice, 63
Hitting, parent accounts of, 178, 367, 390, 392, 393
Hoffer, Abram, 17, 19
Hoffiz, Dan and Jennifer, 154
Holmes, Amy, 45, 160, 225, 247, 248, 391
Homeopathic secretin, 29, 84, 85
Homeopathic silica, 85
Homeopathy, 185, 190-195, 203, 204, 205

Homovanillic acid (HVA), 327
Hooker, Brian, 404
Hoorn, A.J.W., 347
Hopkins, J.N., 375
Hormone-free food, 235
Houston enzymes, 73, 243
5-HTP, parent ratings of behavioral effects of, 383, 384
Hugging, 126
Humming, 239, 357
Humphrey, Dave, 252
Hunter, Kathy, 393
HVA. *See* Homovanillic acid
Hydrogenated oils, 218
Hydrolyzed vegetable protein, 214
5-Hydroxytryptophan, 84-85
Hyman, Susan, 287
Hyperactivity, parent accounts of, 46-47, 63, 106, 138, 193, 220, 222, 273, 315, 316, 351-352, 354, 357, 360
Hyperbaric oxygen therapy (HBOT), 230, 298, 413-415
Hyperlexia, 273
Hypersensitive hearing, 46-47, 63, 111, 158, 273, 274, 354, 395

Ibuprofen, 120, 121
Idebenone, 56
IgA level, 126
Illness, view of, 29
Imitating, 128
Immune defenses, impairments or deficiencies, 31, 72, 90, 99, 100, 106, 110, 115, 126, 234, 235, 261, 290, 311, 398
Immune system, 201, 227
  naltrexone and, 427
Immunizations. *See* Vaccine reactions; Vaccines
Immunoglobulin
IVIg, 115, 227
  oral, 227, 228
Immunostart, 320
*Impossible Cure: The Promise of Homeopathy* (Lansky), 45
Inappropriate laughter, 102
Inattentiveness, 46-47, 221
Indebenone, 321
Individualized Sensory Program (ISP), 158
*Infantile Autism: The Syndrome and Its Implications for a Neural Theory of Behavior* (Rimland), 16, 325, 388, 389
Infections, 72, 87, 99, 106
Inflammation, 32
Insulin-like growth factor-1 (IGF-1), 406
Insurance. *See* Health insurance
Integrative medicine, 27
Interaction, 187, 257, 264, 275
Internet resources
  autism organizations, 441
  Autism Research Institute, 442-443
  autism support group, 151, 152-153, 287-288
  Autism Treatment Evaluation Checklist (ATEC), 24, 443
  Center for Complex Infectious Diseases (CCID), 71
  Childscreen, 73
  dietary support, 217, 218
  film and videos, 272
  GFCF diet, 111
  homeopathy for autism, 208
  medical marijuana, 418
  mercury detoxification, 23
  naltrexone therapy, 429
  parent chats, 151, 152-153
  recipes, 55
  translations of autism materials, 443
  vitamin C, 388
Intestinal inflammation, 236
Intolerance of change, 46-47
Intravenous immunoglobulin (IVIg), 402
  parent accounts of use of, 115, 227, 297
  parent ratings of behavioral effects of, 383, 384
IQ, 140
Irlen, Helen, 38
Iron supplements, 243
Irrational thoughts, 136, 139
Irritability, 143, 144, 146, 307
ISP. *See* Individualized Sensory Program
IVIg. *See* Intravenous immunoglobulin

James, Jill, 119, 239, 409, 423

Jelen, Nancy, 45, 165, 350
Jepson, Bryan, 45, 131, 172
Jonas, C., 373
Joss, Loni, 357
Jumping, 114

Kalokarinos, Archie, 386
Kaplan, Melvin, 38, 64
Kartzinel, Jerry, 112, 113, 118, 120, 121
Kavatrol, 183
Ketoconazole, 399. *See also* Nizoral
Ketogenic diet, 70
Kicking, 366
King, Lorna Jean, 38
Kirkman Laboratories, 18, 56, 83, 112, 152, 272
Kirkman's Companion, 310
Kitt, Edgar, 177, 392
Klonapin, parent ratings of behavioral effects of, 383, 384
Kranowitz, Carol Stock, 109
Krigsman, Arthur, 394, 410
Kugler, Hans, 402
Kun, Lee Dae, 339-340
Kuriyama, S., 375
Kutzin, Alice, 371

Landalf, Helen, 22. *See also* Rimland, Helen
Language use. *See also* Speech issues
  parent accounts of, 70, 106, 109-110, 127, 145, 157, 162, 173, 174, 179, 195, 212, 215, 216, 222, 239, 241, 245, 249, 251, 259, 264, 265, 267, 271, 285, 295-296, 296, 305, 306, 315, 316, 321, 345, 346, 347, 349, 350, 354, 355, 356, 359-364, 366, 368, 404
Lansky, Amy, 45, 185
Late-onset autism, 225, 234, 398
Laughing, 106, 174, 264, 315, 366
Law of Similars, 185
Lawrence, Katharine, 5, 311
Lawson, J.W., 348
Layton, Richard, 311
LDN. *See* Low-dose naltrexone
Lead level, elevated, 52, 126, 129, 158, 161, 304
"Leaky gut," 136, 260, 274, 301, 303
Lecithin, 84
Lejeune, Jerome, 343
LeLord, Gilbert, 327, 331, 341, 361, 373
*Let Me Hear Your Voice* (Maurice), 50
Levin, Alan, 398
Lewis, Carolyn, 45, 209
Lewis, Lisa, 55, 111, 289, 409
L-glutamine, 56, 84
Licensing board, 28
Lieberman, Allen, 304
Lipase, 237
Lipoic acid. *See* Alpha lipoic acid
"Listening therapy," 101
Lithium
  parent account of use of, 73
  parent ratings of behavioral effects of, 383, 384
Loose stools. *See* Diarrhea
Lovaas, Ivar, 16, 38, 40, 50, 211
Low-dose naltrexone (LDN), 230, 427-429
Lupron, 59
Luvox, parent ratings of behavioral effects of, 383, 384
Lyme disease, 74, 75-76
Lypo, 310

Magnesium citrate, 395
Magnesium deficiency, 395
Magnesium glycinate, 395
Magnesium sulfate, 84
Magnesium supplements
  dosage of, 342
  hypersensitive hearing and, 395
  parent accounts of use of, 56, 127, 130, 137, 140, 235, 310, 321, 349
  parent ratings of behavioral effects of, 383, 384
Manganese supplements, parent account of use of, 139
Manic depressive illness, vitamin C and, 389
Mannatech Research and Development Co., 268
Marijuana use, 396, 416-422

Marinol, 417-422
Martineau, J., 373, 374
Massachusetts General Hospital, 236, 254, 394
Mastoid infection, 394
Math, 57
Matt Savage Trio, 277
Maurice, Catherine, 50, 241
Mayes, Frances, 355
Mayo, Gianna and Gus, 398
McCandless, Jaquelyn, 22, 45, 219, 423, 427
McCully, Kilmer, 400
McGinnis, Woody, 138
Mead, George, 232, 311
Mead, Tory, 311. *See also* Shirley, Tory
Measles, mumps, rubella vaccine. *See* MMR vaccine
Measles virus, 290
Medical licensing board, 28
Medical marijuana, 396, 416-422
Mega-B-vitamin mix, 51
Megavitamin therapy, 177-183, 282, 326, 351, 369. *See also* under individual supplements
Megson, Mary, 56, 58, 242, 305, 306
Melatonin
  parent accounts of use of, 296
  parent ratings of behavioral effects of, 383, 384
Melatonin Plus, 56
Mellaril, parent ratings of behavioral effects of, 383, 384
Melnechuk, Ted, 400
Melnychuk, John, 191
Menage, P., 374
Mendenhall, Juliana, 240
Mepron/Zithromax, 74
Mercury. *See also* Mercury exposure
  fetal exposure to, 105, 163, 225
  immune function and, 290
Mercury detoxification, 22-23, 56, 75, 268. *See also* Chelation therapy
Mercury Detoxification Consensus Report (ARI), 23
Mercury exposure
  from dental work, 225
  elevated mercury level, 56, 59, 112-113, 114, 126, 127, 156, 159, 161-163, 234, 242, 253, 304
  prenatal, 105, 163, 225
  from RhoGAM injection, 105, 163
  from thimerosal in vaccine, 224, 225, 232, 249, 264, 314, 317
Mercury poisoning, 32, 68, 70, 72, 127, 128, 155, 224, 247
Metallothionein (MT), 31, 73, 234
Methionine synthesis, 424
Methylation, 311-312, 406-407
Methyl-B12 injection, 312, 423-426
Methylcobalamin, 406-407, 410, 412, 423
Methylsulfonylmethane (MSM), 84, 85
Meyer, Dale, 399
Migraine headaches, 394, 395
Milestones. *See* Developmental milestones
Milk, 18, 128, 188, 189, 286, 287. *See also* Gluten-free casein-free diet (GFCF)
  removal from diet, 383, 384, 395
Milk products, 64, 79
Milk thistle, 84
Miller, Kelli, 245
Miller method, 147
MIND Institute, 234
Mineral supplements. *See also* under individual supplements
  parent accounts of use of, 56, 127, 137-140, 275, 317
Miranda, Ralph, 430
MMR vaccine, 46-47, 70, 80, 123, 246, 290, 314, 315
Mold, in home, 235, 303, 307, 310
Molybdenum supplements, 127
Monihan, Maureen, 345
Montessori schools, 189
Moore, Tom, 369
Moreno, H., 374
Mother's Milk Club, 126
Motor skills, 352, 353
Mouth
  ash color around, 300
  blue color around, 305
  thrush, 299, 397
Movement disorders, 69
MSG, 214, 218

MSM. *See* Methylsulfonylmethane
MT. *See* Metallothionein
MT Promotor, 218
Multivitamins, 140, 182, 272, 310. *See also* Vitamin supplements
Mumper, Elizabeth, 311
Murray, Susan, 354
Muscle tone, 352, 353
Musical ability, 275-277, 287, 321
Music therapy, 167
Mycoplasma infection, 72
Myelin basic protein autoantibodies, 115, 126
Mysoline, parent ratings of behavioral effects of, 383, 384

N-acetyl cysteine, 84, 85, 121
NAET, 100-101
Naltrexone
  for immunomodulation, 427-429
  low-dose naltrexone (LDN), 230, 427-429
  parent accounts of use of, 121, 230
  parent ratings of behavioral effects of, 383, 384
  self-injurious behavior and, 391
Name, responding to, 128, 135, 165, 235-236, 259, 292
Namenda, 230
Nebulizer, 121
Negrón, Lilia, 392
*Nerves in Collision* (Alvarez), 396
Neubrander, James, 423, 424-425
Neural axon filament protein, 126
Neurotransmitter levels, 31
Niacinamide, 73
Nitrates, 218
Nizoral, 304, 310, 399
*Nobody Nowhere* (Williams), 370
Nodular lymphoid hyperplasia, 236
Noises, sensitivity to, 46-47, 63, 111, 158, 273, 274, 354, 395
Noninvasive allergy process, 100-101
Nonverbal autism, 292
Null, Gary, 343
Nu-Thera, 138
Nutraceuticals, 410
Nutrient depletion, 32
Nutrition, 172. *See also* Diet; Feeding/Eating problems
Nutritional supplements, 212, 222
Nystatin
  parent accounts of use of, 51, 55, 56, 112, 166, 242, 253, 398, 399
  parent ratings of behavioral effects of, 383, 384

Oats, 112, 289
Obsessive-compulsive disorder (OCD), 365
Occupational therapy, parent accounts of, 53, 98, 101, 108, 115-116, 140, 147, 154, 211, 213, 246, 306
OIG. *See* Oral immunoglobulin
Olanzapine, safety of, 431
Oligoantigenic diet, 395
Olive leaf extract, 155, 156
Omega-3 and 6 oils, 88, 235, 243
Omega Brite, 321
Online resources. *See* Internet resources
Opioids, 427
Oral chelation, 100
Oral immunoglobulin (OIG), 227, 228
O'Reilly, Brenda, 358
Organic foods, 235, 274, 317
Osmond, Humphry, 17, 19
Ostracism, 28
*The Out-of-Sync Child* (Kranowitz), 109

P2Parents Chat, 152
P5P
  parent ratings of behavioral effects of, 383, 384
  use of, 392
PACE (Personalizing Autistic Children's Education), 115, 118, 259-260
Pain, aggressive and self-injurious behavior and, 394
Pain threshold, 46-47, 109, 241
Paleness, 50
Palmer, Monica Rourke, 358
Palms, sweaty, 315
Pangamic acid, 338, 347
Pangborn, Jon, 19, 20, 21, 409

Panic attacks, 366
Paracetamol, 83
Parasites, 51, 155
Parents, Letters to the Editor, 344-371, 411-412
ParentsChat website, 151
Parent to Parent for Autism website, 152-153
Parrott, Jeri, 251
Parsley, Pam, 354
Pauling, Linus, 331-332, 343
Paxil, parent ratings of behavioral effects of, 383, 384
PDD. *See* Pervasive developmental disorder
PECS. *See* Picture Exchange Communication System
Penn, Joseph, 432
Pepcid, parent ratings of behavioral effects of, 383, 384
Peripheral neuropathy, vitamin B6 and, 333, 334
Personalizing Autistic Children's Education (PACE), 115, 118, 259-260
Pervasive developmental disorder (PDD), 166, 211, 246, 265, 273-274
Pesticides, 218
Petrie, Susan and Garry, 257
Pfeiffer Treatment Center, 218, 234
Phenergan, parent ratings of behavioral effects of, 383, 384
Phenobarbital, parent ratings of behavioral effects of, 383, 384
Phenol sensitivity, 158, 301
Phenol-sulfo transferase (PST), 71
Phillips, Lou Diamond, 442
Phosphatidyl choline, 230
Physicians, 28, 97-98, 172, 225, 289, 335, 400-402
PhytAloe, 84, 272, 320
Phytoestrogens, 269
Picky eating habits, parent accounts of, 52, 53, 55, 87, 91, 135, 253, 301
Picture Exchange Communication System (PECS), 132-133
Pinching, 353
Pink disease, 156
Play skills, parent accounts of, 52, 114, 135, 142, 145, 147, 150, 215, 236, 259, 273, 306, 315, 316, 353
Play therapy, 16
PLUS, 272, 320
Pointing, lack of, 47, 81, 95, 285
Poking fingers, 187
Poor eye contact. *See* Eye contact
Porous intestine, 237
Potty training. *See* Toilet training
Prayer, 196, 317
Pregnancy
  dental work during pregnancy, 225
  RhoGAM injections, 105, 163
Prescreening, for sensitivity to vaccines, 73
Preservatives, 218
Pretend play, 215
Price, Michael Lee, 366
Primal Defense, 73, 320
Prizant, Barry A., 142, 148
Pro-Bio Gold, 56
Probiotics, parent accounts of use of, 51, 91, 212, 218, 224, 235, 243, 261, 310, 320
Project PACE, 115, 118, 259-260
Prolixin, parent ratings of behavioral effects of, 383, 384
Protozoan infection, 74
Prozac, parent ratings of behavioral effects of, 383, 384
PST. *See* Phenol-sulfo transferase
Psychiatric patients, vitamin C and, 388
Psychotherapy, 16
Psychotropic drugs
  for autism, 19, 40
  parent accounts of use of, 179
  parent ratings of behavioral effects of, 383, 384
  safety of, 417, 431
  side effects of, 431
Puberty
  in autistic children, 394-396
  seizures and, 395
Pulling hair, 166
Pushing, 366
Puzzled Media, 272
Pycnogenol, 130
Pyridoxal-5-phosphate (P-5-P), 138

Pyrrole level, 139, 140

*Rain Man* (movie), 22
Rash, 70, 302, 305
Ratner, R.S., 363
RDI. *See* Relationship Development Intervention
Reading, hyperlexia, 273
Reap, E.A., 348
Recombivax HB, 248
Rectal abscess, 315
Redwood, Lyn, 163
Reflux, 263
"Refrigerator mother" theory, 169
Regression in second year, 46-47, 124, 128, 134, 158, 186, 232, 251, 285, 301, 315, 398
Regressive autism, 232, 234
Regulatory institutions, 28
Reichelt, Karl, 224, 288
Reichenberg-Ullman, Judyth, 190
Reid, Jennifer, 119
Reiki, 196
Relational healing field, 230
Relationship Development Intervention (RDI), 103, 118, 239, 261
Repeated courses of antibiotic, 46-47, 123, 263, 264, 302, 397-398
Repeated ear infections. *See* Ear infections
Repetitive behaviors, 285, 293, 349
Rett syndrome, 391, 392-393
ReVia, 427
Reynierse, Peter J., 364
Reznek, Karen, 353
RhoGAM, 105, 163
Rice milk, 302, 310
Rider, Lisa, 346
Rimland, Bernard, 8, 13, 15, 38, 86, 90, 137, 140, 163, 167, 170, 215, 219, 223, 224, 226, 229, 252, 268, 275, 294, 295, 296, 303-304, 305, 311, 325, 329, 333, 336, 341, 344, 372, 374, 375, 386, 390, 394, 397, 400, 404, 408, 413, 416, 430
Rimland, Helen, 388. *See also* Landalf, Helen
Rimland, Mark, 15, 16, 22, 229, 334
Risperdal
  parent account of use of, 58
  parent ratings of behavioral effects of, 383, 384
  safety of, 416-417, 431
  side effects of, 417
Ritalin
  compared to vitamin B6 for hyperactivity, 360
  parent ratings of behavioral effects of, 383, 384
  safety of, 431
Ritualistic behavior, 367, 370
Roben, Miss, 55
Roberts, G.E., 325, 372
Rocephin, 74
Rocking, 46-47, 95, 155, 158, 357
Rosseneu, Sophie, 410
Rossi, P., 374
Rotation diet, parent ratings of behavioral effects of, 383, 384
Rowe, Jason and Angelene, 263
Royal jelly, 321
Rubella titer, 129. *See also* MMR vaccine
Rye, gluten in, 112, 289

*Saccharomyces bouldardii*, 235, 310
Salicylate sensitivity, 116, 301
SAMe, parent ratings of behavioral effects of, 383, 384
Savage, Diane, 273
SCD. *See* Specific carbohydrate diet
Schafer Autism Report, 441
Schimka, Ann and Randy, 352
Schizophrenia
  *Candida* as cause of, 397
  vitamin B3 and, 17, 19
  vitamin C and, 388
Schlapfer, Kelli, 279
Schools, autistic children and, 116, 132-133, 159, 169, 171, 199-200, 239, 243, 250, 270, 280, 353
Scratching, 83, 166, 307, 393
Screaming. *See also* Crying
  parent accounts of, 120, 134, 139, 143, 150, 174, 210, 214, 240, 241, 273, 285, 286, 301, 346, 347, 353, 359,

360, 369, 371
Seacure, 84
Secrepan, 169
Secretin
parent accounts of use of, 29, 84, 85, 116, 120, 127, 131, 140, 156, 169, 223, 224, 227, 237, 242, 260, 282, 296, 307, 310
parent ratings of behavioral effects of, 383, 384
*The Secret Night World of Cats* (Landalf), 22
SecroFlo, 310
Seizures
food allergies and, 394-395
parent accounts of, 70, 128, 129-130, 235, 253, 268, 339, 361, 368-369
puberty and, 395
Selenium supplements, 56, 127, 235
Self-injurious and assaultive behavior (SIB/A)
controlling, 390-393, 395, 416-417
pain and, 394
parent accounts of, 46-47, 182, 367, 404
Self-stimming. *See* Stimming
Sense of touch, 109, 111
Sensitivity to sound, 46-47, 63, 111, 158, 273, 274, 354, 395
Sensory Center Individualized Sensory Program (ISP), 158
Sensory defensiveness, 274
Sensory integration therapy, 117, 140, 158, 168, 239
Sensory Learning Center, 255
Sensory problems, 109, 169, 215, 273
Sensory techniques, 40, 267
Seroussi, Karyn, 45, 96, 111, 147, 212, 241, 285, 306
Shade, Ruth, 357
Shattock, Paul, 82, 83, 85, 86, 288
Shaw, William, 112, 241-242
Shirley, Tory, 232. *See also* Mead, Tory
Shrieking, 174
Shultz, Nicole, 358
SIB/A. *See* Self-injurious and assaultive behavior
SIDS. *See* Sudden infant death syndrome
Siegal, Bryna, 69
Silver, colloidal, 158
Silver level, elevated, 304
Simillimum, 192
Singh, V.K., 202
Singulair, 120
Sinus infections, 300, 302
Sitting, 68
Skin problems
diaper rash, 166, 263, 294, 299
die-off reaction and, 308
eczema, 300, 305, 315, 404
rashes, 70, 302, 305
scratching, 83, 166, 307
Sleep difficulties, parent accounts of, 46-47, 70, 106, 167-168, 210, 273, 292, 293, 346-347, 356, 360, 404
*Smart Moves* (Hannaford), 118
Smiling, 220, 264
Smith, Tyrus, 428, 429
Social skills, parent accounts of, 52, 187, 216, 248, 257, 267, 269, 316, 354, 356, 357, 358-359, 360, 404
Sodium ascorbate, 389
*Somebody Somewhere* (Williams), 370
*The Sound of a Miracle: A Child's Triumph over Autism* (Stehli), 109
Sound sensitivity, 46-47, 63, 111, 158, 273, 274, 354, 395
Soy, 120-121
Soy allergy, 212, 301
Soy formula, 286
*Special Diets for Special Kids* (Lewis), 55, 111, 289
Specific carbohydrate diet (SCD), 152, 158, 239, 404-405, 409-410
Speech echoing. *See* Echolalia
Speech issues, 273
echolalia, 189, 265, 269, 273, 316, 352, 360
parent accounts of, 40, 49, 52, 53, 57, 61, 81, 94, 102, 107, 124, 128, 131, 135, 142, 145, 146, 147, 149, 150, 155, 157, 161, 165, 168, 173, 186, 194, 232, 245, 306, 316, 345, 398
Speech therapy, 98, 101, 108, 116, 135,

140, 147, 211, 213, 246, 252, 347
Spelling, 57, 216
Spelt, 112
Spinning, parent accounts of, 46-47, 107, 174, 187, 239, 305, 310
Spitting, 366
Stamping, 369
Staring, 264
State medical licensing board, 29
Stehli, Annabel, 109
Stelazine, parent ratings of behavioral effects of, 383, 384
Sterolins, 70
Stewart, Gary R., 368
Stimming, 61, 62, 162, 216, 233, 251, 346, 351, 357, 367
  dragging face on floor, 285, 286, 305, 307, 308, 310
  head banging, 46-47, 125, 166, 187, 264, 305, 307, 308, 310, 368, 390-393
  humming, 239, 357
  rocking, 46-47, 95, 155, 158, 357
  spinning, 46-47, 107, 174, 187, 239, 305, 310
  waving fingers or arms, 273, 357
Stittgen, Susan, 352
St. Johns wort, parent ratings of behavioral effects of, 383, 384
Stokke-Johnsen, Ketil and Sarah, 351
Stoller, Kenneth, 413-414
Stone, Irwin, 386
Stools. *See* Bowel problems; Diarrhea
Strattera, safety of, 431
Stubbs, Gene, 240
Sudden infant death syndrome (SIDS), 157
Sugar, removal from diet, 383, 384
Sunderland Autism Research Unit, 82
Super Nu-Thera, parent accounts of use of, 51, 56, 63, 66, 84, 87, 88, 137, 138, 148, 149, 182, 183, 235, 243, 252, 253, 261, 272, 275, 278, 294, 295, 327, 359
Support groups, 115, 218, 244, 287
SV-40, 71
Sweating, 85, 315
Sytsema, Rebecca, 292

Talking. *See* Language use; Speech issues
Tantrums, parent accounts of, 46-47, 49, 51, 91, 130, 135, 146, 212, 213, 257, 258, 262, 264, 273, 302, 347, 352, 353, 357, 364, 367, 404
Taurine, 56, 84, 127, 130, 243
TD-DMPS, 104
*Teaching Individuals with Developmental Delays: Basic Intervention Techniques* (Lovaas), 40
Teeth grinding, 354
Tegretol, parent ratings of behavioral effects of, 383, 384
Temper tantrums. *See* Tantrums
Tenex, 118, 119, 120
Testosterone levels, 58
Tetrahydrobiopterin deficiency, 73
Tetrahydrocannabinol (THC), 417, 419
TF. *See* Transfer factor
Th1/Th2 balance, 427
THC. *See* Tetrahydrocannabinol
Thimerosal
  methionine synthase and, 424
  methylation and, 406
  in vaccines, 224, 225, 232, 249, 263, 314
Thom, Stephen, 414
Thorazine, parent ratings of behavioral effects of, 383, 384
Thoughtful House Center for Children (Austin, TX), 176
Thrush, 299, 397
Tin level, elevated, 156, 304
Titanium level, elevated, 304
TMG. *See* Trimethylglycine
Toe-walking, 46, 155, 273, 285, 287, 354
Tofranil, parent ratings of behavioral effects of, 383, 384
Toilet training, parent accounts of, 46-47, 53, 87, 117, 149, 150, 224, 242, 264, 362
Tolbert, Lelland, 343
Tomatis method, 120, 395
Total EFA, 310
Toxic metals, 100, 114. *See also* Heavy metal toxicity

Transfer factor (TF), 402
parent accounts of use of, 127, 129, 130, 131, 140, 228
parent ratings of behavioral effects of, 383, 384
Treatment Effectiveness Survey, 9, 24, 381
Treffert, Darold A., 420, 422
Trelka, Jeffrey, 404
Trental, 118, 119
Trimethylglycine (TMG)
parent accounts of use of, 56, 119, 140, 239, 424
parent ratings of behavioral effects of, 383, 384
TTFD. *See* Allithiamine
Turuba, Renelle, 356

Unawareness of danger, 46-47
Underwood, Lauren, 363
Unlocking Autism, 441
*Unraveling the Mystery of Autism and Pervasive Developmental Disorder: A Mother's Story of Research and Recovery* (Seroussi), 45, 147, 212, 306
Unresponsiveness, 160, 233
Uranium level, elevated, 304
Urine samples, 304
Urocholine, 242
Usman, Dr., 132
UVBI, 75

Vaccines
autism and, 175, 199, 201, 237, 246-247, 293-294, 304, 315, 402
interesting facts about, 248-249
mercury toxicity and, 133, 154, 156-157, 161, 225, 317
parent accounts of problems following, 18, 22-23, 46-47, 68-69, 70, 73, 80, 94, 100, 106, 123, 124, 127, 133, 165, 232, 264, 300
single-dose presentations without preservatives, 249
thimerosal in, 224, 225, 232, 249, 264, 290, 314, 317
Vaginal yeast infection, 397
Valentine, Sandy, 354
Valium, parent ratings of behavioral effects of, 383, 384
Valtrex, 72
Vancomycin, 235
Vegetable allergies, 301
Venables, Donna and Paul, 370
"Verbal Behavior" approach, 101
Vest, Kimberly Boyd, 299
Violence, parent accounts of, 357, 365, 391
Virastop, 74
Vision. *See* Eyesight
Vision therapy, 64
Vitamin A
parent accounts of use of, 113, 127, 138, 235, 305
parent ratings of behavioral effects of, 383, 384
Vitamin B, parent accounts of use of, 235
Vitamin B3
parent ratings of behavioral effects of, 383, 384
schizophrenia and, 17, 19
Vitamin B6
dosage of, 341-342, 361, 396
Letters to the Editor, 344-371
parent accounts of use of, 17-18, 31, 130, 137, 138, 139, 140, 167, 218, 310
parent ratings of behavioral effects of, 383, 384
safety of, 333-335
side effects of, 333-334, 341
Vitamin B6 with magnesium
dosage of, 341-342, 361, 396
Letters to the Editor, 344-371
parent accounts of use of, 9, 22, 40, 56, 62, 137, 167, 222, 275, 294
parent ratings of behavioral effects of, 383, 384
safety of, 323
self-injurious and assaultive behavior and, 391, 395
studies of, 324-336, 372-375
Vitamin B12
methyl-B12 injection, 312, 423-426
parent accounts of use of, 119, 120, 121, 132, 171, 227, 238, 272, 308, 310, 312, 412

parent ratings of behavioral effects of, 383, 384
Vitamin B15. *See also* Dimethylglycine (DMG)
history of, 338
parent account of use of, 347
Vitamin B complex, parent accounts of use of, 56
Vitamin C
autism treatment with, 386-389
dosage of, 343, 387-388
functions of, 386
parent accounts of use of, 56, 84, 182, 243, 298
parent ratings of behavioral effects of, 383, 384
Vitamin C deficiency, 386
Vitamin E, parent accounts of use of, 56
Vitamin megadoses, 177-183, 282, 326, 351, 369. *See also* under individual supplements
Vitamin supplements. *See also* under individual supplements
megadoses, 177-183, 282, 326, 351, 369
parent accounts of use of, 56, 127, 130, 131, 137-140, 275, 294, 317
Vogt, 47
Voice, 63
Vojdani, Aristo, 410
Vomiting, 70, 263, 294, 301, 304, 351

Wakefield, Andrew, 28, 202, 290, 394, 410
Walking on tiptoe, 46, 155, 273, 285, 287, 354
Walsh, Bill, 234
Waring, Rosemary, 80
Water filters, 235
Waving arms, 273
Waving fingers, 357
"We Cured Our Son's Autism" (Seroussi), 111, 147
Wells, Sue, 55
Westside Early Autism Program and Integrated Preschool, 260
*What Your Doctor May Not Tell You About Children's Vaccinations* (Cave), 264
Wheat. *See also* Gluten-free casein-free diet (GFCF)
gluten in, 18, 112, 136, 286, 289
removal from diet, 383, 384, 395
Whining, 353
White, Patti, 200, 202
Whiting, Paul, 82
"Whole body" tension reactions, 316
Wholesale Nutrition Co., 389
Williams, Donna, 370
Willis, David, 265
Withdrawal, 80, 232
Wolff, Aileen, 356
Writing, 57, 59, 275

*The Yeast Connection* (Crook), 398
Yeast Control, 56, 152, 253
Yeast infection
autism and, 397-399
diaper rash, 166, 263, 294, 299
parent accounts of, 51, 55, 70, 83, 99, 110, 112, 140, 162, 166, 227, 234, 235, 253, 282, 299-300, 304, 310
Yeast infections, 401
Yelling, parent accounts of, 366, 368, 371
Young, Robin and George, 313
YU Natural Organic Rice Beverage, 310

Zarontin, parent ratings of behavioral effects of, 383, 384
Zbylot, Philip, 110-113
Zhivago, Kristin, 369
Zimmerman, Jack, 223, 226, 228, 229, 230
Zinc, function of, 424
Zinc picolinate, 139
Zinc sulfate, 70
Zinc supplements
parent accounts of use of, 51, 56, 127, 139, 140, 218, 235, 310
parent ratings of behavioral effects of, 383, 384
Zithromax, 74
Zoloft, parent ratings of behavioral effects of, 383, 384